Other Books By
Colette Taube Dywasuk

Published by Harper & Row:
Adoption—Is It For You? (1973)
Adoption And After, Revised Edition (1974).

SIXTH OF TWELVE

A MEMOIR ABOUT A DETROIT FAMILY
IN A DYNAMIC ERA

COLETTE TAUBE DYWASUK

PUBLISHERS, INC.

Lakeside Publishers, Inc.
58757 Van Dyke #756
Washington, MI 48094
www.sixthoftwelve.com

Book Design & Layout ©2016 Murder Ink Agency, LLC.

ISBN 978-0-9971169-0-8
ISBN 978-0-9971169-1-5 (ebook)
Library of Congress Control Number: 2016900790
Lakeside Publishers, Inc.

First Edition Printed in the United States of America

Dedication

To my parents Frank and Anne Taube
who selflessly dedicated their lives to their family.
They gave their all and did their best.
Mama and Daddy, you did great.

"To everything there is a season, and a time to every purpose under the heavens. A time to be born, and a time to die; a time to plant, and a time to pluck up that which is planted. A time to kill, and a time to heal; a time to break down, and a time to build up. A time to weep, and a time to laugh; a time to mourn, and a time to dance... A time to get, and a time to lose; a time to keep, and a time to cast away. A time to rend, and a time to sew; a time to keep silence, and a time to speak. A time to love, and a time to hate; a time of war, and a time of peace."

___OLD TESTAMENT: ECCLESIASTES, III, 1-8

Foreword

Growing up in a large family is an unusual experience, especially in today's society in America where you rarely see families of more than two to four children. In the 1940s and early 1950s, when I was a young child in a predominately Polish/German neighborhood on the east side of Detroit, large families were commonplace. Although, even then, families of twelve children were unique.

But this book isn't about families in general—large or small. It is about my family. I am the sixth of twelve children. I grew up with five sisters and four brothers. One younger and one older brother died in infancy. We were a blue-collar family with limited financial resources, but an unlimited supply of love, support, and opportunity. At least that was how it seemed to me. Although we didn't have much, I always knew I could "make something of myself" if I so chose — if I was willing to work hard enough.

Whenever my sisters and brothers and I get together and start talking about our growing up years, it amazes me that each of our individual stories of "how it was" differ significantly. But I guess it makes sense. Each of us experienced some unique and some common circumstances, both happy and sad. Our perspectives would be different based on where we fit in the family as well as our personalities.

This is the story of my family as I remember it. It is a true story although I use fiction techniques to tell it—including ascribing specific conversations and reactions to individuals and occasionally changing names to protect the identity of a character or to avoid confusion. In this way, I attest that each of these elements is, to the best of my knowledge, representative of what the character might have said or done.

Looking back I can see clearly how I became the person I am. The influence of my family has been remarkable. Although I have lived a very conventional life, at heart I remain a free spirit. Somehow both parts of me were encouraged and nurtured by my parents. Woven through all the experiences of childhood was the lesson they most wanted their children to learn: "Be who you are. You are just as good as anyone else. Value yourself and everyone else will value you".

My parents were remarkable individuals. They were strong, dedicated to each other and their family, and ultimately laid down their lives for the future of their children. Along the way they had their ups and downs, their good times and bad. It is with a heart full of love and appreciation that I share my growing up years.

Family Tree

Stanley & Gertrude Wisniewski (Pa & Ma) ──────┐

DOB: 5/7/1883   DOB: 11/18/1882
DOD: 4/26/1969   DOD: 3/25/1955

Felix & Stella Taube (Grandpa & Grandma) ──────

DOB: 4/28/1878   DOB: 4/9/1881
DOD: 5/8/1953   DOD: 10/12/1957

Frank & Anne Taube (Daddy & Mama)   Marvin Taube

DOB: 12/12/1904   DOB: 7/17/1908   DOB: 12/31/1931
DOD: 5/14/1967   DOD: 7/4/1999   DOD: 10/21/1932

Lorraine Taube   Mary Ann Taube

DOB: 1/18/1930   DOB: 2/2/1933
DOD: 9/10/2014

Frank Taube (Buddy)
DOB: 1/12/1935

Donald Taube (Donny)
DOB: 2/13/1937

Colette Taube
DOB: 2/6/1941

Karen Taube
DOB: 12/29/1942

William Taube (Billy)
DOB: 12/19/1943

John Taube (Johnny)
DOB: 12/19/1943
DOD: 12/19/1943

Janet Taube
DOB: 12/11/1945

Judith Taube (Judy)
DOB: 12/11/1945

David Taube (Davey)
DOB: 10/18/1948

Prologue

At the age of 90, my mother fell. She broke her hip. Up until that time, she and my oldest sister, Lorraine, who was in her late 60s, still lived together in a tiny house in Yale, almost 60 miles north of Detroit.

Lorraine had cerebral palsy. Before she was crippled by arthritis, she could manage to get around. Walking with crutches. Holding onto furniture. Now she was confined to a wheelchair. A nurse's aide came to the house twice a week to help her bathe. Otherwise, she managed on her own.

The two kept each other company. But Mama was the provider: cooking the meals; cleaning the house; doing the laundry. "I like to do for myself," Mama said. "It keeps me active. Besides, nobody does it like me."

My youngest brother, Davey, lived next door with his wife, Debbie, and their eight children. They did Mama's shopping, drove her to church and doctor appointments, and managed the outside chores like gardening and snow shoveling.

Mama sat at the kitchen table day after day and waited for company. Meanwhile, she drank pot after pot of coffee, boiled black on the stove. And smoked. Two to three packages of cigarettes a day.

"Those young doctors don't know what they're talking about," she said. "Telling me to stop smoking." Her brown eyes glared fiercely.

"Smoking relaxes me. It was a doctor who told me to smoke in the first place."

There was no arguing the facts with Mama. She knew what she knew. And she wasn't ever shy about sharing her opinions.

"I'm not a phony," she said. "I say what I think. If people don't like it, that's too bad."

Few had liked it. Mama could be sharp and condescending to people she thought were ignorant, foolish, or those who spoke without thinking. Friends. Or family. Neighbors. Strangers. Or doctors.

Mama was a slight woman—medium height, small-boned, delicate looking. She barely weighed 100 pounds. But her feistiness made her formidable. She was intent on speaking her mind, intent on having her way, intent on changing the minds of those who opposed her. She had an internal strength and a spark that defined her—that radiated, "Don't mess with me."

Throughout her younger years she had propelled herself through life with her head held high, shoulders back, eyes flashing, and a burning energy that made her seem always on the move. Now she had slowed down physically, but mentally she was as sharp as ever.

Each of her children was expected to call at least once a week. To keep her posted on what was going on. She used a combination of guilt and embarrassment on anyone who slacked off.

When the phone rang, you'd guess it was probably time for Mama's call.

"You're too busy for your mother?" Those were the first words you'd hear when you picked up the receiver. "One mother has time for twelve children," she chided. "But her child doesn't have time for her one mother?"

It was rare anyone missed calling. There were few acceptable excuses. Trying to explain was a waste of time. "I got tied up with...family, or work, or planting my garden, my," (fill in the blank)... was futile.

"I'm sorry. I'll try to make sure it doesn't happen again." This was the only acceptable response.

There would be a long silence on Mama's end of the line. She wanted to make sure you registered her disapproval. Then she would ask, "When are you coming out?"

Mama loved having her children and grandchildren over to visit. And she always had a lot to say. She talked about the books she'd been reading. The needlepoint she was working on. What was happening in each of our families. Sometime during the visit, she'd demand a game of cards—pinochle or hearts or canasta. If youngsters were around, it'd be Yahtzee or Scrabble or Probe.

But now the ability to do for herself was over.

Mama had fallen during the night when she had gotten up to go to the bathroom. She thought she had tripped—she was not quite sure how it happened. She hit the floor with a tremendous crash, her head just missing the sink as she went down. The pain had been excruciating. She had cried and called out. Lorraine telephoned Davey.

My brother called an ambulance and a short time later she was in the hospital emergency room. An x-ray confirmed what was suspected clinically. Mama had broken her hip. She was given an injection for pain and scheduled for surgery. Now it was late afternoon. The surgery was completed successfully and she seemed to be resting comfortably.

Seeing my mother in a hospital bed, so tiny under the white blankets, I thought of a child-sized mannequin with wide, shuttered eyes. I bent over the bed and kissed her forehead. She opened her eyes and looked at me blankly, showing no recognition of who I was.

"Do you know where you are?" I asked.

"Of course I know," she snarled at me.

"And where are you?"

"At Davey's house."

"I don't think so," I responded gently. "You're in the hospital. You fell at home and broke your hip."

She turned to face me, incredulous. "I did?"

"Yes. Davey found you on the floor and the ambulance brought you to the hospital. You had surgery this morning."

"Well, well," Mama said. She closed her eyes and went to sleep.

I sat by her bed for another few hours. It had been a long day. The doctor said Mama was doing great. When she was awake, she did not appear to be in any pain. She was blissfully unaware of both the fall and the fracture. In addition to the anesthetics used during surgery, which would gradually wear off, she was on a dose of pain medication. And the nurse had just given her a strong sleeping pill. She looked like she would sleep through the night. I left when visiting hours were over.

I was called back to the hospital in the middle of the night. Mama was reported to be confused and combative. I heard her shrieking the minute I got off the elevator.

"Untie me," she yelled. "Let me up! Why am I a prisoner here?"

I walked into the room. A nurse stood by the bed. She held a glass of water with a straw. Mama was twisting her head from side to side. She was lying in bed, her hands tied to the bedrails with soft restraints—padded cuffs wrapped around her wrists, with straps attached. She was wearing a "Posey" jacket—a vest fitted over her hospital gown that was tied to the back of the bed, effectively preventing her from sitting up. She was wide awake, terror in her eyes.

"Why is she restrained?" I asked.

"She kept ripping out her intravenous and trying to get up," the nurse said. "It's not safe for her to walk unassisted but she doesn't remember that. She doesn't know where she is and she doesn't believe me when I tell her she broke her hip."

I took the glass of water. I leaned over and laid my hand gently on Mama's face. "Shhh, Mama," I whispered. I held the straw to her mouth.

"I want to go home," she sobbed. "Get me out of here."

"I'm sorry, Mama. You have to stay here. You remember you fell at home and broke your hip? It has to heal."

"That's right," she said. She took several sips of water. She smiled. "Now can you untie me?"

Some years earlier, Mama had named me her durable power of attorney for health care. She was scheduled for gall bladder surgery at the time.

"If something happens, I want you to tell the doctors what to do," she'd said. "Otherwise they'll be getting directions from everyone in the family."

I was surprised. "What about Lorraine or Buddy? They're older."

"I want you. You're smart. You're responsible. And you've had some experience in these kinds of things."

Of course I knew what she meant. I'd had some challenging times in my life. So had Mama. But she'd always been careful not to talk about them.

I looked into her eyes. There was a flicker of something there... love, compassion, empathy? This was the closest Mama had ever come to bringing up the past.

"Mama, do you think..."

She turned her head quickly. Subject closed. "You know what I'd want. I'll leave it up to you to do what you think best."

"But won't the others be offended?"

"You're right in the middle of all of my children. Sixth of twelve. Nobody will complain about me choosing you."

At the time I'd felt honored... special. It was rare that Mama ever singled out any of her children. She was careful to treat everyone equally. There was always plenty of discussion among my sisters and brothers as to who was "Mama's favorite".

Now, being "the chosen one" didn't feel so good. Mama was disoriented—incapable of making decisions. I was to be responsible for her well-being. The role reversal was intimidating.

I looked at the nurse. "My mother is extremely claustrophobic," I said. "The restraints only intensify her agitation. If you take them off for now, I'll sit with her so she settles down and doesn't try to get out of bed on her own."

"Well," the nurse said. "She does seem to have calmed down with you in the room." She untied Mama's hands. "And I suppose now that she's drinking fluids she won't need the intravenous for hydration. All the medicines the doctors have prescribed are pills. All right. As long as someone is with her, she won't need to be restrained."

As soon as her hands were untied, Mama closed her eyes and drifted off to sleep. I sat in the recliner next to her bed and began to make plans. There were ten of us children who could take turns sitting with Mama—plus sister- and brother-in-laws. Among Mama's 35 grandchildren, several would be able to help out. Providing round the clock supervision during her four- to five-day hospital stay should be simple. I'd start making calls at first light.

The doctor came early the next morning. Mama was sleeping peacefully.

"The delirium is caused by acute illness," he said. "Probably exasperated by the unfamiliarity of the hospital itself. I prescribed Halcion. That didn't control the agitation. Your mother reacted adversely. I hesitate to medicate further."

"Is there a problem having someone from the family with her 24 hours a day?" I said.

"Not at all. We need to keep her calm. The effect of having you in the room has been striking. Obviously, the best strategy for improving mobility and rendering your mother independent is to get her out of bed and on her feet as soon as possible. But as long as she's confused and belligerent, the therapists won't be able to work with her."

Mama was in a strange place and nothing was familiar to her. People, all strangers, came and went. They told her where she was, but she forgot. They poked and pushed, and shoved things in and out and over her. They stuck her with needles, and they wanted her to blow into their bottles. She did not understand and they could not explain that blowing in the bottles forced her to breathe deeply to strengthen her lungs and improve her circulation. When she had to go to the bathroom they put rails on her bed and refused to let her get up by herself.

"The real difficulty will be once your mother is released from the hospital. She'll need physical therapy for a few weeks. A rehabilitation hospital won't take her. She'll be too confused and too weak to tolerate the intense therapy mandated for the hospital to qualify for Medicare reimbursement. There's no alternative but to find a nursing facility where she'll receive physical therapy, though at a less vigorous pace."

"What is the prognosis for my mother?"

"The transfer to a nursing facility is intended to be temporary. In one-third of cases it proves to be permanent. With physical therapy, there is no reason your mother can't gain her strength back, go home again, and return to her previous life." He smiled. "Your mother is one tough lady."

***

I found a nursing facility in Yale, close to Lorraine and Davey. It would require a long drive for me, but I knew Lorraine would be the one spending the most time with Mama. Davey and his family would have to chauffeur her. The facility provided the kind of physical therapy she'd need and was a nice, friendly, clean smelling place.

Over the days in the hospital, Mama remained confused and disoriented. As long as someone from the family was with her, she co-operated with the nurses and doctors and therapists. Then the day came to transfer her to the nursing facility. I tried to explain what was happening as I helped her dress.

"Mama," I said. "Do you remember where you're going?"

"Of course," she said. "I'm going home."

"No, Mama. You're going to MediLodge. In Yale. It's an assisted living place in town. The ambulance is going to take you there. You need physical therapy. You're not strong enough to go home yet. You'll only be there for a few weeks. Then you can go home."

She looked at me. "Why would I want to go there? That's a place for old people. For people nobody cares about."

I shuddered. "No, Mama. It's a place where you can heal."

A nurse walked into the room with Mama's discharge papers.

"I'm going home," Mama told her.

Mama was miserable from the moment she entered the nursing center. She refused to eat. She refused to take her medicines. She refused to do physical therapy. All she wanted was her cigarettes. And to go home.

"Mama, please," I said. "If you don't eat and do your therapy you'll just get weaker and weaker."

"Then take me home," she said. "I'll eat at home. I don't need therapy. I just want to go home. And I want a cigarette. They won't give me a cigarette."

I talked to the director. She showed me a spot outdoors where I could take Mama to smoke.

"Okay, Mama. I'll get you some cigarettes."

Against my better judgment, I went to the party store and bought a package of Bel Air Lights and a cigarette lighter. I returned to the nursing center.

"I'll wheel you outside for a smoke, Mama," I said. I went to the closet for her coat.

"I don't want a cigarette here. I want to go home and smoke. Why won't you take me home? Why do you hate your mother?"

I was shattered. My eyes filled with tears. "Oh, Mama," I whispered. "I don't hate you. I love you. I just want you to get better."

A few days later, I received an urgent call from the nursing center. "Your brother, David, took your mother out for a ride and he refuses to bring her back," the director said.

I was stunned. Yet, I felt a spurt of joy and pride. Mama had found a way to get what she wanted. And I didn't have to bear the responsibility.

"What do you expect me to do?" I said. "Call the sheriff? I'll talk to my brother."

I called Davey.

"I'm so sorry, Colette," he said. "I just couldn't stand it anymore. She begged and begged. She cried. I never saw Mama cry before."

Davey and his family figured out ways to take over Mama's day-to-day care. Other family members helped when they could. Eventually, hospice came. Mama grew weaker and weaker. But she smoked—in bed—until two days before she died on July 4, 1999.

Some have said that Mama was ready to die. I don't believe it. Neither did her sister.

"Even when your Mama was dying, she wouldn't give up," Aunt Bea said. She smiled. "Aunt Evelyn and I visited her shortly before she died. 'Frank will be happy to see you,' I said to her. 'Where do you think I'm going?' your Mama asked me. 'I have no plans to leave just yet. Anyhow, what do you know about Frank? It's been more than 30 years since I've seen him. If I did meet up with him, he probably wouldn't even remember me.' I liked that about your Mama." Aunt Bea laughed. "She was feisty to the day she died. Nobody pushed her around. She had a mind of her own and she let you know it!"

Mama had survived for almost 91 years by being strong, by being tough, by thinking for herself, by refusing to give up. This time it didn't work out so well. But she died in her own bed, on her own terms, surrounded by her children, on the Fourth of July, with fireworks lighting the sky. She left the world as she lived her life—with a bang.

When anyone asks me what my mother died of, I smile. "Stubbornness," I say. I am proud she did not "go gentle into that good night".[1]

After all, I am my mother's daughter.

[1]Thomas, Dylan. In Country Sleep: Do Not Go Gentle into that Good Night, pp.18-19. New Directions Books published by James Laughlin, New York, 1952.

Chapter 1

June 27, 1967. I was in labor. I felt a warm gush between my legs. "Uh-oh, I think my water just broke," I said to Jerry. "Ring for the nurse."

This was our fourth baby in seven years. I felt experienced and self-confident about giving birth. My husband was calm and relaxed.

"Well, at least we're making progress," he said. He smiled down at me and reached for the buzzer.

We are? I thought. But I smiled back. The labor pains really weren't too bad.

The nurse came into the room. "Let's see what's happening here," she said. She lifted the sheet. She took one look and turned around and left. "I'll be right back," she called over her shoulder.

Jerry and I looked at each other. What was going on?

In a few moments the room was filled with medical equipment, doctors, and technicians. I was poked and probed by countless rubber-skinned fingers. "We're calling your obstetrician to come in right now," the resident physician said. "You're hemorrhaging. We'll have to deliver the baby as soon as possible. By C-section."

I gasped. "C-section? Why?"

"Placenta praevia. Afterbirth coming first. Your doctor will explain it all to you as soon as he gets here. You'll have to leave the room, sir. We have to prep your wife for surgery. There's a waiting room down the hall across from the nurses' station. Someone will be there to talk to you shortly."

Jerry's eyes widened. I groped for his hand and squeezed.

"It'll be all right, Colette," he said. He bent over the bed. "You'll see. Everything will be fine." He released his hand, squeezed my shoulders, kissed my forehead, and left the room.

As soon as Jerry walked out, I turned my head toward the doctor. "Is my baby all right?" I asked. "Am I going to be all right?" I looked for the truth in his eyes.

"I'm not able to answer those questions," he said. "Your obstetrician will be here shortly."

I shivered.

Time passed in total confusion. Monitors being hooked up. Something about a clamp. Doctors...nurses...technicians scurrying around. The pain...oh, God, so much pain.

"Please, make it stop! Jerry, help me! Make it stop!"

I wove in and out of consciousness. I was barely aware I was being wheeled down the hall. I heard Jerry's voice calling, "Colette, Colette." I tried to raise my head but it was too heavy.

Then the pain stopped. I was in the operating room. A sheet was draped across my middle. The anesthesiologist sat next to me, watching the monitors.

"We've given you a spinal block," he said. "We don't want to give you any more medications until after your baby is born. You won't feel any pain. Just lie still and everything will be fine."

I felt a pulling on my abdomen. No pain...just pressure.

"You have a beautiful baby boy," Dr. Doyle said.

I couldn't see. The sheet blocked my view. All I could hear was a scurrying. No sound from my baby.

"Is he all right? How come he's not crying?" I tried to sit up. The anesthesiologist pressed my shoulders down against the bed.

"Okay, you can administer the sedative now," the doctor directed.

I watched the anesthesiologist inject something into the IV bag attached to my arm.

"What's that for?" I asked. "What's wrong?"

"Just settle down," the doctor said. "We have to finish with you. The nurses are cleaning him up right now. You'll see the little guy for yourself in just a few minutes."

"A boy. Mark Christopher is the name we chose for a boy." I smiled. I felt warmth spread over me. The sedative. I couldn't stop myself from talking. "We hoped for a girl. A sister for Cheryl...but a boy is fine. Just so he's healthy. You know? That's the important thing. A new brother...the kids will be so excited!"

I thought about our children at home: Jerry, Jr., 6; Jeffrey, 5; and Cheryl, 4 years old. They'd been looking forward to the new baby. That's all they'd talked about for weeks—whether it would be a boy or a girl. Who would be first to hold him or her. How they'd brag to their friends and cousins about their new brother or sister.

Suddenly Dr. Doyle was by my side. "Colette," he said. "Your baby has a problem with his lungs...his breathing. We have to get him down to ICU. The pediatrician is evaluating him right now. He needs to do some tests."

"I need to see him first. Please, I need to see him...just for a second!"

The nurse wheeled a tiny cart over to my bed. I strained, forced my head up to look inside. My baby was perfectly formed—just beautiful. He looked like Jerry. But he was so blue. He had a plastic oxygen mask over his nose and mouth. He wasn't moving. He wasn't crying. He just lay there. I reached over to touch him. He was so cold.

"Let's go. Now!" the doctor ordered.

The next few hours were a blur. Jerry coming in...our clutching each other for support. The pediatrician gave us his diagnosis. "Hyaline membrane disease. A kind of congestion in the lungs," he said. "If your baby survives the next two days, he will be fine. But we need to move him to Children's Hospital to get the best newborn care."

"I'll go with him," Jerry said. He kissed me on the cheek. "He needs me. I'll call you to let you know what's going on."

I wanted to scream, to cry. I wanted to be with my baby. Instead I was stuck in this hospital bed.

Jerry spent the next two days at Children's Hospital. I slept...and cried...and prayed between Jerry's calls.

"Everything's going fine," he reported. "Doctor says he's making progress."

I was half asleep when Jerry walked into my hospital room in the middle of the night. His eyes were red. He was shaking. I struggled to sit up. "The baby?" I asked.

His eyes filled with pain. He nodded. He dropped into the chair next to my bed. He took my hand. "I'm sorry, Colette. I'm so sorry. Mark didn't make it."

There was a screaming in my head. I sobbed. "No, no." My heart ached...my whole body felt heavy. I reached for Jerry. We wrapped our arms around each other and hugged.

Someone shut the door to the room. Jerry and I just held onto each other.

"It was so awful," he whispered. "The doctors did everything they could. I watched them. I was with him. He seemed fine. Suddenly he just stopped breathing. They couldn't get him to breathe again. They tried and tried. They couldn't save him. He was doing so well. Everyone thought he was going to make it."

"I wish I could have been there with him...with you. If only I could have held him just once."

"I didn't get to hold him either. They wouldn't even let me touch him. I could only be there...to watch."

"Oh, God, our poor baby...why him? Why us? What did we do wrong?"

"Shhh, I know." He rubbed the back of my head. "But we didn't do anything wrong—anything to deserve this. Sometimes bad things just happen."

Jerry lay down next to me on the narrow hospital bed. We cried. We talked. We hugged. Finally, we rested.

The sun was coming up when I opened my eyes. Jerry was standing next to the bed. "I have to go. I need to talk to the kids. I have to let everyone know what happened."

"What will you tell the kids? I want them to know they had a brother...to remember him. We don't even have a picture of Mark to show them."

"They're old enough to understand." He pushed the hair back from my forehead and brushed his lips along my hairline. "None of us are ever going to forget Mark. He'll always be a part of our family."

"You're right. We'll never forget him. Give the kids hugs and kisses for me. Tell them I love them. Tell them I can't wait to get home."

"I will. You get some more rest. I'll be back tonight during visiting hours."

At the door he paused. "Your mother's due back from her trip. What should I tell her? Do you want to see her?"

I sighed. Would she make me feel better or worse?

"I don't know. Tell her...tell her whatever you want. I can't think about her right now."

Jerry left. I pressed the buzzer for the nurse. "I need something for the pain," I said. "I just want to sleep for a while."

***

I sat in a chair by the open window. My eyes were closed. The warm, early summer air carried the fragrance of newly cut grass. I tried to keep my mind blank, but the thoughts kept crowding in. The bassinet. The baby clothes. The diapers folded on the changing table. All ready for our homecoming. Why this baby? He was the one we had planned for. Was it because I took the pill? Jerry's right...God doesn't punish people like this. But there had to be some reason it happened. The kids...how were they taking the news? They'd be so disappointed—so sad.

I heard a knock. The door to my room opened. The sounds from the hall floated in. Babies crying...the excited voices of the new mothers. Father Miller came into the room. "Colette," he said. "I am so sorry to hear about your baby." He pulled the chair from next to the bed and sat facing me.

"He wasn't baptized. We didn't think about it...didn't talk about it. We didn't know he was going to die. Will...will he be in limbo, Father? Can he go to heaven?"

"The Church teaches that the desire for baptism ensures salvation for those unable to be baptized with water. Your baby was sick. You couldn't baptize him. I believe he is saved through your wish for his baptism."

"Thank you. I can't imagine a God that wouldn't receive an innocent baby into heaven."

"Me neither. Now, Jerry tells me that you have something else troubling you. Do you want to talk about it?"

Dang. What would Jerry have told him? About me taking the pill? I didn't think so. I couldn't imagine that.

"What do you mean, Father?"

"Well, you know these things just happen. There's no reason for them. Mark's death is not part of God's plan."

Just happen? I didn't believe that for a minute. I believe that there's a reason for everything that happens. Not that God is cruel... just that He has a plan we don't yet understand. If there was no reason for Mark's death, there was no reason for his birth. Obviously this priest and I disagreed. I felt the stubbornness rise inside of me. Was I questioning the wisdom of a priest? I looked at him.

"I know God is not cruel. I'm not blaming Him."

On the other hand, I was still trying to figure out if it was my fault...if I had done something wrong. All I ever wanted was to be a good person...a good wife...a good mother. I felt like I had let my family down somehow. And there was nothing I could do about it. But the priest couldn't help me with those feelings.

"Okay, then. I think Jerry might have been concerned about that."

I hated that Jerry was talking to the priest about me. It made me feel like a child.

"No reason for concern," I said.

He nodded. "I don't know if you've talked to Jerry today. He's made all the arrangements. I'll be saying a funeral Mass for Mark tomorrow morning. He'll be buried..."

Suddenly the door to the room was flung open. My mother walked in, followed closely by a nurse.

"Mama," I cried. "You're home!"

"Ma'am, you can't go in there," the nurse said. "I told you...visiting hours are restricted on this floor."

"I am here to see my daughter," Mama said. "I will see her right now. I have no intention of waiting until this evening. You talk to whomever you need to talk to. I am not leaving."

Father Miller stood up. "Mrs. Taube," he said. He turned to the nurse. "I think there are special circumstances here, Nurse. I'm sure you can get permission for this mother to see her daughter right now."

The nurse looked at me. I nodded. She smiled and shut the door.

"Well, I have other visits to make," he said. "I'll be on my way. Are we all set, Colette?"

"Yes. Thank you for coming, Father. And thank you for taking care of my baby. I wish I could be there tomorrow."

"You'll be there in spirit."

"Good-bye, Father," Mama said.

Mama stood next to my chair. As soon as the priest left the room, she bent down to kiss my cheek. "Why is Father Miller saying the Mass? Why didn't Jerry get Father George?"

I looked at her. I was speechless. Father George had said the funeral Mass and directed the burial service for Daddy a little over a month ago. Afterward, my brother Billy had talked Mama into taking a cross-country car trip with him and Lorraine and Davey. She had just returned. It was the first time I'd seen her in weeks.

"Mama," I said. I grabbed her hand. "How are you? How was your trip? I'm so happy you're here. I've been so anxious for you to get home! Sit and talk with me."

She pulled her hand away. She remained standing. "Father George is the pastor. He should have gotten Father George."

I'd learned over the years that Mama's way of dealing with stress is to create distractions. She'd been through a lot with Daddy's illness and death. But wasn't she going to ask me about Mark?

"Maybe Father George was busy tomorrow. Father Miller will do fine."

"Hmm... I guess he'll have to do. I'd have thought Jerry would talk to me about it."

"You weren't here. Besides, I don't think he'd want to bother you."

She didn't say anything. She just stood there.

"Oh, Mama," I whispered. "It was so awful. I can't believe Mark died. He was so beautiful...so perfect."

"I'm truly sorry for your loss. But you're a strong person. You'll get through it."

I had hoped Mama would be able to share some wisdom...some insight. She would be able to tell me how to deal with the death of a child. She would somehow make me feel better. She had birthed twelve children and lost two. She would know what it was like. Now I knew she would not be able to help me. Worse, I felt a barrier between us. Mama never dealt with feelings. She needed to always be in control. Now I understood why I had dreaded seeing Mama.

"I don't feel very strong."

"God doesn't give you more than you can bear. Sometimes loss is what being a wife and mother is all about. Sacrifice. You'll have more children."

I sat in the chair for a long time after Mama left...thinking about her...thinking about what she'd said. I felt motherless, unsupported. I wondered if there was ever a time in my life that Mama provided the warmth, the love I needed when I needed it most. And I hoped with all my heart that I knew how to be a more nurturing mother than she had been.

***

Sacrifice?   Anger...that was my first conscious awareness of Mama. I was 2-1/2 years old. It was the summer of 1943. Mama was standing inside the front screen door of our house on Mt. Olivet in Detroit. It was early morning. My sisters and brothers were still asleep. I was hanging onto the skirt of her cotton housedress. I wore only my panties. Tears were running down my cheeks. I was hot and itchy.

"Mama, hold me," I cried. "I want up!"

She ignored me. She was focused on Daddy. He was standing next to the car parked at the curb in front of our house. The driver's door was open. He was looking up at Mama. Grinning.

"I don't understand how you can just go off and leave me," she said. "In my condition. With two sick babies. Just so you can entertain someone else's kids. I can't believe you would do this to me!"

"I'll be back as soon as I can," Daddy said. He climbed into the car, rolled down the window, waved, and drove away.

Mama leaned down and brushed my arms away from her skirt. She grabbed one of my hands and pulled me across the living room, through the kitchen, and into the bathroom. She didn't say a word. She sat me on the toilet seat. I shook with sobs. She pulled a chair from the kitchen and set it next to the tub. She filled the tub with cool water and swished it with her hand. She stripped me down and put me in the tub.

"There now," she said. "Just pretend you're swimming." She smiled.

The water felt soothing. Mama sat at my side. I stopped crying. I was content. Then my baby sister woke up.

Years later, I asked Mama about that memory.

"Karen was 8 months old," she told me. "You both had the chicken pox. I put baking soda in the water to stop your itching. I was pregnant with Billy. Daddy had to help out at the church picnic. He was an usher. He had to go. He'd promised."

"Shouldn't he have stayed home with you?"

"No, I managed."

Mama was a proud woman. Public appearance was important to her. She believed in sacrifice...sacrifice of oneself for the good of others. She wouldn't let Daddy stay at home. What would people think? But she wanted him to know that she would be suffering while he was out "having a good time."

I'm the sixth child in a family of twelve—six boys, six girls. I'm smack in the middle—the third daughter. I've thirsted for Mama's attention my entire life. I've thirsted for her approval. I don't know my mother. I don't understand her. She has strong opinions. She lets you know what she's thinking...but never what she's feeling.

Now something else struck me about this memory. Mama had told me she was pregnant with Billy. She didn't even mention Johnny. Growing up I knew that I had a little brother named Johnny. He was Billy's twin. I knew he died...but Mama never talked about him. We learned not to ask. If we did, we were greeted with silent disapproval.

Aunt Bea told me the story.

Mama's parents lived down the street. Aunt Bea happened to be visiting Ma and Pa when Mama started in labor. Her babies were always born at home. Daddy telephoned Ma for help. "Ma and I went right over to your house," Aunt Bea said. "Your mama usually delivered babies quickly. Your daddy had called the doctor and he was supposedly on his way. We waited and waited. Your mama was in a lot of pain. The baby wasn't coming. Everybody was frantic. We didn't know what to do. Nobody knew your mama was having twins."

As it turned out, the doctor had been in his office when Daddy called. Dr. Pete's office was north of the cemetery, on the other side of the railroad tracks. He'd left immediately, but was stopped at the railroad crossing by a train. Billy was born just as the doctor arrived. But it was too late for Johnny. A perfectly healthy baby, he'd suffocated while waiting to be born.

"It was so sad," she said. "To lose a baby that way. Your daddy wrapped Johnny in a blanket and took him to the funeral home. All of us cried and cried. But you know what? I've always said that baby saved your mama's life. Right after he was born, your mama started hemorrhaging. If Billy and Johnny had been born quickly, the doctor wouldn't have been there and your mama would have bled to death. Who knows? God works in strange ways!"

At the time I hadn't asked Aunt Bea how Mama dealt with the death of her son—and she didn't tell me. We were both women who had given birth. We knew how awful it would be to lose a child. Mama bore it. She had no choice.

Now I knew how she felt. So sad, so helpless—like there was a big hole in my heart that nothing could fill—and the emptiness would be there forever. There are no words to describe what a parent feels at the death of a child—the extinguishing of joy in the present and the loss of hope for the future. Survival is possible, but I knew that my life would never be the same.

Chapter 2

When I arrived home my sisters had already been there. The house bore no traces of a new baby. Everything had been packed away. Family and friends came to offer their condolences, to bring casseroles and hams and lasagna and cakes. Someone was always there to help with the children. The activity distracted me. The emptiness inside me was filled with the love I felt around me...with the hugs and kisses of my little ones. Mama did not come.

The days passed. I was feeling stronger...physically. Emotionally, I was on a see-saw...a rollercoaster. The plunges exhausted me. Jerry went back to work. Soon I was on my own. Nobody came. There were few calls, but I managed. Dishes might be in the sink. Clothes lay unfolded in the dryer. We ate a lot of peanut butter and jelly sandwiches, hot dogs, beans, chili and sloppy joes. But I was intent on enjoying my children's company. Their presence was soothing. We played Candyland, Sorry, Monopoly and Go-Fish. We drew and colored pictures. And walked to the swings and slides at the park.

One morning I awoke and for the first time in weeks I saw my situation clearly. The fogginess was gone. Yes, I was feeling down. But no one could help me feel better. It was up to me. I had two choices. I could give up...have a nervous breakdown...or I could go on. I considered my alternatives. A breakdown might remove the memory... dull the pain for a while...but it would accomplish nothing in the long run. Mark would still be dead. Nothing would bring him back. I loved my children. They needed me. I decided to struggle on.

I wasn't sure how to handle my feelings. Talk about them? To whom? My sisters and friends didn't want to hear about Mark. They changed the subject when I brought him up. Mama called only to make sure I was functioning. Jerry was done with the subject. He was distracted by his work. Talk to a priest? Right! Bury my feelings? No. I would deal with them somehow. Over time. I didn't want to become my mother.

And I would not do what she had done...forbid my children to ask questions about Mark. We talked freely about him and what had happened. Now I would stop talking about him—unless someone else brought him up. I wouldn't dwell on my loss. I wouldn't let that become my life's focus. But he would always be an important part of our family's life. If anyone asked how many children I have, I would say, "four." He would not be forgotten.

Then another problem arose. Jerry and I visited Dr. Doyle for my post-operative check-up. Everything was fine. But he issued a warning. "If you have another baby, it's possible he or she will have the same problem as Mark," he said. "The chances of developing hyaline membrane disease are influenced by the previous birth of a baby with HMD."

No, I couldn't go through that again!

"You should also know that once you experience placenta praevia as you did, it is likely to happen in subsequent pregnancies. Of course, you'd have to deliver by C-section in any case." He put his hands on my shoulders. "I don't recommend any more pregnancies for you, Colette. I'm sorry."

I looked at Jerry. I was not ready for another pregnancy. Another caesarean. Another loss. Not now. Probably never. Neither was Jerry. I felt a strange calm...the relief of a heavy burden...then huge concern.

What would we do? We were ready to resume our sex life. We ached for each other. We needed each other. But we didn't want to take any chances. There could be no unplanned pregnancy.

Dr. Doyle wrote a prescription for birth control pills. "Start taking these immediately," he instructed. "Wait at least a week before having sexual relations. Then you should be good to go. There is no chance of pregnancy as long as you take the pill regularly."

Now what? The Catholic Church approved only the rhythm method. We'd tried that. It gave us three children in two-and-a-half years. The pill had worked. But I felt guilty taking it. I still wondered if it was the reason for my problems with the delivery...Mark's death.

"Absolutely not," the doctor shook his head emphatically. "There is no connection."

I took the prescription script and we left the office. It felt hot in my hands. I slipped it into my purse.

I turned to Jerry. "What do you think we should do?" I asked.

"Take the damn pills like the doctor recommended," he answered gruffly. "What else can we do?"

"I know! I'll go to confession. I'll talk to the priest. I'm sure there must be a way out of this dilemma. With Vatican II...with all the changes in the Church."

"Good idea. I'll go with you."

We walked into the church together.

"I'll go to Father Miller," I whispered. "He's young...more modern. He's more likely to understand."

"I'll wait until you're finished. Then I'll go." He slipped into the pew near the confessional.

There were three doors along the side wall. Above the middle door there was a placard with Father Miller's name on it. The light above the door indicated he was inside. One of the side doors opened and a young matronly woman came out. She had a black lace veil on her head. She looked familiar. She smiled and held open the door for me. I nodded, and walked into the dimly lit confessional.

I knelt down on the rubber cushion of the wooden kneeler. It faced a black opaque screen. The great thing about confessionals is that you are an anonymous sinner. The priest can't see you...and you can't see him. You are both shadowy figures. He is there to listen...and to forgive. Not to judge, I reminded myself. The panel behind the screen slid open. I clasped my hands together.

I recited the ritualistic words. "Bless me, Father, for I have sinned. It's been two months since my last confession." I took a deep breath. "I...I have to take birth control pills, Father. I know the Church teaches you're not supposed to. But rhythm doesn't work for us."

"You can take birth control pills for 15 days of the month...and practice abstinence the next 15 days," he said. "The Church approves that method."

"No, Father, I can't. I get terrible migraines. The doctor said it's from unbalanced hormones. And it's too risky. I might still get pregnant. The doctor recommends that I don't have any more pregnancies. It's too dangerous for me and for the baby."

"Well, I'm sorry. But that's the only use of birth control pills the Church allows. It's the modern method of rhythm."

"Besides," I argued. "What's the point? If birth control pills are okay for 15 days, why not for a whole month? It doesn't make sense." I was on a roll. My voice had begun to rise. I trembled with indignation. "Is abstinence a punishment, Father? Is that the idea?"

"I'm truly sorry. I can't help you. I can't give you permission to practice birth control. My conscience won't allow it."

"Permission? Your conscience?" I couldn't believe what he was saying.

"If you want another opinion you can see the priest in the confessional on the other side of the church."

"I have a conscience, too, Father. I don't need to see another priest. My conscience says it's fine to practice birth control in this circumstance. It's perfectly logical to take the pill. For the whole month. For the rest of my life." I got up and walked out of the confessional. My cheeks felt warm. I was still trembling.

Jerry stood up, grabbed me by the arm, and hurried me out of the church. He walked me to the car, opened the door, and guided me inside. He shut the door and came around to the driver's side. He climbed in and shut the door. He turned to face me. His blue eyes were bright with laughter. "I heard every word," he chuckled. "Everyone in church heard every word you said. They couldn't help it. You were shouting at the priest!"

I was stunned. I felt numb. I had yelled at a priest...in the confessional! "Aren't...aren't you going to confession?" I asked.

"You took care of things for both of us," he said. "Good job, Colette. We're free!"

I wasn't so sure. I wondered if my confidence would hold. I was raised with a little voice inside that monitored my decisions. It bullied me and made me afraid of change. It always stepped in when I wanted to challenge the status quo or do anything my parents wouldn't have wanted me to do. It treated me as though I were a child. Today I was able to contact my own authority. I was able to free myself from the voice. Tomorrow, who knew?

At least I was aware of its existence. Now I needed to practice disengaging from the voice. Understanding that it wasn't me. Remembering a time when the voice was silent and I was my essential self. Talk back to the voice like I had talked back to the priest today. Tell it to stuff itself. Live as if I can take care of myself. Yes. "As if" will create a bridge to a new way of life for me. One thing I knew for sure. I was going on the pill.

***

Mama called the next morning. "Christine Lipinski saw you in church yesterday," she said. "At confession. With Jerry. It sounds like you put on quite a show!"

Chapter 3

I didn't feel comfortable talking to Mama about my problems—especially relative to having any more babies. Or about birth control. There was sex involved. And the rules of the church. I was going to do what I had to do. I wasn't looking for her blessing or for her approval. She would eventually figure it out.

**

There were no birth control pills in my parent's day. Rhythm—under exceptional circumstances like danger to the life of the mother or baby—was the only option for devout Catholics. Mama might cast her fierce brown eyes at a priest and question his intelligence, but she would never question his authority. So despite the difficulties, they continued to have babies. And to appreciate them.

I remember the arrival of my last three siblings.

My twin sisters were born on a snowy December afternoon in 1945. My older brothers and sisters were in school. It was two months before my 5th birthday. Karen was almost 3 years old, Billy, almost 2.

We sat on the landing outside the kitchen door with our coloring books, drawing paper, pencils and crayons. Three steps down was another landing and a door that opened to our backyard. A long, open flight of stairs off the landing led to the shadowy basement. We shivered in our thin sweaters. The cold nipped at our fingers.

Every once in a while the curtains on the kitchen door would part and our grandmother would peek out. The next time I saw her, I jumped up and grabbed the door handle. "Ma, it's cold," I said. "We want to come in. Karen has to go potty!"

She cracked the door open and poked her head outside. "In a little bit," she said. "Take your sister to the toilet in the basement."

"It's dark down there."

"You're a big girl. You know how to turn on the lights."

I looked at my sister. She sat on the top step. She looked up at me. Her blue eyes were wide with fear. I leaned over. I put my arms around her. She was shivering. "She can wait a little while. But we want Mama. Where is Mama?"

Billy began to whimper. Karen joined him. I stifled my sobs.

"She's busy right now. You kids be good. You'll be able to see your mama in a few minutes."

No voices emerged from inside the house. There was just the sound of people moving around.

"We want Daddy. Where's Daddy?"

She glanced over her shoulder. "Hush, all of you. Your daddy is busy, too. I don't want to hear a peep. Just be quiet and wait. It won't be long." She stepped back and pushed the door shut.

I sat down next to Karen and picked up a coloring book. "Look, Billy," I said. "Here's a picture of a choo-choo train. You and Karen can color it for Mama."

It seemed like hours before the door was flung open. Daddy stood there. He was grinning.

"Daddy," I called happily. I jumped up. "Ma won't let us in. Where's Mama? Can we come in now? We're freezing!"

"Come and meet your brand-new baby sisters," he said. He pointed to a wicker basket set on the table.

Billy and Karen and I trooped into the kitchen.

"Quick!" Daddy urged. "Shut the door. The babies can't get a chill."

The oven door was open. The heat felt good. Daddy lifted the oblong basket off the table. He set it on the floor. The basket was lined with a thick blue checkered blanket. Two tiny babies lay inside, wrapped in pink blankets. One was bald, one had thick dark hair.

My eyes grew wide. I gasped in surprise.

"That one is Janet." He pointed to the bald-headed baby. "And that one is Judith...we'll call her Judy." He pointed to the dark-haired baby.

"Where did we get them?" I asked. I peered into the basket. Nothing was moving. "Are they doll babies?" I reached out my hand to touch them.

He grabbed my hand. "No, they're real live babies. You mustn't touch them right now. They're too new. You can hold them later." He picked up the basket and set it on the table.

"But where did we get them?"

Daddy pointed to a black bag on the table next to the wicker basket. "The doctor brought them in his bag." He smiled.

I looked at the black leather bag. It wasn't very big. I pictured the babies inside...they were pretty tiny. "Weren't they squashed?"

"The doctor brings babies in that bag all the time. He knows how to be careful. Now. I'm sorry but you'll have to go back outside and wait for a little while longer. Then you can come in and see Mama."

"Is Mama sleeping?" I looked at the closed bedroom door.

Billy and Karen started to sniffle.

"Hush," he whispered. He put his hands on their heads. He turned them around and guided them through the kitchen door to the landing. "You take care of your brother and sister. No, Mama is not sleeping. The doctor is talking to her. When he leaves, you can come back inside. It'll only be a few minutes. I promise."

I walked outside. The kitchen door closed. We sat on the steps and waited...and waited.

Ma opened the door. "You can come back inside," she said. "Don't run. And don't go into the bedroom. You can just stand in the doorway."

Mama was in bed, propped up on pillows, holding a baby in each arm. She looked sleepy. Her hair was mussed. Mama never stayed in bed. It scared me.

"Mama!" I cried. "Are you sick?" She smiled and shook her head.

Daddy sat on the edge of the bed. He was watching Mama. He didn't look up.

"Your mama is fine," Ma said. She pulled us back and shut the door to the bedroom. "Your mama and daddy just need to rest for a while. Who wants a peanut butter and jelly sandwich?"

"Me! Me!" Billy and Karen hollered. They ran to the table.

I looked at my grandmother. Afternoon snacks were a rare treat in our house. And Ma never paid us much attention. Children were to be seen...not heard. She was tall, thin and sharp-edged. Her fingers were gnarled and twisted. She wore her long white hair pulled into a knob at the back of her head. She moved in a slow, shuffling walk. I knew something strange was happening. But when Ma said "move", I moved.

***

The twins were the last to be born at home...but not the last baby. Davey was born in the hospital. He came three years later. I don't know what accounted for the gap.

"He's my surprise baby," Mama said. She laughed. "I never thought I'd have another. I'm too old." She was 40.

I don't remember Mama being pregnant...or acting sick. She's told me stories of how nauseated she was with each pregnancy. Every morning for months. Eating soda crackers. Drinking Vernor's ginger ale. How she bled profusely for weeks after each birth. At the time I was oblivious. I didn't hear any talk. I didn't notice Mama getting fatter...or thinner. To me, each baby was a surprise.

I don't remember Mama being in the hospital either. Davey just showed up one day...not quietly. Something was wrong with him. I was standing in the dining room. The white organdy covered bassinet was in the sun room. The French doors were open. Mama had just laid the baby down after feeding him a bottle.

"Leave him be," Mama said. "He's fussy. I have to change my dress. He spit up all over me. Again." She walked into the kitchen.

Suddenly, I saw a white geyser shoot up from the middle of the bassinet. I heard a gurgling. "Mama," I yelled. "The baby!"

She ran back into the sun room and picked him up. "Oh, my God," she cried. "He's vomited. He's choking!" She wiped his face with a diaper. She flung him over her shoulder and started patting his back. More milk shot out of his mouth. He started to cough...then wail. "Oh, thank God!" she said. "Thank God!" Tears rolled down her cheeks. She held him for a long time.

My tiny brother had been spitting up a lot. He was cute...but stinky. For weeks Mama and Daddy had been hovering worriedly over him. This was the culmination. "He could have choked to death," Mama said. "If Colette didn't happen to be standing there. If she hadn't known enough to call me."

The doctor finally diagnosed him with pyloric stenosis. "It's a condition that stops milk from being digested," Daddy said. "Davey needs an operation. Otherwise, he'll get dehydrated. He could die."

What I most remember is Daddy and Mama's distress and fear during the days they waited to learn how serious the problem was...and the day they took him to the hospital for surgery. "You say lots of prayers," Daddy told us. "All of you. I'm counting on you. With so many of us asking, God has to hear."

Davey was my parent's twelfth baby...he may as well have been their one and only child. It was obvious to me—as young as I was—that his life was precious to Mama and Daddy. To all of us.

Davey came through the operation without a problem. Mama and Daddy brought him home a few days later.

"Let me see where they cut him," I said.

Mama laid him in the bassinet. She removed his snowsuit, pulled up his undershirt, and unpinned his cloth diaper. There was a padded bandage across his tiny stomach. I stepped back. "Is he going to throw up any more?" I asked.

Daddy stood in the doorway. "Nope," he said. "No more vomiting. No more spitting up."

Mama pulled down the baby's undershirt, pinned on a clean diaper, and dressed him in a tiny blue flannel nightgown. She covered him with a fluffy wool blanket. "Thank God," she said.

Chapter 4

Now that I'd been married a few years, I felt I knew something about relationships. I believed Mama and Daddy cared deeply for each other, but I couldn't help but wonder how they ended up together. They were so different. Mama told us she and Daddy met at a cousin's party. Each had come with a date. "It was love at first sight," she said. "I went home with the boy I'd come with—but it was the last time I ever dated anyone else."

"Why did you like him?" I asked.

"He was smart and had a great sense of humor." She looked off into the distance. "He knew so much about so many interesting things."

"What about the one you came to the party with?"

"Oh, he was nobody I was interested in."

Daddy was born in Detroit in 1904, the second child in a family of five. His father emigrated from Germany when he was 2 years old. His mother was born in America of German and Polish immigrants. Grandpa and Grandma Taube both worked in factories—Grandpa on the assembly line at the Packard Automotive Plant and Grandma rolled cigars for a cigar maker.

When Daddy finished eighth grade, his parents removed him from school and sent him to work full-time to help support the family. He wasn't poor, but his parents placed a great value on money. He never had any luxuries growing up. When my parents met, Daddy was working in the same plant as Grandpa Taube.

"I would have stayed in school if I could have," Daddy told us. "I loved school. I loved learning new things. It was my dream to finish high school."

Mama was born in Detroit in 1908. She was the oldest of four children. Both of her parents had emigrated from West Prussia when they were only 5 and 6 years old. We called Mama's parents "Pa" and "Ma". Pa was a tradesman—he owned and operated a shoe store, a hardware store, and a confectionary store. Ma never worked in the businesses. She was a homemaker.

As a young child of Polish immigrants, Pa had experienced severe poverty and discrimination growing up. "I walked to school barefoot... in rags...even in the winter," he said. "Kids called me names like 'Polack and beggar.'" He worked hard to make sure his children had a better life. Mama went to parochial schools and was a high school graduate—a rarity at the time for a young woman in her socio-economic environment. She was working as a secretary at Dodge Brothers Company when she met Daddy.

"I was spoiled growing up," Mama said. "Pa always made sure I had the best of everything." She would tell us stories about how the nuns in her Catholic grade school had to treat her nice—even when she was sassy. "Pa always fitted them with free shoes. They were afraid to punish me. And I knew it. I took advantage of it."

Daddy was easy going, laid back—almost mellow—and much more demonstrative and loving than Mama. He had a dry sense of humor and laughed a lot, crinkling his warm brown eyes. He loved the outdoors— camping, fishing, swimming and walking in the woods. He was of medium build, stocky, with dark brown hair. He read educational books—his thirst for knowledge was unquenchable. He was a hard worker, but he tried his best to find time to enjoy life. He loved to sing. He played the piano and violin by ear—he had no formal musical training. One of his favorite sayings was, "You've got to take time to stop and smell the roses." Spending time with his family was his greatest joy.

Mama was intense—an achiever—and rarely showed her emotions. She had a good sense of humor, but rarely laughed out loud. The greatest emotion I can remember her displaying was righteous anger. Her dark brown eyes would blaze and her mouth tighten into a line as she faced her antagonizer. But it was rarely, if ever, directed at her loved ones. Its focus was toward anyone who attempted to do her or her family wrong. She was a proud woman who had a strong sense of self worth. She worked hard, rarely stopped, and expected everyone to keep up.

When I was an adult, Mama told me that Daddy had promised to further his education and get a professional job after they were married. I can picture him promising that. Daddy was a dreamer. I'm sure he believed what he said—and he might have followed through. But circumstances were against that ever happening. My parents were married on May 29, 1929. Mama was 20 years old, Daddy was 24. Less than five months later, the stock market crashed and the country was in a depression.

My brother Donny told me that Mama once relayed a different story to him about why she married Daddy. As a 20-year-old, Donny had just had his heart broken. He learned that the young girl he was in love with was already married and returning to her husband in Kentucky.

"I was downstairs in my bedroom crying," Donny said. "Mama came and sat on the edge of the bed."

"I know what you're going through," she said. "I was once in love before I met your daddy. My heart was broken and I thought I'd die. I married your daddy on the rebound. But it's all worked out. And it will work out for you, too."

"Mama asked me never to tell anyone," he said. "Heck. I don't know. Maybe it isn't even true. But it made me feel better—and closer to Mama than I'd ever felt."

We looked at each other. Now that made some sense. There is no doubt that our parents loved each other deeply—but it was hard to picture that it came "at first sight". Perhaps it did on Daddy's part. But with Mama, it would have taken more time. We just couldn't see her loving easily or spontaneously. Her love had to be earned.

Daddy always said there were patterns to life and you had to take the good times with the bad. "It's no use crying over things that are beyond your control," he told us. "Whatever will be, will be."

Mama fought with her entire being to control whatever she could before she'd let go. But I never heard her complain about her lot in life. "There's a reason for everything," she said. "No one ever said life would be easy."

Both of them learned the lesson of "letting go" in the earliest years of their marriage.

When her employer learned Mama was getting married, she was "let go" from her job as a secretary. "They didn't actually fire me," Mama said. "It was just assumed that I would leave. Respectable married women didn't work outside the home." It embarrassed her that Grandma Taube worked in a factory. "It's not right. A woman's place is in the home."

How long after the Great Depression started that Daddy continued to work at Packard is unclear, but Mama often retold the story of when he lost his job. "His boss told him to do something that Daddy thought was unethical," she said. "He refused to do it—and quit. He wasn't fired. He quit. During the depression. I couldn't believe it when he came home and told me!"

As adults, we heard the story from Mama many times. We never learned what made Daddy quit, but it had to have been something significant. While Daddy valued his personal honesty and integrity, he was not a foolish man. By then Mama was pregnant and times were bad. He had a family to support.

For a while, Daddy ran Pa's candy store. "But he was always giving free samples to people he felt sorry for," Mama said. She smiled.

"Anyhow, it was a bad time for that kind of business and Pa eventually had to close the store. After that, your daddy stood in lines whenever and wherever work was offered. He took any odd jobs he could get. One time he even sold apples on a street corner."

Eventually his perseverance paid off. "Bower's had one job posted," she said. "There were hundreds of applicants in line. We had been praying a novena to St. Joseph the patron saint of workers to find Daddy a permanent job...and it worked. The man who was doing the hiring walked up and down the line and picked a few people out to talk to. Daddy was one of them. After talking with Daddy, he hired him on the spot. When Daddy came home to tell me, we both cried. Times were tough. We were so grateful."

My oldest sister Lorraine was born on January 18, 1930—just short of eight months after my parents were married. Whenever she told the story, Mama always stressed that she did not "have to" get married. Although this terminology is pretty antiquated now, it was used commonly in those days to mean you were pregnant as a bride. You were expected to take responsibility for having sex before marriage by marrying and raising the child together.

Mama said those closest to her knew she wasn't pregnant on her wedding day because she had her period and stained her white gown. "Yet, some of my bridesmaids still whispered about me after Lorraine was born," she said. It always bothered Mama that anyone would have cause to spread any kind of story about her.

Whether or not anyone ever whispered about Mama, we believed she wasn't pregnant when she got married. It was unimaginable for Mama to let something like that happen to her. She had too much pride—and she always followed the rules even if she didn't necessarily believe in them. Finally, there is no doubt that my oldest sister was born prematurely.

The doctor who delivered Lorraine at home didn't expect her to live. She was too tiny. "The size of a pound of butter," Daddy said.

"She fit in the doctor's hand." The doctor washed Lorraine off in the kitchen sink under the cold water. My parents always maintained that this carelessness on the part of the doctor is what caused her cerebral palsy. But it would be a few years before they even realized there was a concern.

In those days there wasn't the medical technology to diagnose health problems in newborns—especially those born outside of hospitals. It wasn't until a child was recognized as being "slow to develop" physically or mentally that they were examined more carefully. "Mentally, Lorraine was quick," Mama said. "She talked early and showed every sign of being a highly intelligent baby. We thought she was just slow to start walking."

Lorraine was almost 2 years old when my oldest brother, Marvin, was born at home on the last day of 1931. During the months that followed, Mama and Daddy would learn that Lorraine had cerebral palsy and—according to the doctors—would never walk. And they would lose their 10-month-old baby son to spinal meningitis. At the time Mama was five months pregnant with Mary Ann.

Chapter 5

Now Mama's phone call took me by surprise. She had heard about what happened at church.

"Christine Lipinski," I said. "I knew she looked familiar. She's the one who was coming out of the confessional when I was going in. She smiled at me."

Mama didn't say a word. She waited.

"I remember who she is—she's the one who's in charge of the funeral luncheons, isn't she?"

"Yes," Mama said. "And she certainly knows who you are!"

Shoot. Now what? How much did Christine hear? What did she tell Mama?

"It's so nice of her to remember me," I said. "I'm sure she called to see how you're doing."

Time for a diversion.

"Mama, do you remember when I was in second grade and I went to confession for the first time to Father Graeber? He was so grumpy and impatient. Everybody was afraid of him."

"You mean the time you told him in confession that you missed Mass—I don't know how many times—and he started yelling at you?" she asked.

"Yeah. Everybody could hear him. 'Tell your parents they're leading you to hell!' he said. 'Tell them they must take you to church or they're going to hell with you!' I was terrified. I thought I must have done something terrible. I was crying when I came out of the confessional."

"Sister Mary Alphonsus wrote a note and pinned it to your dress," she reminded me.

"You laughed when you read it."

"Well when I asked you what you told the priest, I understood what happened."

"I thought it was a sin to skip Mass on weekdays, so I told him I missed Mass five times...five mortal sins."

She laughed. "He should have questioned you himself. You were only 7 years old."

"And when I was in third grade, I got in trouble with Father Konopka."

"You did?"

"Yes. Sister Cyrilla told us that if the Communion host gets stuck on the roof of your mouth, you should use your tongue to work it down. You must swallow it whole. Never chew the host and never touch it with your finger."

"Right."

"Well, that seemed silly to me. I thought, 'Your tongue is part of your body. So are your cheeks and throat and stomach. If the host can touch all of those body parts, why can't you touch it with your finger when it gets stuck to the roof of your mouth?' I didn't argue with Sister. But whenever the thin wafer got stuck on the roof of my mouth, I secretly used my finger to pry it down."

"And Father Konopka caught you?"

"Sister did. She told Father. He called me out of class to talk to me. He didn't even try to give me an explanation of why it was wrong. He just told me not to do it anymore. He said I shouldn't question things I was too young to understand."

"He should have explained it better."

"Sometimes priests are actually the ones who don't understand. It's frustrating."

"Hmm," was her answer. She didn't ask me any more questions.

***

Mama has always been a follow-the-rule Catholic. Church every Sunday. No meat on Fridays. Abstain from food and drink from midnight until receiving Holy Communion at morning Mass. Fast during Lent. Faithfully attend services every Holy Day of Obligation. She made sure her family followed the rules as well. When my parents married, they promised to love each other "for better or worse, in sickness and in health" and their children could see that they meant it.

Daddy never questioned God's will. He believed that there was a reason for everything that happened and that one day we would "know the reason why". I never heard him blame God or bemoan his lot in life. "We've had a lot of sickness and worse," he said. "But just look at this family. What could be better?"

Meatless Fridays never bothered me. For dinner Mama always made something delicious—fried fish or tuna patties with mashed potatoes and coleslaw, sometimes tomato or potato soup, occasionally potato pancakes. After supper, we would quickly clean up the kitchen and then—family night. Daddy never planned any chores for Friday evenings. He spent time with us instead. Sometimes Mama would participate; other times it was her night to be alone. And it was the one night of the week that we got to have a special treat—potato chips and soda pop. One bag and two bottles divided among us.

Some hot summer nights we would pile in the car and take a ride to Belle Isle where there were free concerts and plenty of space to spread blankets, listen to the music, and cool off. In those days of no air-conditioned homes, entire families spent the night sleeping in the park. We never stayed the night. We would return home late in the evening hours after the sun had set and there was some relief from the intense city heat.

Other times we would take a ride on Jefferson Avenue along the Detroit River to the foot of Alter Road. There was a fishing pier where Lake St. Clair meets the river. Daddy liked to stop and talk to the fishermen. He would park the car, get out, and walk to the end of the pier with us trailing behind. "Any luck?" he'd ask. He would peer into their buckets. In the wintertime when the ice was frozen solid, Daddy would drive right out onto the lake—braking and skidding and spinning the car to our delighted screams.

On other balmy nights, we'd go to the Bel-Air drive-in movie theater on Eight Mile Road. There was always a double feature playing plus cartoons. Only adults in the car were charged admission. Kids were free. Once we pulled into a parking space facing the outdoor screen, we would spread our blankets on the roof and hood of the car, connect the speaker to the driver's side window, and wait until it was dark enough for the movies to begin. Meanwhile, we'd play on the swing sets and slides just below the screen at the front of the theater.

On other Friday evenings, we'd stay home and play family games— Monopoly, Scrabble, Parcheesi, pinochle, canasta, go-fish, hearts, war—depending on our ages and abilities. But there was no coddling or humoring the youngest children. If you were old enough and able enough to play, you were expected to play to win. There was absolutely no cheating allowed, no gloating winners, and no tearful losers. There was a lot of competition; everyone wanted to be a winner.

Neither parent was overly pious. Their religion was a way of life. And Holy Name of Jesus Church was the center. Daddy was an usher and sang in the choir. My brothers were altar boys. All of us attended Catholic grade school and high school—taught by nuns and priests. Only Lorraine went to a secular school because there were "special" schools for the "handicapped".

We said Grace before every meal..."Bless us oh Lord and these Thy gifts which we are about to receive from Thy bounty through Christ our

Lord. Amen." Religion wasn't discussed and references to individual nuns and priests were guarded.

"Who does Father so-and-so think he is?" Mama said. "Talking down to you-know-who. Sister so-and-so has more brains in her little finger that he has in that overstuffed head of his!"

Daddy looked up from tying my shoes. "Little pitchers have big ears," he said.

Mama was not awed by the priests. Some she liked...others she didn't. In her mind, they were the interpreters of the rules...the experts. That's it. She didn't question their authority, but she was never shy about expressing her opinion when she thought we weren't around. "That Father B is a little arrogant," she'd say. Or, "Father G seems a little hard on Father K. He should realize he's still just a kid."

The young assistants assigned to our large parish were in their mid-20s...newly ordained, right out of the seminary. They liked to visit our house. Most were from large families themselves. They were lonely. They enjoyed the noise...the confusion...the rambunctiousness of our large family. They weren't invited to dinner, but often got lucky with homemade apple pie or chocolate chip cookies or molasses cake. And they confided in Mama and Daddy as parental figures.

While Mama wasn't awed by the priests...she was status conscious. Her large family was proof of her devotion. She was following church edicts against birth control. She recognized that others might not be— those with smaller families. Our Catholic neighbors noted the priests frequent visits. That was good enough for Mama.

On Sundays we went to church. A few of us at a time. To the Mass of our choice. Missing Mass was not an option. It was almost impossible for twelve people living in a house with one bathroom to coordinate getting ready for the same Mass.

Taking turns in the bathroom in the mornings was usually done in shifts—two at a time by sex and age. One person used the sink while the other used the toilet. Privacy anywhere in the house was rare, but always being part of a group never seemed strange as a child. It was just the way things were. We were a family. Space was tight. Everyone made sacrifices including Mama and Daddy.

Mama made sure to check out what we were wearing before we left the house. "I don't want you looking shabby," she told us. We wore our best outfits. Our shoes had to be polished. Our hair combed.

There were two days of the year that my five sisters and I always had a new outfit to wear: Easter Sunday and the first day of school. Mama was an excellent seamstress and sewed something special for each of us. She had a good eye for color and design and studied the Butterick, Simplicity, and Vogue pattern books to ensure we wore the latest styles. She was a master at choosing inexpensive fabrics that were perfect for both the season and our age.

Our straw hats were trimmed with matching ribbons. She spent hours gathering spring flowers to make corsages for Mother's Day. "We might not have a lot of money," she said. "But we don't need to look poor."

When Janet and Judy were toddlers, Mama sewed each of them a delicate pink Easter dress with round puffy sleeves. The fabric was dotted Swiss and was accented with a deeper pink grosgrain ribbon wrapped around the waist and tied in a bow at the back that hung to the hem. On their heads, they wore round white straw sailor hats with a piece of matching ribbon wrapped around the brim. The hats were secured to their heads with a fine elastic band that stretched under their chins.

I particularly remember a full-skirted, silky white organdy dress with cap sleeves that I loved. The under slip was navy blue taffeta. Mama tied a navy blue ribbon at my waist and around my hat. I felt like a princess as my sisters and I paraded into church that Easter Sunday each wearing one of Mama's newest creations. Women parishioners stopped us to tell us how pretty we looked. "Did your mama make your outfits?" they asked. "You're so lucky she knows how to sew!"

Mama could sew most anything. One Easter she made a suit for Mary Ann. The fabric was pearl gray light wool. The suit had an A-line mid-calf skirt with a long sleeve bolero jacket. She wore it with a pale pink blouse, pink gloves, and a tiny straw pink hat with a veil. I was 8 years old at the time, my sister was 16. I can clearly remember the fuss everyone made over her when she walked into church. She was stunning. She looked like a Vogue model.

For the first day of school the outfits would be bright cotton plaid dresses or corduroy jumpers with blouses or plaid gabardine skirts with solid flannel vests. My twin sisters always wore matching outfits—exactly the same style and color. When they started first grade, Mama made them navy blue and white plaid dresses with wide shawl collars. The dresses had wide sashes that tied at the back and the collars were edged in delicate white lace.

For Karen and I—who were a year apart in school—she made outfits that were similar in style and pattern, but different color combinations. That year my maroon and white flannel plaid skirt was matched with a maroon-colored vest. Karen's skirt was navy and white flannel with a navy-colored vest.

It was always so exciting when Mama would bring the shopping bags of patterns, brightly colored fabrics and delicate trimmings home from Penney's or Montgomery Ward's or Sear's. "Which one is mine?" I'd cry as I tore open the containers. "I want this one!" The clean fresh smells of cottons and wools and grosgrains and corduroys and tissue paper patterns would overwhelm me.

In the spring of the second grade school year, each of us made our First Communion. To receive the Sacrament for the first time, the little boys wore navy pants, starched long sleeve white shirts, and blue ties. But the little girls wore frilly white dresses, long white stockings, and bridal like veils. Mama would sew each of us our very own special outfits. Even though we were close in age, there were no hand-me-downs for this momentous occasion.

My dress was white organdy with puffy short sleeves. It had a lace yoke and two layers of ruffles in the calf length skirt. A wide sash at the waist tied in a big bow at the back and hung down to the bottom of the skirt. Under the dress I wore a soft taffeta slip, long white opaque stockings, and buckled white patent leather shoes with a tiny bow. For my head, Mama created a wrist length tulle veil edged in lace with a beaded tiara.

But winter dress coats were a different story. These were expensive, store-bought and handed down from sister to sister whenever possible. One Sunday morning Mama attended 10:00 o'clock Mass. Karen and I were coming out of church as she was walking up the steps. It was winter. Our knee high rubber boats sloshed as we walked. "Hi, Mama," I called.

She glanced at me...then turned her head away. I ran to her and pulled on her coat. "Mama," I insisted.

She looked around. "Shhh," she whispered. "I'm late. I have to get into church. I'll see you at home."

An hour later, she stormed into the house. "It was humiliating," she fumed. "How could we miss noticing that Karen and Colette have outgrown their coats? They don't even cover their dresses. The sleeves are way too short. Their bare wrists are showing! They look like refugees." The next day she took us to Federal's for new winter coats.

Another Sunday morning, Mama attended Mass where Donny was serving as altar boy. When he knelt before the congregation, the soles of his shoes were exposed to the entire church. "I couldn't believe it," Mama said. "He had holes the size of half dollars in the bottom of his shoe. I was so embarrassed!" The next day Daddy took him to Sear's for new shoes.

Mama's sense of self worth included where we fit into society as a whole. One hot Sunday morning in early summer, Mama decided we should attend 7:30 a.m. Mass so that we could leave for the beach right after church. Daddy and my older sisters and brothers were at home preparing a picnic lunch and packing the car. Mama sat at the aisle end of the pew and I sat furthest inside with Billy, Judy, Karen and Janet sandwiched between us. The priest—recently ordained and new to our church—was delivering the sermon. I was only half listening. It was early, and already warm. I could hardly wait to be out of church and on our way to the beach.

Suddenly, out of the corner of my eye, I saw Mama sit straight up... her white mesh hat almost popping off her head. "...and you should be proud of your lower middle class heritage," the priest was saying. I turned my head to watch her. She squirmed. She frowned. She shook her head. She could barely sit still. I was too young to absorb the priest's message—or the context in which he said the words—but I'll never forget them. Mama's reaction burned them into my memory. I knew the priest had said something totally offensive.

After Mass, Mama did not stop to talk with anyone else. She corralled her own small family group and nodded to people she knew as we walked out of church. We started down Van Dyke on the four block walk home. She grumbled all the way.

"Lower middle class?" she said. "Can you imagine he had the nerve to call us low class? The pompous idiot. We're just as good as anyone else. Who does he think he is? Uttering such nonsense from the pulpit. You're just as good as anyone else—I don't want you to forget that. This is America. This isn't a class system. You can be whatever you want to be. Nobody is better than you. You're as good as you believe you are."

We walked beside her. We looked at each other. Mama was questioning a priest! We never said a word.

When we got home, Daddy just listened, too. He knew when to keep his mouth shut.

***

Vatican II brought many changes to the Catholic Church after 1962. Communal Penance services. Female altar servers. Standing to receive Communion. No altar railings. Nuns in lay clothing. No hats required for women. Guitar Masses. The kiss of peace. Removal of saint statues and pictures. Talking in church. No more fasting before Communion. No more Latin Masses. And no more meatless Fridays.

"Pope John said it was time to open the windows and let in some fresh air," Mama said. "I think he took off his hat and let his brains fly out! One Friday you're condemned to hell for eating meat—the next, no problem. One Sunday you can't receive Communion because you forgot and had a glass of water after midnight—the next week you can have a full breakfast an hour before Mass and still receive. It's just too much!"

"Too many changes at once," Daddy agreed. "It'll make a lot of people question and reconsider their faith...their beliefs."

Mama kept following the old ways. "It won't last," she insisted. "It'll go back to the way it was."

Chapter 6

Later that evening, I told Jerry about Mama's call. The children were in bed. We sat at the kitchen table drinking our coffee.

"Was she worried about saving your soul?" he asked."Or more about you causing a scene?"

I thought about it. "I don't know. I changed the subject as fast as I could. I didn't want to find out."

He took my hand. "You know, Colette, it's time for us to move on."

"Move on? What do you mean?"

"To move away from here. Out of the city. To the suburbs. Buy a house. Away, away."

I'd lived in Detroit my entire life. I was born nine blocks from where we sat. No doubt we needed more space. We'd outgrown our two bedrooms—and it was a pain living in an upper flat. A tiny, common backyard. Trying to keep the kids quiet when they played. Climbing two flights to do the laundry in the basement. We'd talked and dreamed about having our own home. We'd been trying to save for one. "The... the suburbs? Now? Can we afford a house?"

"Yes, the suburbs. And yes we can afford it." His blue eyes sparkled. "One of the guys at work is buying a house. Ray Gonzales. He's getting a VA loan. No money down. I checked with the Veteran's

Administration, and I qualify."

I stood up. "Oh my God! Our own house! I can't believe it!" I moved around the table. I put my arms around his neck and sat on his lap.

"I knew you'd be happy." He pulled me tight. "We can start looking this weekend. We'll drive around and find some places."

"But why the suburbs? Where are you thinking of looking?"

"Everyone says that's where we can get the best deals. There's a lot of new construction right now. It's cheaper to buy a newly built house and do the finishing—like carpeting, lawn, wall papering and everything ourselves. Finished houses cost more. We can get a lot more room for less in a brand new house. I was thinking we'd just go north a few miles—across Eight Mile Road—and drive around to see what we find."

"It's so exciting...but kind of sad too. The kids were born here. Baptized here. I can't even imagine going to a different church. It'll be strange to live anywhere else."

"It'll be a new start for you...for us...for the kids. A brand new house. Young neighbors. Lots of kids for our kids to play with. A modern parish. Great schools. Our very own place."

I smiled. "Let's start house hunting, then."

He hugged me tighter. "On Saturday."

***

The Detroit I grew up in was still a booming vibrant city—a city of more than 1.8 million people. But Detroit didn't seem big to me. It was safe and comfortable within the small circle of our neighborhood—a neighborhood defined by the boundaries of our Catholic parish. In some ways Holy Name and its parishioners made up a small town. Our family was known. We attended the same Catholic school and knew nearly everyone by name throughout the square mile area whose limits were set by McNichols Road on the north, Lynch Road on the south, the railroad tracks on the west, and Detroit City Airport on the east.

My family lived in the middle of the first block of Mt. Olivet—six blocks south of McNichols or Six Mile Road as we called it. Our tree-lined street ran two blocks east from Van Dyke to French Road (which abutted the airport). The city limit was two miles north at Eight Mile Road.

There was no town center but there were several corner groceries, hardware, drug, dairy and confectionary stores, bars, a funeral home, a Chevrolet dealership, gas stations, two cemeteries, a welding shop, a shoemaker, a dry cleaners, two flower shops, two restaurants, hair salons, and barber shops. Everything you'd find in a small town. Some were situated on Van Dyke—the main thoroughfare. Others were located on corners throughout the neighborhood. Everyone walked to do their daily shopping

For larger items like clothing, there were shopping areas at major cross streets outside the circle of our neighborhood: Federal's Department store at Harper and Van Dyke; Sear's at Gratiot and Van Dyke; Montgomery Ward's at Seven Mile Road and Gratiot. Located near the major department stores were Kresge's and Woolworth's dime stores, shoe stores, and various dress shops and men's wear shops.

For major shopping, we had to go to downtown Detroit. Everyone went there for the most important purchases. It was a busy, bustling city. And shopping downtown was an adventure and a dress-up occasion. Only there would you find J. L. Hudson's, Crowley's and Kern's. These multi-level department stores were located among blocks of shoe stores, dime stores, dress shops, men's clothing stores, hat shops, tailors, and assorted specialty shops. Hudson's alone had 25 floors of merchandise.

To get downtown, most Detroiters took the transit system—to work or to shop. Electric powered streetcars were still running down the center of Van Dyke until 1947 when they were replaced by buses. Streetcars ran down the center of Gratiot until 1956. Daddy drove his car to work, but it was unusual for the time. Most workingmen kept their cars for special occasions—the "Sunday afternoon drivers". By the early 1950s automotive transportation gradually became more commonplace in the Motor City.

I loved to go downtown. J. L. Hudson's, the world's tallest department store with its multi-levels and more than 12,000 employees, was at the heart of the downtown shopping area. It had five basements, 51 passenger elevators, 51 display windows and 706 fitting rooms—and supplied everything a family could need. There were elegantly dressed elevator operators who wore white gloves and delivered shoppers to exactly the right location in the humungous store. Shopping could also be done by phone. Deliveries by a force of 500 drivers and 300 trucks were free of charge.

J. L. Hudson's sponsored the Thanksgiving Day parade which heralded the beginning of the Christmas season. There were festive floats decorated in themes from children's books like Alice in Wonderland, Oliver Twist and Little Women to popular radio and television shows like the Lone Ranger, the Green Hornet and Howdy Doody. The Doodlebug wormed its way down Woodward Avenue along with countless clowns on bicycles and scary and silly characters with huge painted plaster heads. Santa Claus—with his long white hair and beard, wearing his fuzzy red and white suit—always arrived in his sleigh at the end of the parade to the happy shouts of all the kids.

Every year Daddy took us downtown on Thanksgiving morning for the "Christmas" parade—no matter how cold or snowy or icy. We wore layers of clothing—several pairs of socks and gloves, wool scarves and hats and rubber boots to try to keep warm. But the fabrics we wore never kept us warm enough. By the time we climbed back into the car to head for home, our toes and fingers would be red from the cold.

The heaters in those days were too small and inefficient to heat the interior of the car. "Take off your boots and sit on your hands and feet," Daddy told us. "As soon as we all start breathing hard enough, the car will warm up."

At Christmastime the store's decorations sparkled and delighted everyone. The outside display windows featured animated displays from fairy tales to outer space. Daddy would drive downtown just to see the lighted windows at night. He'd stop in front of each window. "Look kids," he'd say. "Look at that one!" Sometimes he would let us climb out of the car to press our faces closer against the glass.

The twelfth floor fantasy area of Hudson's was a Christmas wonderland. And everyone knew that's where you had to go to talk to the "real" Santa Claus. There were merry-go-around and carnival rides and hundreds of toys displayed. One Christmas season Mama sent Karen and Billy and me downtown with Mary Ann to see Santa Claus. We each had 25 cents to spend on hot dogs or cotton candy or a carnival ride.

I chose a "surprise package." I gave my money to Santa's helper and watched as a huge brightly wrapped package cascaded down a chute from the ceiling. I don't remember what was in the package, but I clearly recall the anticipation and excitement as the package tumbled down.

During my growing up years everything north of Eight Mile Road was still rural. My grandparent's cottage was located on the Clinton River in Utica, just beyond Eighteen Mile Road. To get to it, you drove down Van Dyke through mile after mile of farmland—and it seemed to take forever. I can vividly remember Karen and I sitting in the back seat of Pa's shiny black Model A Ford headed for the cottage. Van Dyke was a three-lane blacktop but the side roads were unpaved gravel and so bumpy that our bottoms kept bouncing off of the stiff black leather seats.

The mile roads were the only break in the monotonous scenery. We must have kept asking if we were almost there, because Ma soon taught us how to watch for the crossroad signs so we would know how much farther we had to go: Nine Mile Road, Ten Mile Road...until we finally saw the sign for Eighteen Mile Road and our turn toward Utica Road and the cottage. I can still see those black and white mile road signs.

**

Now a lot of things had changed. Much of the farm country north of the city limits was being developed into suburbia. People began talking about "metropolitan" Detroit. And Jerry and I would be suburbanites. It was hard to imagine living out of the city.

Chapter 7

"You're moving where?" Mama said. "I understand you need more room, but why way out in the country?"

"It's only to Warren, Mama," I said. "We'll be about four or five miles from you."

"I won't see the kids. It's too far. I'll be all alone."

She must be missing Daddy. She wouldn't like it if I brought him up. "What do you mean alone? You'll still have Lorraine and Judy and Davey. Billy, too, now that he's back from the Navy."

"Sure. And they'll all be moving out next. One at a time."

"You can drive out to see us whenever you want. To see the kids. You can help me plant flowers...teach me about gardening. I've never done that. And you can help me sew all the curtains and drapes."

"Well, I guess it's my problem. I don't see why you couldn't have bought a house here in the city. Near me. Of course, you didn't ask my advice. What do I know? Maybe Jerry is too high and mighty to live in this lower middle class neighborhood."

"Oh, Mama, you know what it's like to live in an upper flat. And how exciting it is to get you own house. Be happy for us!"

I was confused. I felt guilty—like I was abandoning my mother. I knew it didn't make sense—but I still felt bad. For her. I was excited about our new house. About moving to a new place. Three bedrooms, a family room, a nice big yard for the kids to play in. We'd have to wait to buy furniture for the living room. For fencing. We'd add a second bath later. And a garage. It wasn't a big house. But to Jerry and me, it was a palace. Everything so new and fresh. All ours. Well, ours and the bank's. It would be great.

***

For the first years of their marriage, Mama and Daddy lived in an upper flat. Above a funeral home. On Van Dyke—a main thoroughfare that runs north from Jefferson Avenue to the city limits and beyond. Lorraine, Marvin, Mary Ann and Frank, Jr. (who we called "Buddy" during our growing up years) were born there.

"To this day I hate the smell of candle wax," Mama told us. "And gladiolus...and the color purple...and men in black suits. They all remind me of funerals. I've seen enough of them to last me a lifetime!"

It's hard to imagine how difficult it must have been living above a funeral home. Trying to keep small children quiet. Being afraid to move around during viewings and services. The funeral fumes. The somber atmosphere. "There was no yard. No place for the kids to play outside. It was hard on all of us. I had to hang the laundry in the basement. It smelled of formaldehyde. It was creepy!"

Mama was expecting Donny when Grandma and Grandpa Taube decided to give each of their five children the money for a down payment on a house. "We were so excited! I fell in love with a beautiful house on Forest Lawn. It was brick. Two bedrooms. It had a big fenced-in yard. A basement."

But there was a catch to Grandma and Grandpa's generosity. They were to decide which house each of their children bought. "They wouldn't even consider my choice. 'Who does she think she's married to? Rockefeller?' Grandma told Daddy. 'She should be happy she's getting any house at all!' The house I wanted was only $100 more. It was so much bigger—and it hardly needed any fixing up!"

The total price of the house on Mt. Olivet was $1100. Mama and Daddy bought it on a land contract. It was an old farmhouse that had been moved to the narrow lot when property was being cleared for Detroit City Airport. There were four rooms on the main floor—living room, dining room, kitchen and bathroom. Upstairs was an unfinished attic that served as one large bedroom. The house needed work before it could even be lived in.

"Ma and Pa already lived on Mt. Olivet," Mama said. "We moved in with them while Daddy and Pa worked on our house. They dug a basement under the house—manually, shovelful by shovelful—and laid cinder blocks. Then they poured cement for the floor and installed a coal burning furnace, coal bin, fruit cellar, electrical, plumbing, and a hot water heater. It was hard work. It took so long."

Mama and Daddy moved into their own house in early spring of 1937—a few months after Donny was born. At the time, the improvements were incomplete and the house was still heated by a wood burning stove in the living room and a gas cook stove in the kitchen. "We slept in the dining room. The baby slept with us, too. The rest of the kids slept upstairs in the attic."

Later Pa and Daddy added two bedrooms to the back of the house— one off the kitchen and one off the dining room—and a dormer to the upstairs attic.

Mama never tired of telling stories about the house. "It still makes me angry whenever I think about it—all the work Daddy and Pa had to do. For a lousy $100! Their own son...how could they do that to him?"

I don't remember what the house was like when Mama and Daddy moved in. I wasn't born until four years later—the first baby born in the new house. I just heard the stories. Repeated over and over through the years.

Mt. Olivet was a paved street lined with tall maple trees that shaded the narrow sidewalks. Lots were 30 feet wide. Houses stood close to each other and to the street. Most of the houses on the block were two-story single family dwellings with wooden siding—although there were a few more expensive brick homes scattered here and there. In some of the larger homes, upper stories had been converted into flats and rented out. There were more than 60 houses on the short block between Van Dyke and Gilbo.

Our neighbors were predominantly Polish and German Catholics with large families. Most had lived there for many years. Neighbors knew each other and the names of each other's children. There were a lot of children in our neighborhood, but with twelve our family was by far the largest. With so many people living in such close proximity, neighbors learned to get along. And most minded their own business.

The Schneemans right next door to the west had five children. Their bathroom window faced our kitchen windows. The houses were so close together that we could hear the father of the house snorting and spitting in the toilet every morning. Waiting for him to clear his sinuses before he left for work as a streetcar driver, became a family joke.

In addition to their five children, Mr. and Mrs. Schneeman's mothers lived with them in their tiny house. Grandma Schneeman was a slightly chubby woman with a friendly sweet smile. She always waved and said, "hello". Grandma Bachmann was a skinny wrinkled old lady who never smiled and only spoke German. She wore black from the cap on her head to the shoes peering out from under her long dress. During the summer she sat on the cement front porch just rocking back and forth.

As young children, we were taught to always be polite to adults. So even though Grandma Bachmann scared me, I had to stop and say "hello" if she was sitting on the porch. But every time I did, the same thing happened. She would peer at me with her piercing black eyes…then start yelling in German. The longer I stood there, the more agitated she'd become—waving her arms and yelling louder and louder.

I would stand frozen in place—not knowing what she was saying, what I did wrong, or what to do. Eventually, Mrs. Schneeman would open the front door and speak to her mother in German. Grandma Bachmann would settle back down and close her eyes.

"It's okay, honey," Mrs. Schneeman told me. "You didn't do anything wrong. She thinks you're someone else. You can go and play now."

But it was upsetting to have an adult yelling at me. After the same thing happened a few times, I went to Mama to ask why Grandma Bachmann didn't like me. "She's old and not thinking very clearly," Mama said. "She thinks you're her little sister who died a long time ago. She's really not mad at you. And you don't have to stop and say hello to her anymore."

Being told by Mama that I didn't have to say hello to someone was a big thing. We were never allowed to ignore our neighbors. We knew the last names of everyone on our street. Whenever and wherever we came in contact with an adult neighbor, we were expected to show respect by recognizing their presence whether we liked them or not. We addressed adults as "Mr." or "Mrs."—never by their first names. And if we were rude, our parents would hear about it—and anything else we did wrong.

Next door to the east of us was a large two-family house owned by the Angelines—an older couple with three adult children. The parents lived downstairs; one of the daughters lived with her husband in the upper flat. Mr. Angeline operated a commercial tile business out of the large barn-like garage at the back of their yard. The lots were deep. While houses bordered on Mt. Olivet, the garages were set at the back of the lots and bordered on Darwin Street.

The properties across from our garage were empty fields with only a few scattered houses. Because it was at the back of our garage, we called Darwin "the alley". Mr. Angeline owned the field across the alley from his barn, where he always had a tall pile of fine sand he used in his work. We were forbidden to play in the sand pile, but it was irresistible to Karen and Billy and me.

We never planned to disobey. We would be playing out back behind the garage when one of us would notice the sand pile. It was like a magnet. The sand was so pure and fine. If Mr. Angeline saw us playing in the sand pile, he would holler at us. He was never cruel or mean, just persistent. Countless times he caught us and sent us home. Countless times he didn't catch us—and we played for hours building cities and forts and castles.

Across from where our street ended at French Road was Detroit City Airport. During my growing up years, the airport was very busy with planes taking off and landing throughout the day. The buzz of single engine airplanes was not disturbing—it was part of the normal sounds of the neighborhood. A training center for airplane mechanics was located on the airport grounds directly even with our street. During the 1940s, students walked from Van Dyke to the school each weekday morning and back again to catch the streetcar at the end of the day.

Our house was a wooden bungalow with white clapboard siding and a green shingled roof. A covered wooden porch ran across the width of the house. Upstairs, three narrow windows hung over the front porch roof. Downstairs, two long narrow double living room windows faced the street. A 2-foot-wide paved pathway centered exactly in the middle of the lot stretched from the public sidewalk to the wide wooden porch steps.

To reach the front door, it was necessary to climb six steps and walk 4 feet across the depth of the porch. The floor of the porch and the steps were painted grey. The porch itself had white wooden side railings, posts and decorative trim. It was supported by cement pillars covered in red brick. A white metal glider with soft green cushions sat under the windows. On either side of our front pathway was a postage stamp sized lawn that Mama watered religiously.

The bedroom that I shared with my three younger sisters was above the porch. The windows opened to the front. The smell of fresh cut grass, cool water, and the spitting sounds of spraying water often lulled me to sleep on hot summer nights. We had no air conditioning or even fans to cool the tiny crowded room. We felt lucky to have an occasional breeze from the front windows.

In the wintertime, it was a different story. The house was heated by the coal furnace in the basement. Daddy used ashes to bank the fire at night. First thing in the morning, he'd stoke the ashes and add coal to start the fire. There was no blower. Heat radiated up through the ducts on the main level of the house, but never reached upstairs. Our bedroom had no heating ducts. On the coldest winter mornings, we would awaken to find the front windows completely frosted over—creating beautiful white designs.

"Look," I'd call. "Come see. Jack Frost was here!" We would examine each window to see what "pictures" Jack Frost had painted for us on the frosted glass.

Daddy was always working on the house. Making improvements—wallpapering, painting. Doing repairs—plumbing, electrical. Cutting the grass. Shoveling ashes and clinkers from the coal furnace. After work. In the evenings. On Saturdays.

I was 6 years old when he redid the upstairs attic. He designed a short hall with two bedrooms—one for the boys and one for the girls. He used two by fours to divide the space. Then he nailed 2-inch-wide wooden laths on each side of the two by fours and filled the pocket with rock wool for insulation.

The rock wool was packaged loose in tall brown paper bags. Daddy would lay each bag on the floor and split it open. As a section of the wall was completed, he'd scoop the rock wool out and pack it into the pocket between the rooms. He let me "help" with the scooping for the lower section of the wall. I remember getting the rock wool all over my arms and legs. It was prickly and itchy.

"Whatever you do," Daddy said. "Don't touch your face—especially your eyes. There's real glass in that stuff!"

Daddy also let me help when he laid the tile floor in the basement a few years later. He designed a checkerboard pattern of dark brown and beige tiles. He bought the boxes of asbestos tile as he could afford it. The tile was hard and brittle. It had to be handled carefully or it would chip and crack. Daddy taught me to remove the individual tiles from the box in alternating colors—one from each box—and hand them to him.

After a while he let me help by warming each tile over the flame of a propane heater so it was malleable. He would apply black goop to the floor, and then press the warmed tile in place. It took months of work—and money—before the entire basement floor was tiled. "You sure are a good helper," he said. "I don't know what I'd do without you."

I liked to spend time with Daddy. He talked while he worked. He talked about his dreams. Of travel. "I want to drive through every state in the country some day," he told me. "That's the only way to learn what's out there. The desert. The mountains. The oceans. The small towns. The big cities. I want to see it all!"

He also talked about learning and how important it was to him. "You can learn almost everything there is to know from reading. It's all in books. Just take The Book of Knowledge—and the dictionary. Between those two you can keep learning new things until you die! And then there's the library. You can get books about anything you ever wanted to know—for absolutely free."

The Book of Knowledge was a blue 20-volume set of encyclopedias published in the 1930s. It was Daddy's greatest treasure—and his only extravagance. I would spend hours poring over the "Little Verses for Very Little People" or "The Child's Book of the United States." The books—geared to grade schoolers—were filled with things to make, things to do, stories of famous people, plant life, science, the earth. Daddy read the encyclopedias every night.

He talked about wishing he could have gone to high school. "Grandma and Grandpa thought it was a waste. Making money was more important to them. 'Why do you need a high school education to work in a factory?' they asked. They wouldn't listen when I told them I wanted to learn more about things. They accused me of thinking I was too good for a factory job. But I think it's important to want to better yourself. I want all of my kids to go to college."

I recognized early on that Mama was the taskmaster. Daddy rarely had the opportunity to slack off with Mama around. He tried. If I saw Daddy lying across the bed fully clothed and taking a nap, I'd pull the bedroom door closed so Mama wouldn't catch him. She couldn't stand to see him doing nothing. When she saw him lying there, she'd poke him awake to do something or other.

One day Daddy was late coming home from work.

"Where were you?" Mama asked. "I was so worried!"

"I was taking a nap in the car by the airport," Daddy told her. "I was exhausted and just couldn't drive another minute."

"It must be nice," she said. "I'd like to take a little nap myself."

"Why don't you then? It might do us both some good!"

Chapter 8

I vowed when I became a parent that I would take the time to enjoy my children—and pay them the attention they'd want and deserve. I was careful to keep that promise to myself. From the time my oldest was a baby, I'd do the work that needed to be done around the house, but allot hours each day to focus on each of my children. We'd take walks, go to the park, put together puzzles, play games, do crafts, read books, bake cookies—whatever activities were appealing to and appropriate for each child's age, interest, and skill level.

When I was growing up, Mama rarely had the opportunity to enjoy her children. She was always working. Her day began as soon as the first child awoke in the morning. She'd climb out of bed, pull on her long chenille robe, and stagger sleepily into the kitchen. There she'd strike a match to light the burner under the pot of thick boiled coffee that Daddy always left for her. In the wintertime she'd also light the oven so the kitchen would begin to warm while she went down the basement to add more coal to the furnace.

She was always cold. "You're as skinny as a rail," Daddy told her. "Like the day I married you. You don't have an extra ounce of fat on your bones. No wonder you're always freezing!" He was proud of Mama's trim figure. And he loved to tease her.

In reality, the house was bitterly cold on winter mornings. Although Daddy added coal to the furnace before he left for work, it took time for the rooms to heat up. We'd grab our clothes and run downstairs to fight for spots by the heater ducts in the living room and dining room or by the oven in the kitchen. That's where we would get dressed.

Meanwhile, we'd be waiting for our turns in the bathroom. There was a toilet in the basement but it was used only for the most desperate of times. The stall was no larger than a port-a-potty. Even as a small child my knees touched up against the wood paneled door. And it was dark and damp and scary down there. We used both the kitchen and bathroom sinks for washing up.

While Daddy was at work, Mama had to keep the coal furnace burning. As a tot, I followed her down the narrow basement steps one day when she went to add coal. The furnace was an enormous silver monster located about 10 feet from the coal bin in the farthest corner of the basement.

"Stand back," she told me. She used a rag to lift the latch and pull open the heavy iron door. Inside were red and white coals. "And don't touch the furnace. You'll burn your fingers."

Mama took a black metal shovel from the coal bin. She scooped it full of coal. She lifted it, and carried the load to the mouth of the furnace. She heaved the coal inside. White sparks flew. Red and yellow flames leaped to consume the fresh coal. She turned to get another shovelful. I moved closer. It was so sparkly. I reached out.

"No!" Mama screamed. She dropped the shovel and pulled my hand back...just as the tip of my finger grazed the hot metal.

I whimpered. I started to tremble. My finger hurt. But I was scared because I knew Mama was upset. I had never heard her scream before.

"Let me see." She grabbed my hand and turned it over. "Thank God. It's only a tiny burn." She dropped my hand and touched my shoulder. "Go sit on the steps. We'll put something on it in a minute."

I went to sit on the steps to wait. Mama continued to shovel coal.

Mama told us she weighed less than 90 pounds the day she was married. Looking at old photos she couldn't have weighed much more than that throughout her childbearing years. I don't know where she found the strength to shovel all that coal. For many of those winters she had to have been pregnant—or recovering from a birth. All of her children except Davey were born in December, January or February. But there was nobody else around to shovel the coal. So Mama did it.

That was only one of Mama's chores. With such a large family, laundry had to be done every day—except Sunday. The green wringer washer was in the basement next to the laundry tub. Mama filled the washer with hot water and added Fels Naptha soap. First she immersed the white clothes and linens in the soapy water. While they agitated, she sorted the rest of the laundry into piles—lightest colors to darkest. After a few minutes, she'd stop the washer and use a wooden stick to pull each item out of the hot water and place it in the laundry tub to rinse.

When the washer was empty of the first load, she'd add the next batch of clothes. While they washed, she'd use the electric wringer to remove the water from the items in the laundry tub. The wringer used two rollers under spring tension to squeeze water out of clothing and household linen. Each laundry item had to be fed through the wringer separately. The wringer could be swung over the wash tub so that extracted water would fall back into the tub to be reused for the next load. As each item was rung, she'd place it in a brown wicker basket. The process was repeated over and over until all the loads were done.

I can still see Mama standing by the washer in her faded housedress—her feet swollen in her blue slip-ons. Her arms and hands red from the hot water—and blistered with fiery patches of eczema from her allergy to the soap.

As the loads were washed, they had to be hung to dry. Most of the year Mama carried laundry baskets of wet clothing and linens up the basement steps and out to the yard. She used wooden clothespins to peg each item to the gray ropes strung between two wooden poles. Mama loved to hang the clothes outside—winter or summer—unless it was too icy or snowy.

"I don't like to hang things in the basement," she told us. "They're not as fresh smelling. Not as soft. Besides, they take too long to dry."

There were no disposable diapers. Cloth diapers were used. Mama was always washing, hanging, or folding clothes. Our yard was dotted with diapers or sheets or towels flapping in the wind. As soon as we were old enough, we helped with the hanging and folding. But only Mama ran the washing machine.

"It's too dangerous," she'd tell us. "The wringer could grab your hair or clothes. You could choke to death before anyone could help. Besides, it's too easy to break the buttons on the clothes if you don't know what you're doing."

When I was a baby, we still had an icebox. I remember the iceman coming into the kitchen door carrying a large dripping block of ice in long scissor-like metal tongs—and opening the bottom of the icebox to deposit it. The icebox stood in the spot where our Frigidaire was installed in the early 1940s. But icebox or mechanical refrigerator, neither was large enough to hold sufficient quantities of food to supply the family for more than a day or two. Food never lasted long in our house. So grocery shopping was another daily chore.

I don't know how the shopping was done before Mama had children old enough to send to the store. I was young when it became my job. Mama gave me a penciled grocery list and a small silver clasped black cloth coin purse. "Be sure to hold onto that money," she'd tell me. "And don't lose the list. I don't want to have to do it over."

Karen pulled Billy in the rusty red wagon. I followed behind—pushing the wagon up and down the curbs. I guarded the money and list carefully. In those days, there were tiny family owned grocery stores located every few blocks. "Be sure to go to Klatt's. If there's not enough money for everything, tell Mrs. Klatt to put back the coffee first, then the cheese, then..." She went on down the list.

We'd park the wagon in front of the store, open the screened door, and walk up to the long wooden counter. I'd hand the list and coin purse to the grocer. She'd fill the order, count out the change, hand me back the coin purse, and place the box of groceries in the wagon.

Right next to the wooden counter was a glass display case filled with penny candy. While our order was being filled, we'd look over the offerings. Mary Janes, Bit O'Honeys, Snaps, Candy Cigarettes, Slo-Pokes, Wax Pops, Circus Peanuts, Candy Pills, Root Beer Barrels, Necco Wafers, Chuckles, Double Bubble Gum. We'd whisper to each other about our favorites.

Most days Mrs. Klatt filled the grocery orders and Mr. Klatt worked behind the meat counter. If Mrs. Klatt happened to be upstairs in their living quarters, Mr. Klatt would wait on us. Then we'd be sure to be treated to a piece of candy. "What would you like?" he'd ask.

We were not allowed to spend money on treats—and we were warned not to take charity. "Nothing, thank you, Mr. Klatt," I'd say. "We're just looking."

"Well we have a lot of extra candy today. It hasn't been selling well. I thought each of you might like to take a piece off of my hands. Help me out. What's your favorite?"

Billy would be pulling on my skirt. "Okay," I'd whisper.

We'd each choose a penny treat. "Thank you, Mr. Klatt."

I poked Billy. I looked at Karen. "Thank you," they'd say smiling happily.

We'd trudge guiltily out the door. "Don't tell Mama," I warned. I didn't need to remind them. We all knew she wouldn't like us accepting "a hand-out". But a free piece of candy was more than any of us could resist.

Preparing meals was another of Mama's daily chores. She had supper ready when Daddy walked in the door from work. Most days Mama would put a pot of soup on the stove early in the day. That would be our main meal. She'd cook fresh vegetable soup with pieces of beef, or creamy stewed tomato soup, or chunky potato soup, or split pea soup with ham and sauerkraut, or chicken noodle soup, or butter bean soup with spare ribs. Other favorites were chili made with ground hamburger and red kidney beans or boiled navy beans baked with brown sugar, tomatoes and ham.

In addition to our clothing, Mama sewed all of the drapes, the curtains, the bedspreads. She did the mending. She ironed for hours. But her love was gardening. Any spare time she had you would find her outside bent over her flowers. She nurtured wildflowers—lily of the valley, violets. Her lilac bushes and rose bushes were her pride and joy. At night you could hear the hose running as she sprinkled the front lawn and her flowers. But the white and pink peonies that grew on the bushes in the backyard were unmatched in the neighborhood.

"Everyone wants to know my secret," she told us. "How to keep the ants away. What I'm doing to make the flowers so lush." She smiled. "I'm not talking. I just say, 'It must be something in the soil.'"

One summer day Karen and I were playing in the backyard. We were pretending to make dinner. We decided to pull the round balls off the bushes to use as food. They fit nicely in our tiny tin cooking pots. Mama came outside to hang laundry. "What are you doing?" she asked. She looked down at us. She looked again.

"We're playing house," I said. "I'm cooking."

"Oh, my God! You've picked all the buds off of my peony bushes!" She set the laundry basket on the grass and ran into the house.

We weren't punished. We never heard about her peony bushes again.

***

It took Mama three weeks after we moved into our new house before she'd agree to come out—and it wasn't for a visit.

Chapter 9

"So, Mama, when are you coming out to see our new house?" I asked. The phone receiver was scrunched between my ear and my shoulder. I sat at the kitchen table. I watched my boys playing happily with shovels and buckets, tractors and trucks in the sandbox outside the window. I folded towels fresh off the clothes line. The phone kept slipping.

"I told you," Mama said. "It's too far."

"Only a few miles. We'd really like to see you. The kids have been asking about you. They miss you."

"You know where I live."

Cheryl sat on the little corner seat of the sandbox sucking her thumb. Why wasn't she playing? Was she ready for a nap? It wasn't even noon.

"Jerry is going to be starting first grade in a couple of weeks. Jeffrey will be in kindergarten. I can't believe it."

"Kids grow up quick. They're going to be gone before you know it."

I stood up and walked to the window. Something was wrong with my 4-year-old. She looked flushed. She was shivering.

"I need to call you back. I've got to check on Cheryl."

"What's wrong?"

"I don't know. She just doesn't look right."

I hung up the phone and went outside.

"Mama," Jeffrey called. "Look. We're building a city."

"In a minute, sweetie."

I bent down over my daughter. I pressed the inside of my wrist against her forehead. Hot.

"What is it, baby? Don't you feel well?"

She shook her head. "My throat hurts," she said. "I'm cold."

I lifted her up. "Let's go and take your temperature."

I carried her into the house. It had to be 80 degrees in the sun—not too hot, not too cold. Her teeth were chattering. I laid her down on my bed, and covered her with a thin blanket. I got the thermometer from the bathroom cabinet, and inserted it. She didn't fight me. She lay still. I put my hand on the back of her neck. I waited. I watched the second hand on the clock. Two minutes. I removed the thermometer. I turned it so I could read it. Almost 105 degrees! How could it be that high?

"Your temperature is up a little," I said. "You stay here. I'm going to call the doctor."

"No shots, Mommy," she whimpered. She looked up at me. Her eyes were bright with fever. She started to cry louder.

"Shhh, don't cry, honey." I sat on the edge of the bed and pulled her against me. "We just need to find out what's making you feel so bad." She calmed. I laid her back down. "I'll be right back."

I went into the kitchen. I found the address book in the hutch drawer. I dialed the pediatrician's office. Thursday—the office should be open.

"You bring her right in, Mrs. Dywasuk," the receptionist said. "Dr. Hahne will be here all day."

"I...I don't know what time I'll get there. I have to find a ride."

"Well just get here as soon as you can. We close for lunch—but we don't leave. If the office door is locked, just knock. The doctor will see you right away."

I hung up the phone. Now what---how do we get to the doctor's office. Jerry's on the road today. No way to reach him. Dang...I wish we could afford a second car. A neighbor? I don't really know anybody that well. We just met the neighbors on either side. They have babies. I don't know if the women even have cars during the day. My sisters? They don't have second cars either. Besides, who'd want their kids exposed to whatever Cheryl has?

Mama is my only answer. Shoot. She's the last person I want to ask for help. No choice. I just need her to drive us to the doctor. Will she refuse? She never babysits for any of her grandchildren. Even in emergencies. "You can help each other out," she told us. "I'm done. I've raised my children." Now I'd have to ask her to come out here. I'm sure I'm going to hear about "living in the country." I don't care. I need her. There's no one else.

I picked up the phone and dialed her number. "Mama," I said. "I need a huge favor." I explained what was happening.

"I'll be there in 20 minutes," she said. "You can take my car. I'll stay with the boys. Now tell me how to get to your house."

***

"We'll need to do some tests," Dr. Hahne said. "Your daughter's lymph nodes—her glands—are swollen. We've got to find out why. And we've got to get that fever down—get some fluids in her. She's already dehydrated."

"But she was fine this morning," I said. "How could she get so sick so fast?"

"It happens. We'll figure all that out. Right now we've got to get her into the hospital."

"The...the hospital?"

"I'll call to have her admitted. Go to the emergency entrance." He looked at me. "Are you okay to drive her?"

"Yes, I am. I'll be fine."

The nurse helped me dress my daughter. We wrapped a white flannel blanket around her. I carried her to the car.

"Mommy," Cheryl said. "I want to go home now."

"We have to go get you some tests, baby. We have to find out why you're not feeling well. We can't go home yet." I laid her on the back seat. "You try to sleep a little, sweetie."

At the emergency entrance the hospital personnel were waiting. An attendant brought a wheelchair. He opened the back door and tried to lift Cheryl out. She squirmed away. "Mommy!" she cried.

"Let me," I said. The attendant moved aside. I picked her up. "It's going to be all right. The doctors and nurses are going to make you all better." I sat in the wheelchair with her on my lap. She clung to me. I handed him my car keys. He wheeled us inside.

After that, everything was a blur. The questions. When did she first get sick? How long has she had a fever? What were the first symptoms you noticed? Why did you wait so long to take her to the doctor? The tests. The probes. The needles. My daughter screaming. They put her in a room...isolation. They strapped her down and attached an IV to her hand. They hooked up monitors. She looked so tiny in the big bed. Finally, she calmed down. She slept.

It was hours before I was able to slip out of the room and call home. "What's going on?" Mama asked. "Why didn't you call sooner? I've been so worried."

I explained what happened.

"Are you sure that doctor knows what he's doing? Isn't he the one who took care of your baby at Children's Hospital?"

I sighed. "I feel comfortable with him," I told her. "It's too soon to... we're waiting for the results of the tests. Her white blood count is high. That's all we know right now."

"Hmm," was her response. She didn't ask me any more questions.

"Look, Mama, Jerry should be home soon..."

"I'll tell him everything. I'll have him take me and the boys home—to my house. They can stay with me."

"I don't know. I don't know what Jerry..."

"You stay there. You watch over Cheryl. Don't leave her. She needs you. Whatever you do...don't leave. I'll take care of things here. We'll work it out."

I didn't argue. The boys were fine. I needed to be with my daughter. I was scared. Tired. Emotionally drained. Jerry would have to work things out at home. Deal with my mother.

***

When I was growing up, visits to the doctor's office were rare—not just in my family but for anyone we knew. The reason may have been lack of money, the war, or just the tail end of a different era. Most illnesses were treated with home remedies. Penicillin was not yet widely known or distributed and there were no sophisticated antibiotics. Sulfa was the only antibacterial drug available—and infrequently prescribed.

For coughs, Mama added whiskey, honey and lemon to a cup of tea. For colds, she rubbed our chests with Vicks Vapor Rub and put a dab under the nostrils to clear stuffy noses. For sore throats, we gargled with a mixture of warm water and salt. For cramps and diarrhea, Mama dispensed a teaspoon of paregoric which was readily available over the pharmaceutical counter. For nausea, we were given Vernors ginger ale.

For high fevers, Mama cooled us down in a tub of cold water. Itches were treated with a plaster made of water and baking soda. For slivers, boils, or skin infections, we applied an over the counter drawing potion called Wonderful Dream Salve. Only if these methods didn't work was a doctor called. And he made home visits.

There was only one time during the 1940s that a doctor was called to our house in an emergency—other than to deliver babies. It was late in the evening. Mama and Daddy were standing by the couch looking down on Donny who lay there moaning and holding his stomach. "Maybe it was too much cherry pie," Mama said.

But it soon became obvious that it was something much more serious. Donny started throwing up. He was feverish. Daddy phoned the doctor. Everyone began scurrying around to straighten the house. When the doctor arrived and examined Donny, he took him directly to the hospital. His appendix was removed that night.

Billy had an appendix attack some years later. He was only 7 years old. It was a hot summer afternoon. Mama was standing in the kitchen ironing. Billy was sitting under the ironing board holding his right side and moaning. "Uh, uh, uh," Mama said. She laughed as she mocked him. For some reason, she thought he was faking.

When Daddy returned home from work, he recognized the symptoms. He took Billy directly to the hospital. His appendix was removed that evening.

In those days, there were no inoculations of babies to prevent scarlet fever, whooping cough, polio, diphtheria, lockjaw, or smallpox. And children were expected to contract red and German measles, chicken pox and mumps at some point. The bugs were passed around from child to child within families, neighborhoods and schoolrooms. Having these diseases was considered a normal part of childhood. But other communicable diseases were considered much more serious.

One summer the Rintz children across the street had whooping cough. The Detroit health authorities nailed a black and white quarantine notice on their front door to warn the neighborhood to stay away.

"Don't go any nearer than three doors away from their house," Mama told us. "I don't want you bringing any germs home."

Mass inoculations against whooping cough, diphtheria, tetanus and smallpox began sometime in the late 1940s. We shivered in anticipation when we learned the health department would be at school "to give out shots". I remember standing in long lines waiting my turn. A nurse in a white uniform dabbed my arm with alcohol and administered the inoculations. There were no combined immunizing agents; each required a separate shot. Some kids cried. I proudly displayed my bandaged arm and complained about the soreness.

Polio was the most feared disease. When there was a polio outbreak, public facilities were closed including schools, pools and beaches.

Everyone knew someone who was permanently crippled or in an iron lung or who had died as a result of polio. When a vaccine was developed and became available, parents everywhere heaved a sigh of relief. I was just finishing grade school when the series of inoculations were administered via a vacuum "gun". Later, sugar cubes were used. Nobody complained about having to be vaccinated against that dreaded disease.

My first visit to a doctor's office was for the medical check-up required to enter Dominican High School. As a result of the physical exam, the doctor wanted Mama to take me downtown to Children's Hospital for an x-ray of my spine. He was concerned that I might have a curvature that would require a brace.

"I'm fine, Mama," I cried. "I don't need to go there. Please don't make me!"

Mama talked to Daddy, neighbors and relatives trying to decide what to do.

"The doctor said it's something she might just grow out of as she gets taller," Mama told Daddy. "I hate to put her through all that if it's not necessary." In the end, my parents decided "to wait and see."

The next time I visited a doctor I was 19 years old, married, and expecting my first child. He never mentioned a problem with my spine. I had totally forgotten there was any concern. It wasn't until years later that I thought to ask the doctor to check. He told me that if there had been a problem, it would have shown up during my first pregnancy or the delivery of my child. He examined me. My spine was fine. There was absolutely nothing wrong with it.

It's a wonder so many of us survived our childhoods and young adult years without permanent physical damage. Our children have the advantage of living in an age of inoculations, sophisticated antibiotics, and exposure to regular and advanced medical care. Of course, in our adult years, so do we.

Chapter 10

I knew why Mama wanted me to stay at the hospital. She was scared for us—for Jerry and me. For Cheryl. Because of what had happened to Marvin.

***

Mama was 5 months pregnant with Mary Ann when Marvin became ill. He was 10 months old—her second child. She never talked about him. One day Karen and Billy and I were playing in Mama's bedroom closet. We found a box of loose photos and began sorting through them. I pulled out a picture of a beautiful baby—a boy—in a little sailor suit with a big grin and chubby cheeks. On the back in Mama's handwriting were the words, "Marvin, July 1932."

I took the picture into the kitchen. Karen and Billy followed me. Mama was stirring a pot of soup on the stove. "Who is this, Mama?" I asked.

She looked at the photo. "Your brother," she said. "He died when he was a baby. Put the picture back in the box. Leave it. Go outside and play. All of you. You have no business digging around in my closet. Go on. Now!"

I looked at Mama. Her face was expressionless. Her eyes were filled with pain. She turned back toward the stove and continued stirring the soup.

"You guys go in the yard," I told my brother and sister. "I'll be right out."

They ran out the back door. I took the picture back into the bedroom and dropped it into the box. I was only 7, but I knew better than to ask any more questions.

Years later, I asked Aunt Bea about Marvin.

"Your mama and daddy were living above the funeral home," she said. "I was 13. I came over to watch Lorraine so your mama could go to the hospital to see Marvin. He was just a baby. He had spinal meningitis. Your daddy was at work. He couldn't get off. It was during the depression. Your mama was planning on taking the streetcar to the hospital.

"We didn't have home telephones then. Your mama had just come upstairs from making a call to the hospital. She used the phone downstairs—in the funeral home's office. She was so excited. The nurse told her Marvin was doing well. She was just getting her coat on when there was a knock on the door.

"Mr. Pitts—the funeral director—came to tell her that the hospital had called back. Marvin had died. It was so awful. I'll never forget it. Your mama sat right down on the floor in the doorway. She started screaming and sobbing, "no, no, no." I didn't know what to do. I ran to get Ma. He was such a beautiful baby—bright blue eyes and blond curly hair. And always happy. It was so sad."

***

Cheryl was still sleeping. I dozed on the recliner next to the bed. I had no idea what time it was. The sun had gone down. The door opened and Jerry walked in. He had a big smile on his face.

"Colette," he whispered. "Dr. Hahne has good news. He was just coming in to talk to you when I bumped into him by the nurse's station."

"What...what?" I mumbled. I looked at Cheryl. She lay still. Her eyes were closed. Her breathing even.

"Come out into the hall. The doctor wants to talk to us. He'll be in to check on Cheryl in a minute."

I saw Dr. Hahne peering over his shoulder. I stood up. I walked into the hall and closed the door.

"It's excellent news," he said. "I was concerned because your daughter's fever went so high so fast. But I believe she's out of danger now. Her temperature is coming down nicely. No nausea. No vomiting. The test results are good."

"What did you think she might have?" I asked.

"Encephalitis, meningitis could occur…"

"Oh my God," I whispered. I thought about Marvin.

Jerry put his hand on my shoulder. "What is wrong with her?" he asked.

The doctor smiled. "Two things. Tonsillitis…she's probably going to have to have her tonsils out when she's a little older. And mumps. That's why it was so confusing…the diagnosis. I wanted to be absolutely sure it wasn't something much more serious. I didn't want to take any chances."

"My sister's kids had the mumps," I said. "We saw them a few weeks ago—just before they got sick."

"That's just about right. Incubation is two or three weeks. Your boys are likely to get sick, too. Usually it's not a big deal. It's a virus. There's no treatment for mumps. Complications are rare."

"The tonsillitis?" Jerry asked.

"We've started her on some powerful antibiotics. We should see a huge improvement tomorrow. Kids bounce back so fast."

Jerry and I looked at each other. He took my hand and squeezed it. My eyes filled with tears. I squeezed back.

"Now I'll just take a peek at her," the doctor said. "I'll want to keep her here for another day or so—just to be sure everything it okay. She'll have to stay in isolation, of course. We'll probably send her home Saturday morning."

We walked into the room behind the doctor. We stood by the side of the bed holding hands while the doctor examined her. Cheryl stirred, but did not wake up. After a few minutes the doctor smiled, gave us the thumbs up and left the room. I followed him out.

"I'd like to stay with her, doctor," I said. "She'll be so scared when she wakes up."

"Of course. Actually, you can use the other bed. They're not going to be putting anyone else in the room. I'll let the nurses know." He turned toward the nurse's station.

"Thank you," I said.

"You're very welcome." He waved his hand over his shoulder as he walked down the hall.

When I walked back into the room, Jerry was standing by the bed. "Why don't you go and get something to eat? Maybe you want to call your mother...talk to the boys. I'll stay here until you get back."

When I returned an hour later, Jerry was dozing in the chair. He opened his eyes when he heard me come in. "She never even woke up, poor thing. The boys okay? Did you talk to your mother?"

"The boys are excited about staying at my mother's. They seem to be having a great time with my brothers and sisters. But she thinks they might be getting the mumps, too. Their cheeks are flushed and their glands are a little swollen. Especially Jeffrey."

"Oh, shoot. Of course, it makes sense. They were all exposed at the same time."

"Mama said not to worry. She'll take care of the boys. She's had enough experience. She knows what to watch for. She thinks they'll have a real minor case."

"Take care of them until when?"

"Mama assumes they'll stay until Saturday."

"That'd be great."

"She wants to know when you're going to bring her car back."

"I think I'll drive over there tonight. I can return her car, see the boys, and have your brother drive me back to pick up my car."

"You're going to work tomorrow?"

"I have to. I took off so much time after Mark. It's only been a few months. And you don't need me here. Cheryl's doing fine. The boys are taken care of. I'll come right after work tomorrow and relieve you. Is that all right?"

"We should be fine. But could you stop at the house and pick up a few things for me?"

"Sure. Make a list of what you need. I'll drop your stuff off at the nurse's station when I pick up my car."

"Great! At least I'll be able to brush my teeth and have something to read. You should probably bring Cheryl's teddy bear, her coloring book and crayons, maybe some playing cards..." I took a piece of paper and pen out of my purse and started writing some items down.

After the list was completed, I handed it to Jerry. He looked it over, nodded, and bent down to kiss my cheek. "I'll be in the office all day tomorrow. Call if you need anything." He bent over the bed and brushed Cheryl's forehead. "When Cheryl wakes up, be sure to tell her Daddy was here...that he loves her." He walked back to where I was sitting. "You're sure you're going to be all right?"

"We'll be fine." I stood up. We hugged. "I love you. I'll see you tomorrow."

"I love you, too. See you tomorrow. After work." He left.

I checked Cheryl to make sure she was still resting comfortably. I turned on the directional lamp next to the recliner. I sat down and opened the Good Housekeeping magazine I had found in the visitor's lounge. But I couldn't concentrate. I started to doze. I thought about my husband—having to go to work. We were lucky he was able to get off when Mark was sick...when he died. He's so responsible—a hard worker. Just like Daddy.

***

When I was growing up, Daddy worked at Bower Roller Bearing

Company on the east side of Detroit. He was a grinder on the production line in the heat treat area of the plant. It was a grimy job. The furnaces were hot. There was no air conditioning. He literally earned a living for his family "by the sweat of his brow." He returned home at the end of the day with his clothes sweat stained and covered in grease.

His day started at 4:30 a.m. when he got up—to a cold house on winter mornings. He added coal to the furnace to start the fire and take the chill out of the house before everyone else was awake. I never saw Daddy off to work. Nobody did. He quietly boiled a pot of thick black coffee, made peanut butter and grape jelly sandwiches, packed his black lunch bucket, ate a bowl of oatmeal and drove to the plant. Five days a week for 24-1/2 years. He never complained. He never missed a day of work.

"They wanted to make him supervisor," Mama told us. "But he refused. It would have been a lot more money but Daddy wouldn't hear of it. 'I don't want to be responsible for other people's work,' he said. 'I just want to be responsible for my own.'"

I don't know how much money he brought home on a regular basis, but I remember Mama and Daddy's excitement the day his take home pay reached $100 for the week. "We're going to Sear's," Mama said. "Everybody get in the car. We're going to celebrate. Everyone is getting a new pair of shoes!"

Daddy just grinned.

When it was time for Daddy to get home from work at 3:30 every afternoon, we'd all be waiting for him. His green 1937 Hudson Terraplane would pull up to the curb next to the tree in front of the house.

"Daddy's home," we'd call out.

He'd climb out of the car—then reach across the seat for the battered rectangular shaped metal lunch pail. His clothes would be rubbed black with grease. Daddy kept an old blanket draped over the driver's seat to protect it.

"Don't hug me," he'd say. "I'm sweaty and greasy."

But I would get as close as he'd let me without actually touching. I loved the sour smell of him—the Daddy smell. It made me feel protected and safe.

We always had the table set for supper when Daddy arrived home. He'd go around to the back yard, open the outside door by the kitchen and basement steps, take off his greasy shoes at the bottom landing, and climb the three steps in his white cotton socks to peek into the kitchen where Mama was cooking.

"Honey, I'm home," he'd call out with a chuckle. "Something sure smells good. What's cooking'?"

"Supper will be ready in 15 minutes," she'd respond. She'd turn and smile at him from the stove. "I made lentil soup," she answered one day.

"You've got to be kidding," Daddy laughed. "I was just talking to this guy at work today. He was telling me how much he loved lentil soup. I told him I'd never had it. Wait until I tell him tomorrow that you made lentil soup for supper!"

Daddy would then turn around and climb down the two sets of steps to the basement. He'd peel off his greasy shirt and begin to wash up using a bar of Fels Naptha laundry soap. He used a scrub brush to clean his fingernails. He kept fresh clothes and a bath towel on a peg by the laundry tub. As soon as we heard him coming up the steps, we'd run to our places at the kitchen table.

Supper was the one meal of the day that the entire family ate together. We had a huge white Formica and chrome table with tiny silver flecks embedded on the surface. Two wide leafs would be inserted to extend the table to fill the kitchen. There were eight turquoise padded kitchen chairs that were part of the set—and additional wooden chairs were brought in from the dining room. Daddy sat at the head of the table by the windows. Mama sat at the foot of the table by the stove.

We waited patiently until everyone sat down. If we were having soup, Mama ladled it from the pot on the stove and we passed the bowls. She also proportioned out any meat or chicken. But the rest of the meal—pots of vegetables, dishes of salads, loaves of bread—were passed around the table. We helped ourselves as well as the youngest children—always careful to leave enough for everyone else.

We sat and waited for everyone to fill their plates and pour milk into the glasses.

"Okay," Daddy would say. "Now let's pray."

We would fold our hands and follow his lead.

"Bless us oh Lord and these Thy gifts which we are about to receive, from Thy bounty through Christ, our Lord. Amen"

As soon as the last "Amen" was finished, we were allowed to start eating. The room would erupt with noise—the clatter of plates and utensils as well as laughter and conversation. Getting our parent's attention was the main challenge.

"Daddy, I got an 'A' on my spelling test today," I'd call out trying to be heard above the noise. But my older brothers and sisters had stronger voices. With so many people, it was difficult to get the spotlight at the supper table. As I grew older, I learned a trick that has served me well in any family gathering over the years. I speak softly—a kind of reverse psychology to get attention.

"What did you say?" one of my older brothers or sisters would ask. "Wait everyone. Colette is trying to tell us something."

And, magically, the room would quiet down.

"I got an 'A' on my spelling test today."

"That's great," Daddy said. He smiled.

"Yeah, swell! Good going, kiddo." I would hear around the table. Even Mama would smile and nod at me. And I would feel proud and recognized.

"How was work today?" Mama would ask Daddy.

For a time Daddy would talk about labor union "goons" who were trying to organize the plant. They were focusing attention on Daddy because he didn't believe unionizing would benefit him. And he was being a little too vocal about it.

"I don't think I'm going to have much of a choice but to join," he told Mama. "The union organizers are getting threatening. Verbal abuse wasn't enough. Today two guys sat next to me at lunch—one on either side. Whenever I tried to eat, one of them would poke an elbow at me to try to knock my sandwich out of my hands. When I complained, they just smirked. 'Need to unionize, Frankie,' they said. They wouldn't move until I finally told them I'd think more about it."

"Then you're just going to have to sign up," Mama told him. "It's too dangerous working around all that hot metal to take a chance on things escalating."

"I know. I just hate being forced into something I don't believe in."

As it turned out, both parents were right. Other employees were seriously injured when union organizers escalated the recruiting. The plant was eventually unionized and Daddy joined. But he felt it never benefitted him. Help wasn't there when he needed it most.

After dinner, Daddy always had work to do. He focused on whatever happened to be the highest priority that day. During the war in the 1940s, Daddy had a small garden at the back of the yard. He planted tomatoes and cucumbers that Mama canned. He also raised a few chickens. I can remember him slaughtering one of the chickens for dinner. He used an axe to chop off the head. To my dismay, the chicken ran around the yard spurting blood until it fell over. Then Daddy took the carcass down to the basement, boiled hot water, and steamed and plucked the feathers over the laundry tub. Mama roasted the chicken for dinner, saving the wings and neck to make chicken noodle soup.

Daddy did all of the repairs on his car—even the most complicated ones. Our garage stood at the furthermost back end of the yard and was open to the street behind. He would pull the car into the garage, put blocks under the axles, and spend hours taking it apart and rebuilding the various parts. He had a car book that he used for directions.

One time Daddy spent days rebuilding the engine of our old car.

After it was reassembled on the garage floor, he had to hire a tow truck to hoist the engine and replace it under the open hood. I stood outside the garage and watched Daddy directing the tow truck operator. I was so proud of my Daddy when the repairs were completed and the motor actually started!

Daddy wasn't a great mechanic. As with most of his projects, he never had any formal training. He studied books from the library about how to do something and then figured the rest out for himself. The lessons he taught me were "you can learn what you need to know from books" and "you can do anything you put your mind to". I've carried these values with me my entire life. I owe my successes to my Daddy's inspiration and example. And I'm passing them on to my own children.

Besides repairing his own car and tending the garden and chickens, Daddy did all the yard work and handyman chores, kept the ashes shoveled out of the coal furnace, and always had major and minor house projects in process—from adding more living space to wall papering and painting. Finally, just before bed, he would sit down with his Book of Knowledge to read for a while. And that's where I would find him for a kiss good night.

Chapter 11

I called Jerry early Saturday morning to pick us up. The doctor had already been in and had signed the release. Cheryl's fever was gone but her cheeks were still swollen, her throat hurt, and she was irritable.

"Here's a prescription for antibiotics," the doctor said. "Continue to give her the medicine until it's gone. Make sure she drinks plenty of fluids, but avoid tart drinks such as orange juice and lemonade. Drinking them can be painful because they stimulate the inflamed salivary glands. Your daughter may be soothed by warm, moist towels around her neck."

"Do we need to bring her back to the office?" I asked.

"Yes, we'll want to re-check those tonsils. But wait another week to make an appointment. She's still contagious. We don't want to start an epidemic."

I told him about the boys.

"You don't need to bring them in unless they exhibit unusual symptoms. It sounds like they're doing fine. I'd guess it's good your children were all exposed at the same time. They'll be quarantined for a few days and you'll be done with the mumps."

"How many days will they be contagious?"

"The virus is spread by exposure to the saliva of an infected person. I'd give it another week or ten days before you let other children around.

It should be safe after that."

"Any other precautions?"

"Call me if Cheryl's temperature goes over 101 degrees. But I don't think there'll be a problem. She's doing well." He smiled. "Are you ready to go home, sweetie?"

Cheryl had her thumb in her mouth. She nodded.

***

Focus during the next days was on keeping my children happy—and getting them well. We played card and board games—war, go-fish, old maid, Candyland, Parcheesi, Chutes and Ladders, Sorry. We colored in coloring books. We created human figures, animals, vases and dishes out of Play-Doh. As they felt better, I sat in the yard and watched while they played in the sandbox. They ate chicken noodle soup, and Jello, and popsicles until their tongues turned purple. Slowly, day by day, the swelling went down in their glands.

I enjoyed the isolation, the time spent together. The boys would be starting school in just a few days. As a first grader, Jerry would be full time. As a kindergartener, Jeffrey would go half days. Only Cheryl would be home to keep me company. I had sewing projects planned— drapes and curtains for the house—and some fall gardening. That would keep me busy for a while. But I didn't like to think about being idle.

I talked to Mama on the phone. She called each day to get a report, but she hadn't been over. I still couldn't believe that she had been willing to keep the boys while Cheryl was in the hospital. Especially with Jerry and Jeffrey coming down with the mumps. And she didn't complain. I knew I didn't have any other options. She knew that, too. Still, I was surprised she didn't take the opportunity to make a big issue out of the fact that we lived so far—out in the country.

"I told you the boys would have a mild case of the mumps," Mama said. "I'm glad I was right."

"Me, too. They're doing great. Are you going to come over and visit soon?"

"I'm busy right now. I've got a project going."

"What is it?"

"I'll tell you about it later. Right now I'm doing a thorough housecleaning. The house hasn't been gone over completely in a long time."

I knew Mama had been busy taking care of Daddy before he died. I was sure there were things to clean up and put away. It was good she was keeping busy. I decided not to press her. "Well, you know you're always welcome here, Mama," I said. "I don't know what I would have done if you hadn't taken the boys."

There was only a silence.

"Maybe you'll want to come over sometime and help me sew the curtains and drapes for the house. You're so good at it. Or help me plan my garden—and plant bulbs for the spring."

"I might like to help with your gardening. But that can wait a few weeks. We'll see."

***

Too soon, the day came for the boys to start school. I planned on walking them and making sure they were deposited and comfortable in their classrooms. I would be sure to meet their teachers. They were going to a public school, as there were no parochial schools in our new neighborhood. I couldn't believe my oldest was going to start first grade. I could remember clearly my first day of school.

I was 6 years old when I started grade school in 1947 at Holy Name Parish in Detroit. Nobody I knew attended kindergarten—if it even was available then. Karen was 4, Billy 3, and Janet and Judy were 9 months old. Daddy was at work. Mama was busy at home. Mary Ann was in high school. So my brothers Buddy, 12, and Donny, 10, were assigned the task of walking me to school on the first day.

They were supposed to see to it that I found my classroom. Instead, they walked me to the entrance of the school, pushed me inside, and disappeared. There were kids everywhere. And there were tall ladies dressed in long black skirts with veils that covered their heads. I stood mesmerized, not knowing where to go or who to ask for help. It was the first time I had ever been alone in a crowd of people where I didn't know a soul.

Eventually, an older girl noticed me standing frozen in the doorway and took charge. "Are you starting first grade?" she asked.

I nodded my head.

"You need to go into that room." She pointed to one of the nearby doorways.

I walked over and looked inside. There were rows and rows of desks with boys and girls my size sitting there. A lady dressed in the special clothes smiled at me. "What's your name?" she asked.

"Colette Taube," I said. Daddy had told me to be sure to add my last name whenever an adult asked.

"Welcome to first grade, Colette. I'm Sister Mary Frances. I'm going to be your new teacher. We've been waiting for you. Your seat is right there."

I looked at the seat she was pointing to. It was in the middle of the last row, next to the windows. My cousin Jimmy Taube was in the seat behind mine. I smiled and walked to my assigned seat. I realized later that the seating had been arranged alphabetically. I knew I was going to like school. It was orderly and Sister was nice.

Daddy's brother Sylvester and his family lived in our parish two blocks from the school. As in my family, all of my cousins attended Holy Name before going on to high school. Starting with Mary Ann, there was usually one of the cousins in the same grade as each of us. They were the "Tumey Taubes"—referring to the street on which they lived. We were the "Mt. Olivet Taubes". They were much more studious than we were. Grades were important to my Aunt Alice and Uncle Syl.

Mama and Daddy liked the discipline and love of learning they believed the nuns and priests at Holy Name School instilled in our elementary education. There were more than 50 students in each classroom and teaching methods were stern. But we got a good solid education in reading, language skills, math, science, geography and history along with religious education. There were only a few times any of us complained about getting rapped on the knuckles with Sister's ruler.

I was shy and introverted as a child—a good girl who rarely disobeyed or publicly challenged authority. Inwardly was a different matter. I questioned everything. Sister Cyrilla was the only teacher I ever openly challenged in grade school. She was a short chunky nun that demanded discipline in her classroom. She carried a ruler to enforce order. Sister had divided the students into reading groups based on ability. As I loved reading, it was an area in which I excelled. I was able to read well above my grade level.

One day Sister Cyrilla "called" my group and said we had to "fly" from our desks to the circle of chairs where we did our lessons. "Flying" consisted of skipping and flapping our arms up and down as we proceeded from our desks to the front of the room. I hated flying. It made me feel stupid. I decided that day to walk to my chair. I stubbornly refused to fly, even though she rapped me on the knuckles with her ruler and made me stand in the corner. For some reason, it was the last time she ordered any of the children in the classroom to fly.

By the time I got to sixth grade, the Sisters already knew my family. Although Donny was in Sister Grace Imelda's class four years earlier, she remembered him well. He was the class clown. He kept the class laughing with his antics. Discipline was strictly enforced at Holy Name School. Even so, one wonders why Sister was assigned to teach this grade level—where hormones start raging and peer pressure becomes so important. She was much more equipped emotionally to teach the lower grades.

Sister Grace Imelda must have cringed when she saw "Taube" on her class list. Instead of assuming I was like my brother, she took a special interest in me. I loved Sister and her gentle ways. She worked hard to teach her students the importance of learning, and she never lost her temper. She achieved discipline through mutual respect. I worked harder in school that year than I ever did before.

"You're not like your brother at all," Sister told me.

I asked Donny what she meant.

"Oh, I used to tease Sister all the time," he said. "When her back was turned I used to do things like hide the erasers and mix up the papers on her desk. I made everyone laugh."

For the most part, Mama and Daddy left our education to us and to our teachers. They checked our report cards and signed off. As long as we were getting As, Bs, or Cs—and there were no discipline problems being reported—we were fine. High grades weren't important. They trusted that a love of learning would naturally provide us with the education we needed. As haphazard as it sounds, it worked.

I loved school in the early grades and always did well. As I entered the upper levels, I focused on language skills and eased up on science and math. I was frequently a finalist in spelling bees. I loved to diagram sentences. My book reports received high grades. I memorized all the states and their capitals. I learned my multiplication tables. But I hated fractions. I rarely studied for tests—unless I needed an "A" to balance a "D". Nothing lower than a "C" ever appeared on my report card.

"You can get all "A+s" if you put your mind to it," Sister Grace Imelda said.

I smiled.

"I'll make you a deal. If you get all "A+s" on your report card for the rest of the school year, I'll let you take my fern home for the summer."

Sister loved that plant. It was like a child to her. She had nurtured it for years. The convent and school would be closed for the summer and she needed someone to care for the plant. The pot was 8 inches round and the dark green foliage reached 12 inches high—draping over the pot and extending 24 inches down. Everyone in the school knew she only entrusted it to her favorite student. I had never been a teacher's pet. A lot of girls in my class were hoping to be chosen for the honor of taking Sister's plant home for the summer.

I didn't care about the plant, but I was interested in the fact that the other girls didn't consider me competition. I figured I could excel in every subject if I tried. And I liked Sister Grace Imelda. She was kind and caring. She was my homeroom teacher and taught language skills—my favorite subjects. Another Sister taught our class for Math and Science. Those were the subjects I'd have to work at.

"Okay, Sister," I said. "I'll do it." And I did. I also won the spelling bee and got on the Honor Roll that year. Most importantly, I took Sister's fern home for the summer.

Unfortunately, that was the summer we had a house fire. The plant was in the room where the fire started. When I told Sister Grace Imelda at the beginning of the next school year that her plant had been destroyed, she just smiled.

"That's okay," she said. "The sacrifice was well worth it. Nobody was hurt in the fire and the spirit of that plant will always be alive in you."

It was years before I understood what she meant.

The grade school was four long blocks from our house. We walked back and forth to school and went home for lunch every day in the coldest or hottest weather, rain or shine. There were no buses and school was never closed for "snow days". Being tardy was a cause for reprimand and detention—something we were careful to avoid. At lunchtime we barely had time to get home, have a peanut butter sandwich, and get back to school in time—especially in the winter when we had boots, leggings and layers of clothing to deal with. But students weren't allowed to stay for lunch unless they lived more than six blocks away.

I'm sure some of the things about school in those days were the same—public or parochial. The air raid practices where sirens would bellow and all students had to get under their desks and cover their heads. The inoculations where we had to line up for the public health nurses to administer each newly developed vaccination against whooping cough, tetanus, diphtheria, or smallpox. The geography projects where we had to make elevated maps using a homemade plaster of flour, salt, water and food colorings. The science projects.

But in Catholic school we had additional activities. For example, we saved our pennies to help the Missions. We had bake sales and sold greeting cards. Every $5 a homeroom collected would pay to support an orphaned baby. I don't know what charity the money was sent to, but I remember the excitement of the class as the stamps representing each penny were posted to a card and we edged closer and closer to the $5 goal. We even got to name the baby.

Religion was incorporated into our school days. We studied it as a subject and practiced it daily. Talking about God and saints was natural. We had Christmas and Easter pageants. We sang religious carols and songs. In second grade we prepared for and received the Sacraments of Penance and Holy Communion. In sixth grade we studied for the Sacrament of Confirmation.

Confirmation was especially important because it was an individual profession of faith for each of us. Our parents had us baptized and entered us into the Catholic religion. Within this sacrament, we confirmed our belief. It was exciting. We got to choose a symbolic new name and a sponsor. Girls got to wear grown up clothing for the first time—nylon stockings and garter belts, a navy blue skirt with a white blouse, elevated heels, and a round felt hat.

I chose a favorite "Tumey Taube" cousin, Estelle—who is just a few years older than I—to be my sponsor and Catherine, as my new name. A bishop of the Archdiocese of Detroit came to Holy Name Church to confirm us. Next to eighth grade graduation, it was the most exciting day in grade school. We thought we were now entering our adult years!

Attending Catholic grade school exerted a huge influence on my growing up years. Even the after school and summertime games we played were shaded by our classroom experiences. One of my favorite pastimes was playing school. I would talk Karen, Billy, Janet and Judy into being my students. As the oldest, I was always the teacher. I tried my best to make the game interesting. I would make addition and subtraction flashcards out of scraps of paper to teach my "students" math, and borrow books from the library to teach them how to read. I usually managed to keep their attention for at least a little while.

Of course, I thought all teachers were nuns. So I would dress my part of teacher as a Dominican order sister. For the long white robe, I would use one of Mary Ann's white rayon slips which came down to my ankles. For the scapulars, which ran lengthwise from shoulder to floor, front and back, I pinned white bath towels together at my shoulders. For the cross drape and neck collar, I used white dish towels. For the wimple (the head covering which wrapped around my hair and under my chin), I used another white dish towel.

I borrowed Daddy's black belt and wrapped it twice around my tiny waist. From the belt I looped a dangling rosary. I borrowed one of Mary Ann's black wool skirts and pinned it to the "wimple" by the bottom hem to make the veil. Although I neglected to get her permission, Mary Ann never complained about my borrowing her clothes. Mama never objected to my use of the towels, nor Daddy to the use of his belt. But borrowing Ma's rosary without permission was a big mistake.

I had noticed the ivory beaded rosary sitting on the dining room table at Ma's house. It was perfect for my "costume". I had no idea that the rosary was a special treasure of my grandmother's. It had hand carved beads, was imported from Italy, had a relic entombed in the crucifix, and had been blessed by the Pope. By the time Ma noticed the rosary missing and confiscated it from me, I had lost a few of the beads. I had never seen her so upset. But I learned a valuable lesson: Some people have personal possessions that mean a lot to them. Everything is not meant to be shared. There are boundaries.

Another game we liked to play was church. Karen and Billy and I would set up a small table as an altar using doilies and fresh wildflowers. For Communion hosts we rolled white bread into tiny round balls. Sometimes we were lucky enough to have flat white Necro candy wafers to use as pretend Communion hosts. When everything was arranged, we would take turns pretending to be the priest distributing Communion or the parishioner kneeling to receive. In May we set up an altar with a statue of Blessed Mother Mary and pretended to have crowning ceremonies complete with dressing up in our First Communion dresses and veils, suit and tie.

I had no hesitation as a child to walk up and down the street dressed as a nun. Nobody ever commented—whether or not they recognized what my costume was supposed to represent. I wasn't teased. It was as accepted as dressing up like a fairy princess, or a cowboy, or a pirate. Although not everyone in the neighborhood was Catholic, nobody hid his or her religious beliefs. Christianity in some form was part of everyone's life. If it wasn't, they didn't advertise their lack of belief. And we had absolutely no experience with diverse religious or ethnic groups.

***

My children's experiences in school would be much different.

Chapter 12

Cheryl was taking a nap when the phone rang.

"Hey, Colette. It's Karen," she said. "How are you doing?"

"I'm doing good," I said. "How's my favorite sister?"

"Well, I was just thinking about you and thought I'd give you a call. I was wondering if you're over it yet."

"Mumps are all gone, thank heavens. The boys started school. Cheryl is still getting her energy back. She's taking a nap right now. It's pretty quiet around here."

"Oh, that's great to hear. But I was talking about Mark."

"Mark?"

"Yeah—his death and all."

I was flabbergasted. Karen is my closest sister. She has been part of my life for as long as I can remember. Born in December, she is 22 months younger than I, but was only a year behind me in school. From the time we were toddlers, we were seldom apart. We played together by choice. As we grew older, we had mutual friends. Most of my experiences growing up included Karen. We shared a bedroom until the day I was married.

Karen had gotten married 3-1/2 years after me—just before she turned 21. She had two boys. She knew what it was like to be a mother, to have children. But obviously she didn't know what it was like to lose a baby. I love my sister with all my heart. She is my dearest friend. I wanted to say just the right thing.

"You know," she said. "Bad things happen. You just have to get through them. We banged up our car last week. Nobody was hurt. But it was pretty upsetting."

"Karen," I said. There were tears in my eyes. "One of the worst things about losing a baby at birth—and I'm sure it's true of a miscarriage or stillbirth—is that nobody can truly understand what it's like unless they've lost a baby. I realize that. You didn't carry Mark for 9 months. You never knew him. Neither did I. And that's the saddest part. Nobody else misses him. But I do.

"I'll never see him smile. Never hold his hand. Never see him grow up to be a man. I know you don't mean to be cruel...and I appreciate you even bringing him up so that I can talk about this. But I'll never in my entire life get completely over Mark. I'm sure the deep sorrow will fade after a while, but I don't think the feeling of loss will ever leave. It's like having a hole in my heart."

"I'm so sorry. You're right. I'm fortunate that I don't understand. I love you, Colette, and I just hate to see you in pain. I don't know what I can say or do."

"You can't take the pain away. You can remember him. You can bring him up in conversation every once in a while. It's a funny thing. Talking about him helps. You'd think it would be the opposite. Most people are afraid to say anything. But it really helps to know that he's remembered. That his birth and death happened. That it meant something. That it impacted other lives—even in a small way."

"It doesn't feel good to talk about it."

"Honest. It feels good to me. It's a comfort to know you care so much that you'd risk bringing Mark up at all."

***

I was almost 2 years old when Karen was born. Although I don't remember her birth—or even her as a baby—I do remember one summer having to play in the yard by myself. My guess is that it was in 1943— just before my brothers Billy and Johnny were born in December. Mama would have been heavily pregnant with the boys and Karen only 8 months old. It's the only time I can remember not having a built-in playmate.

We had a beautiful fenced-in back yard. Along the back of the house was a cement patio-like area. A narrow sidewalk ran from the patio through the center of the yard to the garage. One side of the yard was shaded by a huge old apple tree which stood just next to the small pear tree that Daddy had planted. The other side of the yard was divided in half, the back, a white picket fenced area that contained a vegetable garden, the front, a green grassy area where Mama hung clothes to dry on ropes strung between two white wooden poles.

I had to stay out of the garden and the garage, but the rest of the yard was my playground. I'm sure Mama or my older sisters were keeping an eye on me for I felt safely alone. I can remember lying contentedly on the grass watching the ants busily carrying tiny bits of crumbs here and there. Mama brought me water in a tall metal cup and showed me where to pick spearmint leaves to make tea. I put the leaves in the cup and left it in the summer sun to brew. Every once in a while I would taste the warm liquid to check whether the flavor had taken hold.

"It's ready now, Mama," I said.

"Okay," she said, nodding her head. She went into the house and brought out tiny flowered metal teacups for our tea party. She set them on a patio table and sat down next to me. She poured the warm water into the cups. She handed me one of the cups. "Your tea, madam." She smiled.

My older brothers would have been 6-1/2 and 8-1/2 that summer— too old to play with me, too young to be relied on to watch me. But Buddy had a small round magnifying glass that fascinated me. He showed me how I could use it to make the ants larger, then left me on my own.

"If you hold the glass in the sunlight over paper, it'll burn," he said. "So don't hold it over the ants too long. It'll make them too hot."

After watching the ants for a while, I found some newspaper and held the magnifying glass over the paper. It took a long, long time holding the glass in the sunlight focused over the tiny bits of paper, but eventually brown singe curled the edges and consumed the paper. The sheer power of the sun amazed me.

In another vivid memory, I am 3 years old. It is a warm spring day. I am at Ma and Pa's cottage in Utica. I am twirling round and round at the bottom of the grass-covered hill that rolls down from the cottage to the Clinton River. Mama is sitting near the bank on a gray blanket, her legs curled under her. Karen is a toddler, sitting next to Mama. She is leaning over, plucking at the yellow faces of the dandelions that dot the hillside. Mama has a pile of flowers next to her, and is smiling contentedly as her fingers busily weave the stems together to make a crown. As I spin round, I see Mama looking up at me her brown eyes sparkling.

I am wearing my favorite navy blue, Swiss cotton dress embroidered with tiny white dots. It has short puffy sleeves and a narrow white collar edged with lace. Over the dress I wear a white organdy pinafore with wide ruffles along the shoulders and hem. It has a sash at the waist that is tied into a puffy bow at the back. My sun-streaked light brown hair is long and fluffy. I wear on my head a wreath of dandelions that Mama has weaved for me. My feet are bare. As I dance, my dress swirls and my feet crush the grass; moisture oozes up between my toes. I smell the damp grass, the dandelions, the flowing river, and I feel the soft spring breezes caress my face. I am alive. I am joyous. I am at peace. I am totally happy to be me.

Even as young children, day by day we begin to lose the gift of living in the present moment. Once in a while, we may experience a tiny glimpse of absolute bliss—a whiff of apple pie, the call of a mockingbird, the fluttering of a hummingbird, the sound of ocean waves crashing against the shore, the pungent smell of a fresh cut Scotch pine—a jolt of remembered joy. But why do we have to search backwards in time for our bliss? Can't we find such moments in present time? Childlike wonder is buried deep within us. We simply need to get in touch with our inner child—the one lost through layers of time. Whether this memory is accurate or not, I know this child is my true, unencumbered self.

In one of my earliest memories of playing with Karen, we are in the yard. It must have been the following summer, a beautiful sunny day. We are each taking turns sitting in the white metal baby tub on the patio while the other runs fresh cold water from the garden hose over our head and down our body. Mama is hanging laundry on the line in the grassy area of the yard. Karen is in the tub. I am trying to be careful not to spray toward the clothes. Suddenly, I trip and the water splashes at Mama who is facing me behind something she is pinning on the line.

"Hey," she said. She lifted the clothing and ducked under the line. "You know you have to keep the hose on the patio or I'll have to shut it off." She smiled and walked over to us. She was wiping her face with her wet paisley apron. "But I do have to say that felt good. God knows, those diapers will get wet again soon enough—with or without any help from the hose." She slipped off her shoes and took the hose from my hand. She let the water run over her feet, then handed me back the hose. "Just try not to spray towards the laundry."

Karen was my constant playmate. One of our favorite games—as we grew older—was jacks. We would sit on the warm cement patio and play for hours. We had a round, 1-inch rubber ball and ten spiky metal jacks. Using one hand, we'd bounce the ball. As the ball bounced, we'd try to grab a jack and catch the ball before it hit the cement again. First one jack, then two, then three—until the last grab was for all ten. If you missed, it was the other person's turn. When your turn came again, you started from your last successful grab. The first person to successfully grab all ten jacks without the ball hitting the cement was the winner.

Another game we liked was playing cutouts. We tore figures of people from the newspaper to use as our play dolls, then fashioned make believe clothes for them out of newspaper scraps. We sat on the staircase to the upstairs bedrooms and used separate steps for each of the pretend rooms—with furniture, appliances and bedding also created from newspaper scraps. We occupied ourselves for hours playing with our makeshift cutouts. The year Santa Claus brought us paper cutout books—with lifelike colored figures, clothing and accessories—we were ecstatic!

There was a chicken coop at the furthermost corner of the long backyard, next to the garden and across the cement path from the garage. The enclosed wooden structure was about 6- foot square with a step-up plywood floor, a narrow door, and a glass window that could be pushed open to let in fresh air. When Daddy decided to stop raising chickens, he cleaned the chicken coop for our playhouse. Mama hung curtains on the window.

We had a child's size wooden table and chair set inside and used wooden boxes as our stove and refrigerator. Mama made cradles for our dolls out of a discarded Quaker oatmeal package. She cut the round cardboard carton in halves lengthwise and wrapped fabric inside and around the outside. Each 10-inch half made a perfect rocking cradle for our baby dolls.

Of course, we prepared meals in our little kitchen. We would take slices of white Silvercup bread, peel off the brown crusts, and roll the soft centers into small balls using the palms of our hands. The crusts were our meat and the balls were our vegetables. We served the meal to Billy and to each other on tiny flowered metal dishes. I can still picture those balls of bread, gray with the dirt of our hands. But we ate them with gusto—dirt and all.

One day when Karen was 5 or 6 years old, she decided to make peanut butter. I watched as she took some of Daddy's salted peanuts from the pantry shelf, chewed them thoroughly, and delicately spit them onto a small metal plate. Then she stirred a teaspoonful of softened butter into the mashed peanuts.

"Look, Colette," she said. "I made peanut butter." She spread the mixture on a piece of bread and took a bite. She held it out to me. "Do you want some? It's good."

I declined. There is a limit to togetherness—even for children. But I felt proud of my younger sister for being so creative.

Looking and acting young for your age is an inherited family trait. As a child, I hated that people thought me younger than I was. I was a tall, skinny kid with little fat on my bones—what people used to call "a late bloomer". Plus, I was a bit of "a tomboy". Being a tomboy meant that I liked to do "boyish" things—like climb trees, ride bikes, play curb ball, build forts. I liked being physically active and Mama and Daddy encouraged it for both their boys and their girls. I had to wear dresses all the time, but that didn't slow me down. I was always on the move.

One summer Karen, Billy and I decided to build "a space ship" along the side of our house. We were inspired by Flash Gordon, Buck Rogers, and Tom Corbett's Space Cadet comic books and radio programs. We had saved cereal box tops and mailed away for our free space ranger kits. When they arrived—plastic rings, sky guides, secret codes, cardboard sun glasses with kaleidoscope lenses—we knew we were ready for outer space adventures.

Our space ship was erected in a narrow 3-foot-wide area bordered by the fence next to the Angelines's yard on one side, and our house on the other. We used weathered two by fours and plywood scraps to build a roof, with an open hatch to climb in and out. The wire fence served as the steps. But our makeshift space ship never took off. One morning Karen climbed up the fence, through the hatch, and onto the roof of our spacecraft. The roof collapsed and Karen fell and broke her arm. Mama and Daddy made Billy and I dismantle the ship and abort the launch.

When Karen and I were a little older, we each received a teenage doll for Christmas. The dolls had long hair that could be combed and styled. The hair on Karen's doll was brown; mine was blond. The dolls came with one outfit each, but Mama gave us fabric scraps from her sewing to make more clothes for our dolls. We would spend hours cutting and hand sewing skirts, blouses, dresses and coats out of the tiny brightly colored pieces of wool, corduroy, cotton, and rayon. When Mama saw how much we enjoyed creating the doll clothes, she began to teach us the basics of creating our own clothes—starting with simple summer cotton skirts.

Karen and I slept in the upstairs front bedroom. It was the furthest possible room from the kitchen where Mama and Daddy sat in the evenings after all of their children were in bed. The bathroom was just beyond the kitchen. When I was 6 years old, I went through a period where I had trouble sleeping. I would lie in bed listening as my sisters and brothers settled down for the night and the house grew quieter and quieter. I was petrified of being the only one awake in the house.

First, I would try to prevent Karen from falling asleep. I talked to her about the day; I sang to her; I told her stories; I asked her questions. Finally, despite all of my efforts, I would sense she was beginning to doze. "Karen," I whispered. "Are you listening? Don't go to sleep."

"No, I'm awake," she said. But after a while she would begin to drift off. "Mmpph," she would respond to my repeated inquiries until finally she wouldn't answer at all. Even poking her with my elbow and shaking the bed didn't wake her. I knew she was already sleeping.

Then I would climb out of bed, turn on the hall light, tiptoe down the steps into the living room, and peek around the corner to see if any lights were still on. Mama and Daddy's bedroom was off the kitchen; they didn't turn the kitchen light off until they were in bed. If the light was on, I would make as much noise as possible—clumping through the living room and into the kitchen.

"What are you doing up?" Mama would ask, as I walked into the kitchen where she often sat late at night drinking her coffee out of a squat white mug.

"I got to go to the bathroom."

As I came out of the bathroom a few moments later, I would ask: "Are you going to bed soon?"

"Not yet. Why are you still awake?"

"I can't sleep."

"Just lie there and close your eyes. You'll fall asleep soon enough. Try saying some prayers while you wait."

"Okay, Mama." I knew she would be up for a while and that comforted me. I wouldn't be alone. I headed back upstairs to my bed.

On the nights Mama was still awake, it calmed me and I would climb back into bed and fall right to sleep. On nights when the kitchen lights were already out, I would make enough noise so that Mama would call from her bedroom. "Who's there?" I'd know I'd awakened her, but it made me feel better. After using the bathroom, I would scurry back up the stairs and climb under the covers. I wasn't afraid of the dark, of monsters, or of burglars. I just felt lonely. I wasn't used to the quiet or the absence of activity. It was eerie. The emptiness spooked me.

I'm not sure over what period of time I had this problem. It could have been days; it could have been weeks; it could have been months. I didn't worry about it or think about it during the day. It never occurred to me to tell my parents. Eventually, I just got over it. And it was the only period in my life that I ever had concerns about falling asleep. I'm a deep sleeper—and I learned to enjoy alone time.

Reading was my favorite pastime as a child. The closest Detroit library branch to our house was on McNichols at Gratiot—more than two miles away. A bookmobile came to the grade school once a week during the school year, but selections were extremely limited. Getting books to read during the summer months meant we had to walk to the library and carry the stacks of books home.

I devoured books. Once a week I would talk Karen and Billy into walking to the library with me. Neither were serious readers at the time. The library limited the number of books each child could take out to five. Generally, my sister and brother only wanted one so I could choose 13 books if they both went with me. And they helped me carry the stacks of books home—not always willingly. There was a lot of coaxing, bribing, dropping and complaining involved. Even today, Karen isn't much of a book reader and she doesn't like to walk.

Finding a solitary spot and privacy to read was a challenge. If I tried to read in the upstairs bedroom, I was constantly interrupted by one of my sisters or brothers. And then there was Mama.

"Colette," she would call up the stairs from the living room. "What are you doing?"

"I'm reading, Mama."

"It's a nice day. You should go outside and play."

"In a minute, Mama. This book is good. I just want to finish this part."

Several times she would be back calling up the stairs for me to go outside before she lost her patience.

"Come down right now," she would finally holler. "You shouldn't be locked up in your bedroom on such a beautiful day."

So I would have to leave my book and go outside. This continued until one day I came up with a brilliant idea. The apple tree. The trunk of the apple tree was almost 3 feet in diameter. The thick branches of the tree were perfect for climbing. I loved to climb that tree. I could climb higher than any of my sisters or brothers. When I wanted to be alone, I'd climb branch by branch up into the tree where the trunk grew narrower and narrower. Then I would fling my leg over a branch, lean back against the trunk, and just sit.

I decided that this was the perfect spot to do my reading. It was private. It was outside. I just had to figure out a way to carry a hardbound book while I climbed. The solution was simple—if unsanitary. I used my teeth. As long as the book wasn't too thick, it worked perfectly. I can't tell you how many hours I spent 20 feet up in that apple tree reading books.

When Janet and Judy were old enough to move upstairs, they moved into the bedroom with Karen and me. There was only room for one set of twin beds so we had to sleep two to a bed. Karen and I shared one narrow bed. It didn't seem strange to us. We also shared our clothes, our thoughts and dreams, and whatever games and toys we owned.

On Saturday nights after our baths, we rolled each other's long straight wet hair onto small round metal curlers with rubber clasps. Ideally, our hair would dry during the night and the next morning we would have tiny round curls for Sunday Mass. One week we were short a curler and decided to share. We wrapped both of our hair on one curler and attempted to go to sleep—our heads locked together on the pillow. Of course, it was impossible logistically—and because we got the giggles.

Even as adolescents and young teens, Karen and I hung around together. We mingled her friends and mine. Being a grade apart was never a problem. We were both good girls and watched out for each other. We went to "sock hops" together and double-dated as we got older. Neither of us was "boy crazy" or cared much about make-up or stylish clothes. And we weren't concerned about peer pressure. We talked over most everything and recognized that the most important opinions were each other's.

***

Now Karen had once again proven to be a great comfort and a friend to me.

Chapter 13

The doorbell rang.

"Uncle Billy's here," Jeffrey called. He ran from outside into the family room through the side door, across the kitchen, and into the living room. He pulled the picture window curtains aside.

"Uncle Billy. Uncle Billy," Jerry and Cheryl were hollering as they, too, ran into the house. Their voices echoed against the hardwood floors in the hall and living room. The room was bare. We had not yet been able to afford carpeting or furniture. The couch, chairs, tables and lamps from our upper flat in Detroit were set in the family room.

I opened the inside front door. The late afternoon sun outlined the muscled frame of my brother through the screen.

"Hey, Billy," I said. "What a nice surprise."

"I had some business at the college and I was so close I thought I'd stop by." He smiled. "Are you busy?"

"Never too busy for you."

Billy is my closest brother in age. He is less than three years younger than I am, and was a constant playmate growing up. He had joined the Navy after high school, spent three years in service, and returned home a couple years ago. He was now a firefighter with the Detroit Fire Department. He was single and attending classes at Macomb

Community College. The school was a mile from our house, so he stopped by frequently. The kids loved him. He always took the time to play rough house games with them, and to tease them.

"Hey guys," he said. "Get your balls and mitts. We'll play some catch in the yard. And if you're lucky, I might hang around for a while." He looked at me. "Any chance I can have some of whatever you're cooking that smells so good?"

"It's lasagna. And there's plenty. We'd love to have you stay for supper, Wouldn't we kids?"

They ran into the room with their balls, bats, and baseball caps. "Hooray! Uncle Billy's going to stay for supper," they yelled.

"Go outside," he told them. "I'll be right out." He turned to me. "There's something I need to talk to you about, but it can wait until these troopers settle down."

"Something important?"

"Let's just say something significant."

"Hmm. Sounds interesting."

"It is." He walked into the kitchen, through the family room, and outside through the sliding glass door.

I looked after him wondering what it could be. As far as I knew, he wasn't dating anyone special. But whatever it was, it sounded serious.

**

Although there were six boys and six girls born into my family, only four of the boys survived infancy. Because of the birth order, most of us had a same sex sibling to provide companionship: Lorraine and Mary Ann, Buddy and Donny, Colette and Karen, Janet and Judy. Some were very close—like Karen and me. Others were only close in proximity, but still had each other to complain to, or fight, or argue with. Billy and Davey were the exceptions. They were separated in birth order by my twin sisters—and a little too far apart in age and temperament to be best buddies.

To Davey, it didn't seem to matter. He was the baby of the family and got a lot of attention. He was easy going and mellow—like my daddy. And he was more of a loner. He loved to explore, loved animals, and kept himself entertained. But for Billy, it was a different matter. The death of Johnny, the twin he never knew, seemed to impact him throughout his childhood. He didn't have a buddy. Karen and I included him in our games and adventures, but he was a boy. He needed more. He was too often left on his own, and his craving for attention only made matters worse.

Billy was constantly getting himself into trouble. I'm not talking about breaking the law kind of trouble—or getting kicked out of school kind of trouble. I'm talking about the kind of trouble that draws negative attention to oneself with parents, adult relatives, neighbors, and the nuns at school. The getting grounded, time outs, spankings, slaps on the wrist with a ruler, can't play with my kids, stay after school, demerits, extra homework kind of trouble.

When a lamp with a bare lighted bulb was left under a blanket in an upstairs bedroom and a smoldering fire started, everyone knew "Billy did it." When all the neighborhood kids were playing kick-the-can in the street in front of the house and the can accidentally hit the side of a car, everyone escaped except Billy. When we were all jumping up and down on our beds when we were supposed to go to sleep, only Billy was still jumping and got caught by the time Daddy pounded up the steps. Billy always seemed to draw negative attention to himself. It might have been his way of saying, "Hey. Look at me. I'm here!"

When Billy was only 5 years old, the family left for a Sunday outing to Ma and Pa's cottage one hot summer day. We had all gone to early Mass, packed our picnic lunch, filled the gallon red and white thermos with Kool Aid and ice cubes, stored our swimming trunks, towels, lawn chairs, bats and balls in the trunk, climbed into our green Terraplane and headed to Utica.

The four-door car was designed for six passengers. Loading twelve people into it was an art. Each of us had a designated spot. Our parents sat in the front with the youngest sibling on Mama's lap. My oldest brothers and sisters took turns sitting between my parents on the front bench seat. The rest of the family had to fit in the back. The oldest three had full seat rights. That left five of us to squeeze between sets of legs or on laps. For most of the ride, the shortest of us stood—our heads not yet reaching the roof of the car.

I'm sure we were quite a sight. In those days, cars were not air-conditioned so all the windows were open and our heads would be sticking out to feel the breeze. At stoplights, we were accustomed to people in cars next to us pointing and exclaiming. "Wow. Look over there. I wonder how many kids that family has." Mama taught us to hold up ten fingers and smile. We weren't embarrassed. It was a game to us. We were proud of our family and delighted to be noticed.

On this particular day, we were driving along Eight Mile Road near Hoover when the red lights by the railroad track started flashing and the guardrail dropped. Billy loved trains. It was summertime, but he had already decided he wanted a choo-choo train set for Christmas that year.

"Look, Billy, a train is coming," Mama said. No answer. "Billy?" she repeated. She turned around to look in the back seat.

We looked at each other. "He's not here," someone shouted.

Daddy leaned over the seat to check the floor, then made a swift u-turn and headed back home.

"I can't believe we left him," Mama said. "I just can't believe it!" She kept repeating the words over and over.

When we pulled up in front of the house 15 minutes later, there was Billy sitting on the front porch steps. Tears were running down his cheeks. His hair was chopped unevenly—shaved almost bald in some spots and greased and standing like a rooster's comb in other spots. We all piled out of the car to stand around him and stare. He reeked of after shave lotion.

"You forgot me," he said. He sobbed pathetically. "You left without me. You forgot about me!"

Daddy crouched in front of Billy, placing a hand on each bony knee. "We're so sorry, Billy," he said gently. "We didn't mean to leave without you. Where were you? What happened to your hair?"

"I was at Gary's house. We were playing barber."

"Wasn't his mother home?"

"Yeah. She told me to go home. She said you were going to be mad."

"Come on. Let's go," Daddy said. He took Billy's hand and pulled him up. "I'll talk to Mrs. Smith later. We're going swimming and on a picnic. We're going to have a great time. And I'll bet we won't forget you ever again. Okay, everyone. Climb back in the car. Let's get going."

Everyone rushed to take their places in the car. Billy sat on the edge of the seat in the spot that was his—next to me. I felt bad for not having missed him in all the excitement and anticipation of our Sunday outing. "I'm glad you're safe," I whispered. I put my arms around his skinny shoulders. "I love you, Billy." He looked up at me solemnly with his big brown eyes and nodded his newly shorn head.

Of all my brothers, Billy probably endured the most punishment from Daddy—the most spankings and the cruelest words. He seemed to draw anger and frustration from a man who was usually easy-going and mellow-tempered. But that day, Daddy was gentle and loving with him.

Billy made his way through Catholic grade school and high school constantly calling negative attention to himself and making passable grades by the skin of his teeth. After graduation, when he joined the United States Navy, he seemed to find his niche. He'll tell you he learned self-discipline and how to apply himself. But I think he found his missing brother—his buddies there. And he certainly found himself.

It was another sibling who set the more serious fire in our house. It was an August afternoon. Janet and Judy were 5 years old, Davey was 2. Billy was innocently taking a bath. Karen and I were walking home from visiting our Taube cousins on Tumey Street. Mama was outside in front of the house talking to neighbors. Daddy was at work. The only other one in the house was Lorraine. She was in the kitchen reading—when she suddenly smelled smoke.

By the time Lorraine made her way on her crutches from the kitchen to the dining room, smoke was pouring out from her bedroom, which was divided from the dining room by leaded glass French doors. Mary Ann and Lorraine shared the bedroom. We later learned that someone had been crouched on the floor of the wooden armoire experimenting with lighting matches.

Dresses, skirts, and blouses hung across the top of the closet from a round pole. Along the floor in boxes, Mary Ann had carefully stored her trousseau—hand embroidered pillow cases and crocheted doilies—and her wedding shower gifts. The thin white tissue paper in which everything was wrapped had caught fire. When Lorraine arrived on the scene, the fire was blazing. The perpetrator had run outside to play—totally oblivious to the havoc she had caused.

"Fire, fire, fire," Lorraine screamed. She headed rapidly as she could to the front screen door.

Mama ran up the steps and pushed open the door. She saw the smoke pouring out of the bedroom. "Go outside and down the steps," she hollered. "I'll call the fire department."

"Billy is in the bathtub," Lorraine said. She made her way out the door.

But 7-year-old Billy, hearing the commotion, had opened the bathroom door. "I've got water in the tub, Mama," he yelled. "We can make the fire go away until the firemen come."

When the fire department arrived, they found little Billy—naked as the day he was born—running back and forth from the bathroom, through the kitchen and dining room, to the bedroom door. He was carrying pots of water from the tub to Mama. She was pouring the water on the raging flames as tears poured down her cheeks.

One firefighter wrapped Billy in a towel, took him down the front steps, and placed him in Mrs. Schneeman's arms. Another firefighter touched Mama gently on the shoulder and said, "We'll take it from here, ma'am. You need to go outside now. You and your son have done everything you could. Is there anyone else in the house?"

"No, I don't think so," Mama said. "I...I didn't think to check. Oh, God. How could this have happened?"

"We'll check all the rooms and the basement just to be sure there's nobody left inside. Really, the fire isn't as bad as it looks. We'll have it out in a just a few minutes. You go outside with your children, now."

As Karen and I rounded the corner by Gilbo and started down Mt. Olivet, we saw the fire trucks in front of our house.

"Look, fire trucks," Karen said.

We started to run down the street and were met by excited neighborhood playmates. "It's your house," someone said. "And Billy's naked!"

Although I wasn't there to see and hear all that happened, the story was recounted over, and over, by Mama and Lorraine. The room where the fire occurred was destroyed, the furniture burned. The firefighters had chopped a hole in the roof. The rest of the house was filled with the smell of smoke. Kind neighbors took us children into their homes to sleep for the next two nights until the smoke smell abated. But Billy got the most attention.

"You were outside naked," neighborhood kids teased him. "We saw you without your clothes on!"

"You're special, Billy," I whispered. I put my arm around his bony shoulders. "What you did was very brave. Don't let them bother you. They're just jealous. People who put out fires are heroes. You're a hero—just like the firemen."

He must have taken it to heart because my brother has put out hundreds of fires throughout his years as a Detroit firefighter. During the 12th Street riot this past summer, he worked around the clock to fight fires in homes like those we grew up in—for people like us. Billy remains my hero—and he is very special to me.

***

Later that evening—after the dinner dishes were done and the children had settled in for the night—Jerry, Billy and I sat in the family room with our hot cups of coffee. The fire burning in the fireplace cast a warm glow over the room.

"So, Billy, spill," I said. "What's the big news? You met a nice girl. You're falling in love?"

He laughed. "I haven't been that lucky yet. I can't seem to find anyone special. I guess I'm not as fortunate as Jerry. He found you. One in a million."

"Right!" I looked at Jerry. He smiled. "Come on. What is it?"

"Mama's talking about selling the house. She's serious. She's sprucing it up--getting it ready to go on the market. She's been bugging me to make some repairs."

"Oh my God! She didn't tell me. I wonder why? All she said was that she was working on a special project. What's she being so secretive about? I can't believe it. Where is she thinking of going?"

"She's talking about moving to Utica—to be near her father. She misses Pa since he moved to the cottage after Ma died."

"I'm sure she does. But what about the rest of you at home? How do you feel about it? Don't you have to live in the city?"

"Mama's worried everyone's going to try to talk her out of moving. But I think it's a good idea. She wants to find a place with room for a big garden. She's looked at a small house with 1-1/2 acres of land a few miles from Pa's—near Uncle Stanley and Aunt Coalletta. It wouldn't be a big problem for me. I can rent a room in the city. And Judy and Davey and Lorraine seem all right with it."

"Really, Lorraine and your mother matter the most in the decision," Jerry said. "Judy and Dave won't be around for many more years. And Bill either. It won't be long before they'll each find someone special and get married."

"Talk about moving out to the country. I can't believe it. Mama was upset when we moved out here. Now she's talking about moving more than 10 miles farther north!"

"Well at least she'll be near her father and brother. And it won't be totally strange for her. She's familiar with the town. It'll be good she and your sister are settled in a place they feel comfortable---I mean for after Judy and Dave and Bill move on."

"Would Dave and Judy move with them?"

"It sounds like it," Billy said. "Dave said he could get a new job out there and Judy said she could commute."

"Wait until I talk to Mama. I can't believe she didn't tell me. I don't think Karen knows either. I talked to her the other day and she didn't say anything."

"As far as I know, you're the first of the married kids to hear. You're not going to discourage her, are you?"

I laughed. "I doubt it would do much good. When Mama makes up her mind to do something, nothing will stop her. It's just hard to imagine her not living on Mt. Olivet. Our family not owning that house. Daddy put so much of himself into it. We all grew up there. It's kind of sad."

Jerry put his arm around my shoulder and gave me a hug. "It won't matter in the long run. That house will live forever in your memories."

"That's true," Billy said. "And I really think it will be a good move for Mama. She's been at loose ends since Daddy died. A lot of the old neighbors are already gone. How long ago was it when Pa moved to the cottage? It was around 1955—that's twelve years ago. I think Mama's kind of lonely. She's worried about her and Lorraine being left alone in the city after everyone leaves home. I think she's ready for something new. Maybe she'll finally get the house she always wanted."

'She deserves it, that's for sure. I do support her in this. I hope everyone else in the family does, too. I can understand how she must feel—like everyone's leaving. Let me know any way I can help."

"You can let her know you support her," Billy said. "Your opinion matters a lot to her. Even though she tries not to show it, she respects you. You've always been her favorite."

I laughed. "Her favorite. Right. If I am, she sure doesn't show it."

Billy and Jerry laughed, too. Mama never showed favoritism. It was a long-standing joke in our family—speculating on who was Mama's favorite. Even the in-laws knew this game. The winner was still to be decided. And Mama wasn't exposing any of her cards.

Chapter 14

After Billy left, I thought a lot about Mama moving to Utica. It was too late to call her, but I was anxious to talk with her. To tell her how much I supported her decision to move. I totally understood her desire to make a change—and it was a good idea for her to be closer to Pa. He was in his 80s. Who knew how much longer he'd be around?

I thought also about my brother saying my opinion meant a lot to Mama, that she respected me, and that I'm her favorite. Truth be told, I have always worked hard to nurture a special relationship with Mama. I recognized that we were alike in many ways. Like her, I'd also chosen being a wife and mother as my lifework. Now I considered how much Mama's opinion of me had always mattered—and how the circumstances of my life had led to that career decision.

**

Growing up, I got a lot of razzing about being Mama's favorite. "Queenie" was what my brothers and sisters called me when they wanted to irritate me. Queenie is a referral to a 1950s television show entitled, Queen for a Day, that we all used to watch. Each week on the program a woman was selected out of the audience and awarded all manner of special gifts and favors. What they were really saying is that I was treated differently—spoiled—because I came after a four-year gap in family births.

There is a picture of me taken when I was a year old. It is winter. Mary Ann is holding me upright on the flat pillar of our front porch. I am wearing a beautiful white coat with a fur collar and a hand crocheted cap. Mary Ann told me the outfit was a gift from my godmother, Aunt Coalletta. I look like a princess. But if I was queen of anything in our family, it was reigning over my younger brothers and sisters. I'm not complaining. I loved my place in our family—right smack in the middle. But I certainly wasn't spoiled. Karen was born before I was 2 years old.

I knew my siblings were just teasing me. But I couldn't seem to help myself. Too often, I took the bait—even though I realized teasing was part of the dynamics in a large family and that reacting disclosed sensitivity that invited more of the same. Being able "to take it" was a key to survival in our family. Arguing as one against the throng was useless. Yet, being told I was treated special in any way was still a sore spot with me. How could anyone feel privileged among so many?

The other aspect of why it bugged me was the inference that I had more in either attention or material goods than the rest of my sisters and brothers. Being spoiled would be considered a negative in our family dynamics. It would mean that growing up you took more than your share of the meager supply of individual attention available from Mama and Daddy. Sharing was vitally important in such a large family. You were always careful to take only your fair share of food at mealtimes, warm clothes on cold days, underwear and socks, and money for school expenses. You never asked for more than you absolutely needed. So taking more than your share of attention would be a selfish thing to do.

As children, we were taught to share everything—toys, clothing, treats. It wasn't until I grew older that I began to understand the concept of yours and mine. In our home, even as teens, we shared much more than most of our friends seemed willing to share. We had little, so sharing benefited each of us. In our Catholic high school Karen and I were required to wear uniforms. We had only a few good casual clothes.

But we were the same sizes so we were able to borrow each other's wool sweaters and skirts as well as jewelry, purses and shoes. It was the only way to have a minimally diverse wardrobe.

In borrowing, we learned to respect each other's possessions. We asked for permission and returned the property in good condition. We also learned to barter and negotiate especially when we both had in mind to wear the same outfit to a sock hop or date. As an adult, I've learned that having my own things is important to me—not in a hoarding sense, but in an exclusive sense. I've noticed that same tendency in my sisters and brothers. Now that we can afford to have our very own things, we fully enjoy the pleasure of individual ownership.

As one of twelve children, I frequently felt shortchanged by my parent's lack of attention. Mama was never a demonstrative person. Daddy was warmer, but not cuddly. I knew I was valued by my parents— and yes, loved—but I never heard it said. It was mostly conceptual. I am here. I am fed and clothed. I have a place to sleep. I must be loved. But it was not a subject we talked about. I don't ever remember being told I was loved, or saying it to my parents as a child.

There was a part I enjoyed about being called "Queenie" by my brothers and sisters. It felt good to be singled out. Maintaining individuality in a large family was a mammoth struggle. To outsiders, you were always "one of the kids" or "one of the Taubes". You counted on your sisters and brothers to know you as a separate person. When they singled me out, they acknowledged my individuality and they showed their love. They were telling me they were proud of me—proud that I'd made something of myself. "Of course," they were always quick to add: "You did have some advantages—being spoiled and all." And when I defended myself, we all knew it was just part of the game.

Deep down, I knew what my sisters and brothers meant when they teased me about being Mama's favorite. They recognized, as I did, that Mama respected me. And that's important in our family. I don't believe she loved me more than any of the others, but I did feel her respect.

Even as a young child, I knew she trusted me and valued my opinions. As an adult, I know that she is proud of me. Although she's never said it.

And I respect her. My family grows strong women. Our grandmas on both sides of the family were matriarchs. Mama is one of the strongest individuals I have ever known. Whenever I think about her, she reminds me of the childhood story, The Little Engine That Could. Women in my family have been independent and capable long before it was acceptable in our social group. As young girls, we learned to hide our intelligence and talent lest we be accused of "trying to wear the pants" in our families or be called "nags". It wasn't until recently that I've begun to understand that being strong and smart and capable are good things.

I've studied Mama. As a child, I used to watch her carefully trying to get to know her and what she was thinking. She rarely expressed her feelings and was careful to show little emotion. I learned to read her slightest facial expression—it was an important survival technique. I got along with Mama because I knew what to expect from her. A slight twitch at the corner of her mouth meant amusement. A hardening of her eyes meant anger. A pursing of her lips meant impatience or irritation. A very slight softening around her eyes meant she was touched by something. She always seemed so much in control.

Each of the names she was called—Anne, Annie, Onya, Mama, Mom—elicited a different response. Her father, Pa, seemed to make Mama the happiest. She liked him and tried to please him. "Onya," he called her. Mama's eyes would always soften whenever he called her name. Daddy wasn't always so lucky. Sometimes she liked him, and sometimes she didn't. He mostly called her "Anne". When he called her "Annie" it was a good sign. It meant Mama was in an especially good mood. Those were the best of times. To us children, Daddy always referred to her as "your Mama".

Mama was extremely perceptive. She has what she called "feelings" or "an intuition" about things—but would abhor being called psychic. When we were children and the phone rang, she would call out before we picked up the receiver, "Tell Mrs. Schmidt I can't talk right now, but I'll call her back." And it would be Mrs. Schmidt on the phone.

We learned to take in stride how often Mama was correct on who was calling. And it was kind of amazing considering the number of family members or friends or neighbors who could be on the other end of the line. She was also an excellent judge of people. She hated phonies and could always spot a liar or a sneak. With her intuitive abilities, you couldn't put much over on Mama.

Mama liked to tell the story about when she was a child in grade school at Holy Rosary Catholic School. She was naughty in class one day. Her teacher, Sister Vincent de Paul, was frustrated because she felt unable to discipline Mama. As mentioned earlier, Pa used to fit the Sisters in the parish with free shoes at his shoe store whenever they needed them—and Mama took advantage of his charity by acting like a spoiled brat.

"Even as a young child," Mama said, "I knew the Sisters were afraid to offend Pa."

Like most kids, I had a difficult time imagining Mama as a little girl—no matter how many photos I looked at. And to think that she was ever a naughty or spoiled little girl was unimaginable. But Mama wanted to remind us that she had privilege and social position when she was growing up.

"You come from good stock," she said. "Don't forget that. Other people might have more money and material things than you, but that doesn't make them any better. What really matters is how smart you are, how willing you are to learn, how hard you are willing to work, and—most of all—how much you believe in yourself."

Pride runs deep in my family heritage. Mama's parents were proud people—even in adversity. During the Great Depression, Pa lost most of his real estate holdings and businesses. But never his pride in who he was or what he was doing.

One summer afternoon, Mama was in the basement doing laundry. Daddy was still at work. The rest of us were scattered throughout the house. I was in the kitchen fixing a peanut butter and jelly sandwich when I heard Mama holler, "Oh my God!" I pounded down the basement steps and ran to the laundry area. Mama stood there, her eyes wide, her hands immersed in the hot suds of the ringer washer.

"What's the matter, Mama," I asked. I thought maybe she had caught something in the ringer. But everything looked normal.

"I can't believe it," she whispered. "Sister Vincent de Paul told me that one day I would be sorry for being so sassy in class. She said, 'The day I die I'm going to pull on your slip to remind you of your naughtiness.' I just felt a tug on my slip. I know it was her. There's no mistake. I know it was her."

I looked at Mama incredulously. She wore a faded blue and while bib apron; it was looped around her neck and tied at her waist. Underneath the apron, she wore a flowered cotton housedress. The lace of her white rayon slip hung slightly below the hem of her dress. I didn't know what to say. It was one of the few times in my entire life that I could remember Mama openly expressing a thought or feeling. And there was no mistaking her conviction that Sister Vincent de Paul had fulfilled a promise made many years before.

As a child in a large family, you never get as much of your parents as you'd like. And it was extremely rare to have one on one alone time with either parent. So it's only natural that those times would stand out. The first time I can recall, I was very young. The streetcars were still running down the center of Van Dyke so it had to be in the mid 1940s. Mama took me with her by streetcar to shop in downtown Detroit.

While we were downtown, we stopped to see Pa. He was working as a guard at one of the stately banks. The floor and walls of the bank were lined with rich gray marble. There were rows and rows of caged tellers and it was very quiet. Pa stood by the entranceway wearing a stiff gray uniform. He smiled broadly when he saw Mama and me, and he brushed his hand lightly over my head. Even as a small child, I sensed the pride he took in Mama—dressed in her finest dress with a veiled hat on her head—and in the job he was doing.

The next time I was alone with Mama was just before I was to graduate from grade school. She went with me to find a dress. It was to be my first store bought outfit and she wanted it to be special. We went from store to store until we found something that I liked, that met her satisfaction as far as how well it was made, and one that was affordable. It was a pink dress with a wide collar; it was flocked with white flowers. I wore it for my graduation under a maroon cap and gown.

During my childhood, I would get Mama's solicitous attention when I was ill and had to stay home from school. She would install me in her bedroom where she could keep an eye on me while she went about her daily schedule. Although some of my younger brothers and sisters were around, she would make frequent stops to see how I was doing. I would be lying all warm and cozy under her fluffy feather tick. She would sit on the edge of the bed and place her cool hand on my forehead.

"You're a little warm," she might say. Or, "how is your tummy? Any better?"

Truth be told, sometimes my only illness was the need for some of Mama's one on one attention. And I like to think she knew it.

One of my favorite things about learning to drive was the opportunity to spend time alone with Mama. She was an excellent teacher. She was patient as I learned to work the clutch and to shift gears. The jerking motions didn't bother her. She gave instructions quietly and didn't get excited when I made mistakes. She smoked her cigarettes one after the other and seemed to enjoy just getting out of the house. During those short trips, I had her undivided attention—and her praise as I gradually improved.

When I was preparing for my wedding, Mama came downtown where I was working to shop with me for fabric for my wedding gown.

I took the afternoon off and we spent hours looking at styles, patterns and fabrics for the entire bridal party. Afterwards, we went to lunch at a little deli and had corned beef sandwiches. The next time we went downtown together to shop for fabric, it was for a baptismal gown for the baby I was expecting.

Nobody ever asked me what I wanted to be when I grew up. Daddy stressed the importance of getting a good education but it was focused more on the acquisition of knowledge than on a career path. As with most children, my future dreams were based on my limited experiences in life.

When I first went to school, I admired the Catholic sisters who taught me. As I had no experience with lay teachers, I thought you had to be a nun to teach. So that's what I decided to become. My desire to teach had nothing to do with having a religious vocation; it had a lot to do with imparting knowledge—and being in charge. When I learned that religious sisters couldn't get married or have babies, I lost interest.

As my literary horizons expanded, the Cheryl Ames nursing series for young readers inspired me. I was particularly impressed with the book, Cherry Ames Student Nurse. I pictured myself going to nursing school, learning exciting new things and, of course, wearing the white stockings, shoes, and uniform—including a starched cap and a blue wool cape.

I asked for "a nursing kit" for my birthday. It came in a white leather case with a tiny red cross etched on the outside. Included inside were an imitation stethoscope, a thermometer, a shot injector, a roll of gauze, a metal case with tiny candy pills, and a stiff paper nurse's cap. When I opened the gift, I could hardly wait to start playing hospital.

I borrowed a white rayon slip from Mary Ann's dresser drawer to use as my uniform and attached the cap to my head with a bobby pin. I set up the hospital in a corner of the parlor—piling flannel blankets on the floor to make a bed. I talked my younger sisters and brother into "being sick". One by one I took their temperatures, gave shots, applied bandages and, most importantly, dispensed the tiny candy pills. Not having any experience with real doctors and nurses—or what they actually did—I soon grew bored. And once the candy was gone, my patients disappeared.

Ma and Pa gave me my first diary as a Christmas gift and started me on a love for writing. The diary became my journal. I wrote in it every night—a full page. I found that putting my thoughts down on paper was powerful. As my love for reading and the magic of words grew, I decided I wanted to be an author. I wrote story after story creating characters that came alive in my imagination. But I soon realized I enjoyed most writing about real people and things. I loved writing in my journal, doing book reports, and writing assignments for school.

In the early grades, we had learned phonics. We were taught to read by sounding words out. I loved words—they were fascinating to me. I could literally see them in my mind's eye. I remember as a small child lying on the carpet with a paper and pencil and dictionary trying to figure out how to spell the word, "drawer". I tried different variations by sound, checking the dictionary to see if the spelling was correct. "Droor?" No. "Dror?" No. "Droer?" No. It was driving me crazy. Finally I had to ask. Mama was working in the kitchen.

"Mama," I called. "How do you spell drawer. I can't figure it out. I tried sounding it out, but none of the spellings I look up in the dictionary are correct."

Mama came through the dining room wiping her hands on her apron. "Sometimes words are tricky," she said. "They are difficult to sound out. Drawer is one of them. I guess it comes from drawing something to you. Draw-er. D-r-a-w-e-r."

"Oh, I get it." I smiled. To think there might be logical explanations to the spelling of words fascinated me even more.

By the time I got to high school, family circumstances were such that I knew going to college was just a dream and that, instead, I'd have to find a job after graduation. I took typing and shorthand courses so that

I would have a marketable professional skill. But I also took pre-college academic classes—Algebra, Geometry, Sciences, Latin—so that I was prepared to go to college if a miracle occurred. I absolutely loved the Latin language. I learned that it was the root of the English language and the source of so many of the words I loved.

Having a professional skill was important to Mama. "If you know shorthand and typing, you'll be able to get a good job in an office," she said. "Especially knowing how to take and transcribe shorthand. Stenographers and secretaries make a lot of money today."

My interest in shorthand had started when I was small. I was looking for a pencil in the secretary desk in the living room. For whatever reason, it was almost impossible to find pencils in our house. We had a pencil sharpener with the base screwed to the edge of a shelf in the pantry, but pencils were in short supply. "Who stole my pencil?" and "Who's got a pencil I can use? I got to do my homework!" Both were common cries in our house. Sometimes we'd have to go down the street to Ma and Pa's house to borrow a pencil.

The secretary desk was mahogany, about 3-feet wide and 6-feet tall. The upper section had narrow double glass doors framed in wood and criss crossed with flat narrow wooden pieces that formed a diamond shaped design. The doors opened to reveal two bookshelves. The bottom half had three drawers—one 8 inches high, the other two much deeper. A hinged 12-inch drop down door at the center of the unit was designed to be a writing desk.

In the open position, the writing desk revealed a dollhouse-sized door that held bottles of ink. On either side of the door were slots originally intended for sorting mail. Beneath the slots were three tiny drawers with pearl-sized decorative pull knobs. I loved to kneel on a chair in front of the open desk and search the child sized drawers and compartments—looking for treasures.

One day, I decided to stand on the chair and examine the bookshelves. On one of the shelves I found a blue hardcover book filled with pages and pages of tiny squiggles. I thought it might be a secret codebook. I took it to show to Mama.

"What is this book?" I asked.

Mama reached down, took the book, and began to leaf through it. "It's my Gregg Shorthand Manual." She smiled wistfully. "Each of those symbols represents words or a combination of words. It's so you can write words really fast when someone is talking. It is a kind of a code."

"Do you know what those squiggles mean?"

"I do. I was a secretary. A man would tell me what he wanted to say in a letter and I used the symbols to write it down. Later, I would read the symbols and use the typewriter to print the words. Then I would give it to him so he could make sure everything he said was in the letter, and he would sign it."

"Did you like to do that?" I looked up into her smiling face.

"I loved taking shorthand." She handed me back the book. "I was very good at it."

Rarely had I seen Mama talk so excitedly about something. If Mama loved shorthand, it must be important. I took the book back into the living room and sat down at the desk. I spent hours copying symbols and pretending I was a secretary. Then I would take the sheets of paper and show them to Mama for her approval. She would smile and nod. "You're doing well," she said. "You just need to keep practicing." That year Santa Claus brought me a toy typewriter for Christmas.

In high school, I took two years of shorthand and typing. I thoroughly enjoyed shorthand—and I was very good at it. Mama was so proud when I showed her my shorthand papers marked with "A+". "It must be an inherited talent," she said. She smiled. "And look. I can still read the squiggles!" I was also a fast typist. I started earning money as a part-time secretary while I was still in high school.

Ultimately, I knew that my actual career in life would be as a wife and mother. No matter what job I took, everyone around me—friends, neighbors, parents, relatives, church leaders and the nuns at school—

conditioned me to assume those roles. When I got engaged at the end of my senior year in high school, I was considered to be on the path to success. It was just the way it was then. I was not alone. Many of my friends and schoolmates married within a year of graduating high school.

**

My interests and Mama's have always been similar. I'd expected to have a large family—just like her. Now that wasn't going to happen. I wasn't physically able to bear any more children. Truthfully, I wasn't sure how many more I would have wanted. The 1960s were bringing changes in society that I couldn't help but notice. And I was beginning to recognize just how much I still looked for Mama's love, attention, and approval. Was that normal or healthy for an adult woman? Do we ever outgrow that need?

Chapter 15

I decided to wait for a few days before I approached Mama about her decision to move out of the city. I needed to get used to the idea. I never thought of Mama as a person who loved the outdoors. It was Daddy who was the nature lover. When Daddy was single, he drove all over Michigan camping and fishing. It was a time when roads were undeveloped and unmapped—but that didn't stop him and his friends.

Daddy loved to talk about all the places he'd been. Once he married and had a family, his jaunts were limited but his love of adventure and the outdoors persisted. So on Sundays—spring, summer, winter or fall—we frequently went on rides with open-ended destinations. We went exploring.

"Okay, everybody," Daddy would say. "Let's climb in the Terraplane and go for a ride."

He loved that car and always called it by name. It was a 1937 Hudson that had a floor shift with a round black knob and a choke starter. There was no power steering, power brakes, or power windows. The blower barely kept the windows defrosted. There was little heat and no air conditioning. To signal a turn, Daddy had to roll down the window—winter or summer—and stick his arm straight outside. Turn signals and automatic transmissions were inventions of the future.

I knew every inch of the inside of the car. Daddy used to keep it parked next to the curb under the tree in front of our house. He never objected to me sitting in the car behind the steering wheel pretending I was driving. I was so small I could barely see over the steering wheel, but I loved to get my younger brother and sister to climb into the car with me and go on make-believe trips across the country.

In the spring Daddy would drive into the countryside looking for one-room schoolhouses. As they usually had outhouses, well water pumps, picnic tables, playground equipment and plenty of play fields, these were great places for our family outings. We would drive a couple hours north along country roads until we found the perfect spot. Then we would unload our belongings, eat our lunch, and be ready to enjoy our surroundings.

We played on the swings, teeter totters and merry-go-around while Mama and Daddy read The Detroit News or snoozed on blankets spread under shady trees in the tall green grass. After a while, we would talk Daddy—and sometimes Mama—into playing field games. We played frozen tag, spud ball, hide and go seek, red rover and croquet. Everyone old enough participated except Lorraine.

She kept an eye on the youngest children who played contentedly with their toys in the wood-slatted playpen—and she was the referee and umpire whenever anyone in our competitive family called, "foul". Her decisions overrode Mama and Daddy when it came to game rules and fair play—a rare and unusual power in our family.

On hot summer days, we would head to the beach. Daddy rarely chose the closest parks. He drove for hours to find the ideal place—as far north as Caseville, Port Austin and Harbor Beach; west to Brighton, Whitmore Lake and Dundee; south to Canada's Pointe Pelee; and northeast to Marysville, Lakeport, Lexington, Port Sanilac and Canada's Imperwash Beach. It could be a public beach or it could be a deserted spot along one of the Great Lakes. Each time, it was different.

After the long drive, we could hardly wait to get into the water. If there were bathhouses, we changed there. If not, we draped towels over the windows and took turns changing into our bathing suits in the car. Then we would head for the water where we stayed except to come out to eat. We played tag, had splashing contests, sat on each other's shoulders to play king of the mountain, and tipped each other off the inner tubes. We tried to avoid coming out to eat because once you ate you had to wait 30 minutes before you could go back in the water. At the time, it was believed that swimming too soon after eating caused cramps and the danger of drowning.

Mama wasn't a swimmer. She loved to go to the beach, but I never saw her in a bathing suit. She claimed she knew how to swim, but I never even saw her put a toe in the water. Instead, she would sit on a blanket in the sun for a while and watch us swim. Then she would put a lawn chair under a tree and read. Daddy paid close attention while we were in the lake. If he wasn't swimming, he was sitting on the edge of the water—always counting heads.

My older brothers were notorious for ducking me and my younger sisters and brothers. They would swim underwater, grab our legs, and pull us under as we bobbed in the water on our inner tubes. Sometimes they would swim up, push our heads under the water, and hold us there for several seconds that seemed like hours. I don't know why this was their idea of fun, but I soon learned how to stop them.

"Don't duck us," I'd yell as either Buddy or Donny approached. "Help, Daddy! They're bothering us!"

"Stop that horseplay," Daddy would holler. "Or you're getting out of the water right now. It's dangerous. You're old enough to know better."

Daddy loved the water. He was the one who taught me how to swim. Ma and Pa's cottage was on the Clinton River. We swam there when I was very small—before it became polluted. The river had a strong current and many hidden drop offs. I was only 3 years old when Daddy insisted I learn.

"If you're going to be in the river, you have to at least learn to float," he said. "Sometimes the current is so strong it will pull at you—your feet will be lifted right out from under you. It will take you by surprise—and it'll be too strong to fight. Let me teach you how to float." He would lay me down on the water with his arms beneath me. "Just close your eyes and relax. Pretend you're lying on a soft, soft bed."

"Don't let me go, Daddy. I don't want to get water in my nose."

"I won't," he promised.

But as soon as I lay back and totally relaxed, Daddy would remove his arms. He didn't do it to be cruel. He was checking to see whether or not I was floating. Time after time, I would sink and end up with water in my nose. As bizarre as his teaching method was, I soon learned to float. Eventually, I could lie on top of the water, pillow my arms under my head, and float for as long as I wanted to as though I was lying on a rubber raft. Once I learned to float, Daddy taught me swimming strokes. Although I never took a swimming class, I became a strong, confident swimmer. So did each of my brothers and sisters.

When I was in sixth grade and on a Girl Scout outing at the beach on Lake Huron, I saved a fellow scout from drowning. Barbara was several inches shorter than I. We had walked out a little ways from shore when all of a sudden the waves pulled us out into water over her head. When she realized she couldn't touch bottom, she didn't yell or scream. She just thrashed around. I was a few feet away. I noticed her flailing her arms. Her eyes were filled with terror.

I didn't know any lifesaving techniques, but I knew she was in trouble. I swam over to her and grabbed her. She pulled me under, but I was confident in the water. I simply walked along the bottom—letting the water go over my head—and brought her back to where she could touch bottom.

"I...I can't swim," she whispered. She bent over. She coughed and sputtered. Finally, she caught her breath. "Thank you. I didn't mean to go out so far. All of a sudden the water was over my head. She looked around to see if anyone else had noticed. "Please don't tell anyone I went under. If my mother finds out, she'll be real mad. I'm only supposed to go up to my ankles. Please, don't tell."

"You should learn how to swim," I said. "It's easy. You need to take lessons." I was amazed that anyone wouldn't know how to swim.

Apparently nobody else noticed what had happened. I never told anyone at the time, and I doubt that Barbara did either. I don't know if she ever learned to swim. I like to think that she did.

As the summer day cooled down, we would come out of the water one by one with blue lips, shivering, and go to change into dry clothes. Then we would play games on the grass until the mosquitoes started biting and we were ready to pack up and head for home. It would be dark by the time we got back, tired and sunburned.

When autumn arrived, Daddy liked to take us exploring in the woods. He would find places in the country for us to walk while Mama waited in the car with the babies and toddlers. "See how the leaves change colors?" he'd say. "You can tell what kind of tree it is by the shape and colors of the leaves. See, this is a maple. Its leaves are wide and red. That's an oak. Its leaves are narrower and bronze—and it has tiny acorns. And notice the smell of autumn." He would sniff the air. "If I woke up from a long deep sleep and didn't know what month it was, all I'd have to do is take a deep breath. Without even opening my eyes and looking around, I would know it was fall."

One of our favorite destinations in the winter was Belle Isle Park which sits in the middle of the Detroit River near Lake St. Clair on the southernmost edge of the city. Across the river is Windsor, Canada. The park featured a large, natural wooded area that was the home of a wide variety of small animals and birds. It included a half-mile swimming beach; interior waterways for ice skating, fishing and canoeing; an aquarium with hundreds of exotic fish; a year round flower conservatory filled with rare orchids, and tropical plants; a beautiful white marble outdoor fountain; a band shell for summer concerts; an indoor casino that served hot drinks in the winter, cold drinks in the summer, and snacks and meals year round.

There were horseback riding trails and two stables where horses could be rented by the hour. There was a canoe concession which provided rental canoes. There were fishing piers, playgrounds, picnic shelters, and handball, tennis and basketball courts, baseball fields and even a cricket pitch. Tables for picnicking were scattered throughout the park. At the eastern tip of the island were a marble lighthouse and the U.S. Coast Guard Station. And there were lots of nature trails.

The MacArthur Bridge—a half mile stone expanse —connected the 2-1/2-mile-long, 985-acre Island Park to Jefferson Avenue. A cement stairway descended under the busy street and fascinated us as children. It looked like a secret tunnel. "Let's walk in the tunnel today," someone always begged as we started across the bridge.

"Someday we will," Daddy said. "But you won't like it under there. It's a dark, gloomy place and you can't even see the water. Look out here." He pointed to the blue expanse on either side of the bridge as we drove across. "It's beautiful. You can even see Canada—a whole different country than ours. Not too many people in the United States can make that claim."

One winter afternoon Daddy parked the car and we finally climbed down the steps to explore. We followed the underground passageway with its many twists and turns to the bottom—where it ran in an open fenced-off area along the Grand Boulevard auto underpass. When we reached the other side, we waited while Daddy went for the car. It was an adventure, but he was right all along. I didn't like the dark, closed-in tunnel at all.

Belle Isle had many short drives that crisscrossed the interior of the island, north and south between the main east/west roads. The drives had steep concrete bridges over the canals which, when properly traversed by car, could give passengers the illusion of being on a roller coaster. We called them "tickle hills".

"Uh, oh," Daddy would call. "Tickle hill alert!" He would step on the gas just before hitting the rise, and the tires would leave the pavement for a second as we descended the hill—making us feel that the car was flying and sending our stomachs into euphoric flips. We would start squealing before he even stepped on the gas.

On Sundays during the winter, Daddy frequently took us to Belle Isle to ice skate on the frozen canals. We visited the "flower house" and "fish house" which were adjacent to each other and open year-round. On Easter Sunday, it was a family tradition to visit the conservatory dressed in our church clothes—our newest outfits including dresses and hats and gloves. The flower house with its 85-foot high central dome and its collection of continuously blooming plants was one of Mama's favorite places.

On hot summer evenings we took rides around the island with the car windows open to the fresh cool air as we listened to the music from the concerts wafting over us. We stopped at the fountain which was shaped like a huge tiered wedding cake and bubbled day and night. We sat at the base and put our hands—and sometimes our feet—into the cool water. At night, the fountain was illuminated by multi-colored lights.

Although we talked and dreamed about canoeing along the canals and horseback riding along the trails, we never did. The rental rates for such a large family were beyond our means—as well as our expectations. And we only visited the casino for potty stops. When we visited the island, Mama always packed our food and drinks.

On our rides, we never went out to eat and rarely stopped for treats. There was one exception. The Sundays we headed out to Ma and Pa's cottage. Along the way was a general store that sold dipped ice cream in cones. Sometimes we stopped. As we approached the store, we would always quiet down—waiting, hoping. If it was a good day, Daddy would say, "What do you think about stopping for some ice cream, Annie?" That was our cue.

"I scream, you scream, we all scream for ice cream," we'd chant.

Mama was the decision maker when it came to spending money. I couldn't see to read her face because she was in the front seat and didn't turn around. But I knew that on the good days there would be a twitch at the corner of her mouth and a twinkle in her eyes. And it was usually a good sign when Daddy called her "Annie". On those days, she would give a small nod and Daddy would stop in front of the store.

Then everyone except Lorraine and Mama would pile out of the car, climb the steep cement steps and each take a turn at the ice cream counter choosing the flavor for our single dip cone. Daddy would choose three flavors—one for himself, one for Mama, and one for Lorraine who couldn't climb the open-ended steps with her crutches. The ice cream cones were a rare and wonderful treat—and Mama in a good mood was even better.

On other days, we just quietly drove past the store. It didn't necessarily mean Mama was in a bad mood. It just might mean that Daddy didn't have the money to spend on twelve ice cream cones. And we knew better than to ask for something we couldn't afford. It's one of the most important lessons you learned growing up in a large family.

Sometimes on family outings, the car would balk. Daddy would pull over to the side of the road and turn off the engine. He'd get out of the car, lift up the hood, and peek inside. He always carried his tools and extra water in the trunk. He wasn't a mechanical wizard, but he seemed to be able to diagnose and fix the problem—whatever it was. He was an expert in making do. We were never stranded at the side of the road.

One time stands out in family lore. It was a hot summer day. The engine started chugging...chug...chug...chug. Daddy pulled to the side of the road and turned off the ignition. It wouldn't restart. He got outside and lifted the hood. We were all waiting anxiously to see if the problem could be fixed. He slammed down the hood and got back into the car.

"It needs air in the mix," Daddy said. "Buddy, you get out and take the cap off of the gas tank. Then you can help me push the car to get it started rolling. I'll jump inside. You run beside the car and blow in the gas tank. I'll try to start the engine. If the engine starts, keep blowing in the gas tank. When the engine stops chugging, run and get back inside the car. I'll drive slowly."

I don't know what the problem was, but Daddy's solution worked. The engine started, Buddy jumped in the car, and we were off again. The car worked fine the rest of the trip.

When Aunt Bea and Uncle Harold bought a lot and began to build their house on Elkhorn Lake in Orion Township, we would occasionally drive out to visit them. We swam in the lake, fished, ice skated, and sledded down the hill. To get to their house, we always took Orion Road between Rochester and Lake Orion. It was a narrow, hilly, two-lane blacktopped rural road with many curves and dips. We called it "snake road".

We were returning home late one Saturday evening when an unexpected ice storm hit. Unfortunately, we were half way between two villages. The area was remote—scattered houses, but no stores or gas stations. The road was a sheet of ice. Daddy was driving slowly. Suddenly, the car turned and began sliding sideways down a steep hill. There was absolute silence in the car.

"Everybody close their eyes and start praying the rosary," Daddy said. He clutched the steering wheel tightly. "I'll let you know when we're safe."

"In the name of the Father, and of the Son and of the Holy Ghost," Mama said. We all chimed in with the proper responses.

I peeked at Daddy's white knuckles on the steering wheel, and then looked out the window. It was black all around us. The only light was from the glare of the headlights on the trees along the side of the road. There were no other vehicles around. Our car was going sideways—but slowly—and stayed in the middle of the road. Soon the car reached the bottom of the hill and Daddy straightened out the wheel. I closed my eyes and joined the prayers. I was confident he wouldn't give up—that he would get us safely home. If anybody could get us out of this danger, it would be him—with God' help, of course.

⁎

Now I wondered about all those family outings. Was getting out in the country Mama's idea of a good time, too? She rarely talked about her likes and dislikes—about her desires. I had always assumed Mama was just going along for the rides—to please Daddy. With her now talking about moving to the country, I began to look at those times differently. I wanted to understand Mama. I needed to. And I wanted to support her as best as I could.

Chapter 16

When I finally called her, Mama wasn't interested in talking about her dreams—past or present. She was in action mode.

"I'm getting the house ready to sell," she told me. "I'm too busy to talk."

"What's the big hurry?" I asked.

"Everyone's moving out of the city. I don't want to be left behind."

"Why Utica?"

"Pa is there. So is Uncle Stanley. I know the area. I like it. You know I've been going out there since I was a little girl."

***

Mama's Uncle Frank and Aunt Mary had a farm on Van Dyke near 23 Mile Road. She told us stories about taking the train from Detroit to stay with them for weeks at a time during the summer. Uncle Frank would pick her up at the train station in town in a horse and buggy. When we were small, we visited them occasionally. But they were no longer farming. The area was rapidly growing into a rural suburbia.

Ma and Pa built their small cottage in Utica around 1915. It was a two-bedroom structure surrounded by pine trees sitting atop a hill that swept down to the Clinton River. The long narrow property included 2 acres and combined pockets of stately white pines and open fields. A dilapidated carriage house served as the storage shed. Along the side nearest the house were the outhouses—one for the boys and one for the girls.

After Pa retired, he and Ma would stay summers at the cottage. On designated Sundays, the extended family gathered there for picnics and reunions. We swam in the river and played outside games like baseball, frozen tag, red rover, and hide and go seek. During the winter we drove out to slide down the steep hill on our sleds. Everyone in the family looked forward to what we called "going to Utica".

Karen and I loved staying for a week at a time during the summer at the cottage with Ma and Pa. We weren't allowed to swim in the river without Daddy there, but we could cool down by putting on our bathing suits and filling the metal tub that stood by the well with the cold, cold well water. It was fun to pump the metal handle up and down as the water poured out over us. It was also the way we bathed as the house had minimal indoor plumbing.

And that was the one thing we hated about being out there. We had to use the outhouse—day or night, summer or winter, rain or shine. Pa had installed makeshift plumbing for a modern toilet inside the house off the kitchen. However, there was little water pressure. Some cold water ran from the faucet in the kitchen sink, but flushing the toilet usually required carrying buckets of water into the house from the well. The indoor toilet was strictly for use by Ma who was crippled by rheumatoid arthritis and couldn't navigate to the outside facilities.

The outhouse was located about 50 yards from the cottage. It was a long wooden structure divided into two tiny rooms by a floor to ceiling wall. The inside wall was the outside of the shed. The other two walls ran from the wooden plank floor to 10 inches from the roof—leaving openings for ventilation. Cut into the old wooden bench in each unit were two large circular holes. Unfortunately, the openings invited free access to all manner of flying insects that were attracted to the pungent odors. The doors to the rustic outhouse usually hung open a few inches.

Spiders loved to build their webs inside!

The first thing you would do when you opened the wooden plank door would be to check for critters. Next, you would take a big gulp of fresh air before entering to avoid inhaling the smell for as long as possible. Then you would check for buzzing insects—especially bees and wasps—that liked to fly around just inside the bench openings. This was crucial if you didn't want to experience a butt sting. Finally, you would do your business as fast as possible and escape before you needed to take a breath.

My brothers loved to tell stories about children who had fallen through a bench opening into the human waste below.

"When Aunt Josephine was small, she accidentally knocked her favorite doll down there," Buddy told us.

"And she fell in headfirst into the guck trying to get it," Donny said. "They almost couldn't get her out."

"And when they did she was covered with you know what."

"You better be careful you don't fall in!"

Karen and I devised all kinds of plans to avoid using the outhouse. We found the open fields and behind bushes and trees were much better places to pee. If we had to do what we called "number two", we had no choice but to use the outhouse. Unless, of course, Ma and Pa weren't paying attention or weren't around. Then we could sneak through the kitchen and use the prohibited indoor toilet. There was always a chance the water pressure would be up and the flushing would be successful. But there were countless times that "number two" mysteriously appeared in the indoor toilet and nobody admitted to knowing how it got there.

Having to go to the outhouse during the night was particularly fraught with trauma. It was pitch black outside. The porch light didn't reach as far as the storage shed. Our way was lighted only by the beam of a flashlight and the moon and stars on a bright night. All of the usual concerns applied—magnified by the darkness and spooky night noises. Karen and I tried to avoid drinking anything in the evenings so we wouldn't have to get up during the night. Unfortunately, we were both frequent bed wetters the nights we spent at the cottage. But Ma and Pa never complained about our accidents.

Pa grew lots of vegetables at the cottage—tomatoes, cucumbers, lettuce, peppers, corn, green beans, squash and pumpkins—as well as cantaloupes and watermelons. He let Karen and I eat as much as we wanted when we stayed there as long as we didn't waste anything. I can remember going out to the vegetable patch on hot summer days to find ripe red tomatoes warm from the sun. We would pick the juicy fruit, rub it against our clothing to clean off the dirt, and eat it right in the field.

Watermelons were also a favorite. It seemed to take forever until they were ripe enough to eat. As soon as Pa told us the watermelons were ready, we would run to the field. We would pick an oblong green striped melon, dash it against a rock to break the rind, and each take a jagged piece. There was nothing sweeter than that delicious pink pulp still warm from the sun. As we gorged ourselves, we would spit the seeds at each other, laughing and ducking, totally ignoring the juices that ran down our chins and onto our sundresses.

Some mornings, Ma would send us out to the unfarmed fields to pick wild berries. Little girls wore dresses in the 1940s—we were not allowed to wear "boys' pants" even for playing outside. The field where the blackberry bushes grew was overgrown with weeds and prickly bush. By the time we got to the berry bushes with our pails, our arms and legs were scratched and bleeding. But we ignored the discomfort once we saw the fat black jewels. We picked and picked, filling our metal buckets and eating as we picked. We knew if we picked enough berries, Ma would bake a pie—she never let the berries go to waste.

Ma and Pa taught us how to play card games—canasta and pinochle— and we would play far into the evenings. Sometimes, Karen would fall asleep right in the middle of a game. Ma or Pa would shake her to make her finish the hand. When we finally climbed into bed in the room next to theirs, we could hear them talking companionably as we fell asleep. The smells of the fields and river and the sounds of crickets and frogs wafted in through the screened windows. There were no traffic sounds and only the stars and moon lit the night. We felt cocooned in safety.

Ma and Pa were not huggers. I knew in my heart that they loved me—as did my parents, sisters and brothers, aunts and uncles—but it was rarely demonstrated or expressed to me in words or actions. I'm not sure if it was the times, our social conditioning, or our ethnicity, but the only ones I can remember hugging me occasionally was my sister Lorraine and my Aunt Coalletta. It was rare, in fact, to be singled out for any attention whatsoever.

Being one of twelve children in a large family with lots of cousins doesn't allow much room for feeling special or even noticed. I was "one of the kids". As a result, I tried to find ways to get positive attention— and oftentimes, just a word in edgewise. But so did my brothers and sisters and cousins from both sides of the family. Our gatherings were filled with energetic, lively individuals all on the same mission.

As a small child, I was quiet and shy. When we had visitors at home, Karen and I would hide under the dining room table. If anyone noticed and talked us out of our hiding place, we would put our thumbs in our mouths and climb quietly onto any inviting lap. We always knew who would be the best snuggler—and who didn't like children.

Aunt Coalletta was one of my favorites. She was married to Uncle Stanley, Mama's only brother. She was young and beautiful and especially mine because she was my godmother. In the 1940s Uncle Stanley and Aunt Coalletta lived down the street on Mt. Olivet in an upper flat at Ma and Pa's house. At the time, they had two children. Their oldest son, Stanley, is Karen's age, and Beverly is a year younger. I loved to spend time with my aunt. Everything she did seemed glamorous to me. And she never made me feel like I was intruding.

One day I sat for a long time watching Aunt Coalletta running clothing through an Ironrite mangle. It was a 3-foot square electric appliance that used a roller and cast iron shoe to press cloth. Mama didn't have a mangle. She stood before an ironing board in the kitchen and used a plain electric iron. Aunt Coalletta sat in front of the Ironrite and fed wrinkled clothing through the hot roller. The machine did all the work. It was magic and modern in the 1940s when steam irons were yet unknown. I ached to try the mangle, but my aunt insisted it was too dangerous.

Most everything had to be ironed in the days before permanent press or wash and wear—pants, shirts, blouses, skirts, and handkerchiefs. Clothing was stiff from hanging on the lines. There were no clothes dryers to soften fabric. And shirts and blouses were heavily starched. As Mama unpinned the dry clothing from the backyard or basement lines, she put the items that needed to be ironed into a separate basket.

On ironing day, she used a glass Coca Cola bottle filled with warm water and capped with a metal rubber-banded sprinkling head to moisturize the items to be ironed. Each piece had to be sprinkled with water, rolled to spread the dampness evenly, and placed back into the basket. Then they had to be pressed individually with a hot iron.

One hot summer day I watched Mama as she stood at the ironing board pressing Daddy's Sunday shirt. Her hair was damp from perspiration. Rivulets of sweat ran down her face.

"Mama," I said. "You should get one of those new ironing machines like Aunt Coalletta's. It's called a mangle. She can sit down while she irons. And she irons everything with it—even sheets and underwear and socks!"

Mama didn't tell me we couldn't afford something so extravagant.

"Irons underwear and socks?" she scoffed. "I guess she must have too much time on her hands!"

One day at lunchtime I was allowed to go to Aunt Coalletta's so she could curl my long, straight, medium brown hair for a music recital in which I was performing at school that afternoon. I was so excited! I knew my aunt would transform me into someone beautiful and glamorous—just like her. The curling iron she used looked much like the ones we use today, but it was not electric. It had to be heated in the gas flames on the stove.

Aunt Coalletta would heat the iron by laying it in the open flame. After a few minutes, she would test the temperature by clamping it on newspaper to make sure the paper didn't turn brown. The iron couldn't be too hot or it would singe my hair. Next, she would take a lock of my hair, dampen it with a comb dipped in water, spit on the iron to make sure it sizzled, and then apply the heated iron to my hair. It was a long and tedious and painful process. But I felt elegant when I looked in the mirror and saw my long curls.

When I arrived home from school later that afternoon, I was still excited about my new appearance.

"Look, Mama," I said. "Don't I look beautiful? Aunt Coalletta did my hair for me. Everyone at school liked it!"

She looked at me, and then turned away.

"Some people are fortunate enough to have the time to fuss," she said.

I realized then, as young as I was, that Mama was jealous of my attachment to Aunt Coalletta. I never went back to get curls from my aunt, and I don't remember spending much time with her after that. However, that could have been a coincidence because Uncle Stanley and Aunt Coalletta moved out to Utica around that time. And she grew busier and busier as they started construction of their new house and as their family continued to grow.

Like Mama and Daddy, Aunt Coalletta and Uncle Stanley were hard workers. In the 1940s and early 1950s, most blue collar workers couldn't afford to just buy a new house. There wasn't easy financing, and people who grew up during the Great Depression considered borrowing suspect and dangerous. Instead, they saved. First for a piece of property, then for the building materials. And friends helped with the construction.

Uncle Stanley had a good steady job in a Ford Motor plant repairing machinery. He and Aunt Coalletta lived in the upper flat at Ma and Pa's until they saved enough to purchase a few acres of land on Shelby Road near 22 Mile Road. Uncle Stanley, Pa, Daddy, and all of my uncles helped clear the property for a home site. Next, they sunk a well and built a garage. The garage was the family's rustic living quarters until the house was started. And this took time and money. The work was done on weekends as weather permitted.

Once the basement was dug, the men used cinder blocks to construct the walls. Then they poured a concrete floor and installed electrical, gas, and plumbing. Finally, a roof—which would eventually be the floor of the house—was constructed and covered with black tar paper. Basement steps were cast and a door installed. The basement was then divided into kitchen, bathroom and bedroom areas—and the family moved in. Uncle Stanley and Aunt Coalletta and their family lived in the basement while their house was under construction.

Meanwhile, they cleared and planted the fields with corn, tomatoes, potatoes, peppers, cucumbers, lettuce, squash, and pumpkins. They fed their young family, canned the surplus, and shared the vegetables with all of the relatives who came to help with the building of their house. As busy as she must have been, Aunt Coalletta always invited Karen and I to come and stay with our cousins for a few days every summer. Her family eventually grew to include eight children.

***

In the years since Pa sold the house on Mt. Olivet and moved to the cottage, he had lived on his own with support from Uncle Stanley and Aunt Coalletta. Until recently, he planted vegetable gardens every summer, cooked, canned, baked, and managed most of his own chores. But five years ago, he'd discovered a lump in his left breast that was diagnosed as breast cancer. The treatment took a lot out of him.

"It's ridiculous. Men don't even get breast cancer," Mama said. "What kind of hack is he going to?"

Mama had been frustrated. She would have loved to be involved in Pa's medical care and concerns. But he lived in Utica—and Daddy needed her. She had her hands full and could only observe from a distance as Aunt Coalletta and Uncle Stanley chose Pa's doctors and transported him to and from appointments. Uncle Stanley was still working full-time, so it was Aunt Coalletta who was most involved. To Mama, it just wasn't right that a daughter-in-law, not a daughter, was in charge.

"Aunt Coalletta has weaved some pretty wild stories in her life," Mama said. "But this has to be the most ridiculous. Obviously Pa had a lump on his chest—but breast cancer? That's just stupid!"

Pa had surgery and recovered. But he wasn't as active as he had been. His clear blue eyes sparkled with mischief and he still loved to tease—now his great grandchildren. He continued to live on his own, but he'd stopped his planting. When Jerry and I visited Pa, we would lay our youngsters down to sleep on the bed and sit down to play three-handed pinochle—a game Pa still loved. We laughed at some of his favorite expressions.

"What's your meldt?" he'd ask as he marked down each player's score. "Cut your troat?" he challenged as he offered the shuffled deck to the person on his left to cut the deck. "It's all over but the cryin," he boasted when he had an especially great hand dealt to him.

As children, we learned competitiveness in games from Pa and Ma. They taught each of their grandchildren how to play cards—war, hearts, double solitaire, and canasta—but pinochle was always their favorite. They would play for hours and never tire. There wasn't any special consideration given for age or ability. We learned to play to win. If we lost, we had "to grin and bear it"—and try for a rematch. Nobody wanted to be called "a baby" or "a poor loser". We couldn't understand anyone who didn't play to win.

Teasing we learned from my grandfather. Pa was a master at teasing. Although he didn't mean to be cruel, it was difficult to deal with as a young child. One scenario particularly stands out. It was replayed at the beginning of every school year.

In grade school, we each had to bring in an empty cigar box to keep in our desks for school supplies—pencils, erasers, paste, scissors, crayons. Pa was a cigar smoker. He must have saved his empty cigar boxes throughout the year so he would have some in September when we came asking. I can see Karen, Billy and I standing nervously on the landing by the side door of the house on Mt. Olivet as Pa leant across the steps to the kitchen, a big grin on his face, his blue eyes twinkling.

"Pa," I'd say. "Do you have any cigar boxes?"

"Did you ever see a cigar box?" he'd tease.

If you answered, "Yes," he would chortle, "You saw a cigar boxing? I don't believe that for a minute!" If you answered, "No," he would say in mock outrage, "You are telling me that you never saw a box of cigars?" So we would just stand there waiting. Then he would smile, say "Wait here," and go get an empty cigar box for each of us.

It wasn't until we grew older that we learned to appreciate Pa's sense of humor.

***

Mama's move to Utica would be good for both her and Pa. She had happy memories there, and she would be able to spend more time with him in his declining years.

"I'm happy for you, Mama," I said. "Pa would love having you out there. I hope you find a place you like."

"I have my eye on something," she said. "But I have to sell our house first. Hopefully, it will all work out."

Mama usually managed to make everything work out.

Chapter 17

I never knew my husband's father. He died when Jerry was 16 years old. His mother was an independent woman who supported herself and lived on her own. I tried to include her in all of our family events. Our children were close to Grandma Dywasuk. They loved her. But, like most women, in my daily life I was much more involved with my mother than my mother-in-law.

***

Growing up, we were much closer to Mama's family than we were to Daddy's. Mama didn't like Daddy's parents. She thought they had taken advantage of his good nature from the time he was a child. Most importantly, they had forced him to quit school at 14 years old and go to work full time. He wasn't allowed to fulfill his dream of going to high school and she never forgave his parents for that. Mama especially disliked Grandma Taube.

"She's bossy, tight with money, opinionated, and lacks a sense of humor. What's to like?" Mama said. "I could enjoy Grandpa Taube's company if they didn't come as a pair."

So Daddy went to visit his parents without Mama. Karen, Billy and I would go along to keep him company. Visiting Grandma and Grandpa was like entering a different world. Daddy grew up on Joseph Campau in Detroit. His parents owned a two-family home and lived in the lower flat. We never went to the front door. We entered their property from the alley, through the back yard, up the steps to the screened-in back porch, and across the porch to the kitchen door. I shivered as I waited for my grandmother to answer the door.

Although Grandma Taube was the only one of my four grandparents to have been born in the United States, she was the one who seemed "old country" to me. She was a tall, large- boned woman who wore her white hair in a tight bun at the back of her head. She didn't smile or seem happy to see us. Instead, she would answer the door with a finger on her lips telling us to keep quiet so we wouldn't disturb the family who lived in the upper flat.

Grandpa always sat at the kitchen table facing the door. He would wave when we walked into the house. Our grandparents didn't call us by name, never hugged or kissed us, and barely acknowledged our presence during the visit. Grandpa had an empty can on the floor by his feet. Every once in a while he would pick up the can and spit into it. Even as a child, it amazed me that Daddy, with his good humor, interest in learning new things, love of adventure and gregarious personality could have come from these parents.

Billy, Karen and I would stay by the door trying to be as quiet as possible. We were afraid to move. On the sewing machine—which stood next to the back door under the window facing the back porch— there was a fish bowl with a huge goldfish. The goldfish was 5 inches long and 3 inches wide. We would stand for what seemed like hours watching the fish swim back and forth. We weren't allowed in any other part of the house. We weren't offered anything to eat or drink. Mostly, we stood around while the adults visited.

"We won't stay long," Daddy told us.

He always promised this as we climbed out of the car. He knew how uncomfortable it was for us to visit his parents. He didn't seem to enjoy it that much either. But we came because we wanted to spend time with

Daddy and because—once in a great while—Grandpa would get up from his chair, go out of the kitchen, and come back with 50-cent pieces for each of us. And that was a fortune to us!

"Come here," Grandpa called. He would beckon to me to stand beside him. "Now, which one are you?"

I answered him in a whisper. He would take my hand, spread it open, and press a cool round coin into my palm.

I was afraid of Grandma Taube. There was no warmth about her. But Grandpa was a kind man. He was about the same height as Daddy—5 feet 10 inches or so—only much rounder. He had white hair and bright blue eyes that were scrunched into slits above his chubby cheeks. I know he loved fishing and had a good sense of humor because I listened while he and Daddy laughed and talked together. It's difficult to judge our grandparents by today's standards. In those days, children were to be "seen and not heard". But Grandma and Grandpa didn't seem to enjoy children very much.

The kitchen was divided from the living room by pocket doors. The doors were kept closed to keep the heat in the kitchen. On one visit, Grandma asked if we wanted to listen to the radio. When we nodded, she slid open the door and led us into the living room. The living room had a polished wood plank floor and overstuffed furniture. The windows were draped and there were tiny slivers of light shining into the cool, dark room. A wooden Zenith floor model radio stood against the wall opposite the windows.

"Sit there," she told us. She pointed to the floor in front of the radio. She turned the radio on and started flicking the control dials to find a station. "Just sit quietly. Don't move. Don't touch the radio or anything else. And don't sit on the couches."

Grandma and Grandpa didn't have a car. They walked to church for Mass and to neighborhood stores to do their shopping. For family events like Baptisms and First Communions, Daddy went to pick them up to bring them to our house. After a short visit, they were ready for Daddy to drive them back home—even though the party was still going on. Lorraine would often go along for the ride. Grandpa knew Lorraine's name. She was his oldest grandchild and he seemed to enjoy her company.

One day she returned home from the ride barely able to contain her excitement. "Guess what?" she said. "Grandpa gave Daddy money to buy us a television! I'm going to be able to watch Eisenhower get nominated at the Republican convention!"

"Yeah," Daddy said. He looked at Mama. "Apparently my mother gave all my brothers and sisters money for televisions a while ago. My dad noticed we didn't have one. He was mad! He said Lorraine should have been the first to get one."

Mama just rolled her eyes.

Television seemed like a miracle. The first time I ever saw one operate was in 1948. Uncle Harold and Aunt Bea had a tiny television that was set on a high shelf in their living room. The black and white screen was probably no bigger than 6 inches by 8 inches. It had a magnifier in front of it to enlarge the picture. Reception was poor—the images wavy and blotched with what we called "snow". The room was crowded with relatives whispering excitedly.

Later, one or two families in our neighborhood got televisions. It became a social event for adults to gather on Saturday evenings to watch television. One program they whispered about—supposedly out of earshot of children—involved a performer named Dagmar. All we gathered was that she was busty and risqué. There was not much selection of channels or programs in the early days of television.

Daddy bought our television in 1952. We had three channels in Detroit: 2, 4 and 7, as well as channel 9 from Windsor. "Rabbit ears" were used to pick up the signals. The television was only turned on for specific programs; we were warned to be careful not to wear out the tube. Programs I remember watching were Howdy Doody, Soupy Sales, Perry Como, Milton Berle, Ed Sullivan, I Love Lucy, Your Hit

Parade, Bishop Fulton J. Sheen's Life Is Worth Living, Kraft Television Theatre, Father Knows Best, and I Remember Mama. The news came on at 11:00 p.m. and all programming ended shortly after midnight.

Before television, we would sit around the radio listening to favorite programs. There was a kid's program on Saturday mornings that Karen, Billy and I especially liked. It was called No School Today. It opened with a jingle I still remember: "If you go down to the woods today- You're sure of a big surprise...Today's the day the Teddy Bears have their picnic." Although I have no memory of what the show was about, the jingle remains in my head even after all these years.

Others shows we listened to were Flash Gordon, Buck Rogers, The Lone Ranger, Ozzie and Harriet, Hopalong Cassidy, Gene Autry, The Adventures of Superman, Our Miss Brooks, Dragnet, The Shadow, My Friend Irma. Later some of these shows were adapted for television and we were excited to switch from just listening to seeing our favorite characters.

Grandpa Taube died suddenly at home in the spring of 1953 just after his 75th birthday. I was 12 years old. The wake was held at Grandma and Grandpa's house. The funeral Mass was celebrated at St. Albertus Church in Detroit where my grandparents had been married 53 years before. One summer day a few weeks later, Mama called Karen and me into the house.

"Grandma's lonely," she said. "She called to ask if the two of you would go to her house and stay with her for a few days. Daddy would like you to do it."

Karen and I were stunned. We barely knew Grandma and had never felt comfortable in her house. But we wanted to please Daddy. And we were curious.

"What would we do there?" I asked.

"I don't know. You'll just have to play it by ear. If you don't like being there, just call. Daddy will come and pick you up. Nobody's making any promises about how long you'll stay."

I don't know how many days we spent with Grandma Taube, but she was like a different person. We felt comfortable in her house. She walked with Karen and me to the dime store and bought white linen hankies, crochet hooks, and brightly colored thread. Then we sat for hours—on the couches in the living room—while she patiently taught us how to crochet elegant lace edges on the hankies.

Grandma talked about her work as a cigar maker, her growing up years, and about Grandpa. She asked us about what books we liked, about school, and about places we liked to go and things we liked to do. She made meals for us and was never stingy with how much we ate or drank. She bought candy and cookies for special treats. Yet, when she heard some of our cousins coming through the yard to visit, she jumped up.

"Hide the cookies in the cabinet," she told us. "Be quick. They'll eat me out of house and home."

I looked at her. She wasn't joking. I hid the treats.

Those days after Grandpa died was the only time I ever spent one-on-one time with Grandma Taube. Shortly after, she sold her house and moved in with her youngest daughter and her family of eight children. Although we visited her at Aunt Lucy and Uncle Mike's, it was always hectic. Grandma knew my name, but she didn't seem interested in talking to me. She died four years later at the age of 76. I value the few days Karen and I spent with her. If she didn't have so many grandchildren, we might have had a closer relationship. I wish I had known both her and Grandpa better.

Ethnic background was not discussed much in our family. Ma and Pa and Grandpa Taube had come to America when they were small. They told us they had vague recollections of the boat trip across the Atlantic, but no memory of the old country. Borders changed, so their exact provincial origins were vague. We knew our ethnic heritage was partly German and the rest mainly Polish, but it wasn't important to us. Our parents were born in the United States—we were Americans.

The food that was cooked for holidays and special occasions reflected our heritage. We called them by mispronounced Polish names: Goo-ump-kee (stuffed cabbage, actually Golabki); Keesh-ka (blood sausage, actually Kieszka); Chi-neen-na (duck's blood soup, actually Czarnina); Keel-bah-sa (Polish sausage, actually Kielbasa); and stuffed green peppers (Nadziewana Papryka). I loved the stuffed cabbage and green peppers Mama and Ma made, as well as the delicious Polish sausage Pa made from scratch and smoked. But I refused the duck's blood soup the first time Mama placed a bowl in front of me. It was dark brown and smelled vinegary; it had sour red cherries floating on top.

"It's dirty," I told her. "I don't want it."

"I guess it does look dirty," Mama said. "But it's good. You don't have to eat it, but you'll be missing out on something special."

Soon everyone in the family—sisters, brothers, grandparents, aunts, uncles, cousins—were laughing about me calling the soup dirty. It became a yearly ritual at holiday celebrations to offer me the soup to see what I would say. I was only 4 years old when I first refused the duck's blood soup. I had no idea what the ingredients were. Later, when I learned actual duck's blood was used to make the soup, nobody could ever convince me to try it!

I never knew any of my great grandparents; they died before I was born. English would have been their second language so I assume my grandparents grew up understanding Polish and German. But none of them had an accent or regularly spoke the languages. Mama and Daddy knew a few Polish and German words and sometimes tried to use them when they didn't want us to know what they were discussing. But the foreign words were so interspersed with English, that it was simple to get the drift of an interesting conversation.

"Did you know that the Vatue boy was caught pachniec (smelling) in the park yesterday?" Daddy asked.

"Really, pachniec?" Mama smiled broadly. "Don't you mean palic (smoking)?"

"Oh, that's right. Palic."

They looked at each other and began to laugh. Soon tears were rolling down their cheeks. Although we didn't know exactly what had been said, we got the gist. We knew they had gotten the words mixed up somehow and it was funny. We all laughed with them. Mama and Daddy certainly weren't fluent in Polish or German, but they each had a great sense of humor and we enjoyed their attempts at speaking the language of our heritage.

There was one Polish phrase and one German phrase we used regularly in our extended family. We said, Jen-koo-ye (Dziekuje), the Polish phrase for "Thank you," and Ges-und-hite (Gesundheit), the German phrase for "God bless you" when a person sneezed. We probably didn't pronounce them correctly, but we knew what the words meant and used them correctly.

Ma and Pa always came to our birthday celebrations; Grandma and Grandpa Taube never did. Sometimes our godparents would come. All were invited. Our birthdays were enthusiastically celebrated, but they were group celebrations. Considering how our family birthdays are clustered, there was little choice.

According to the family calendar, the first birthdays are in December—Janet and Judy's on the 11th, Daddy's on the 12th, Billy and Johnny's on the 19th, Karen's on the 29th and Marvin's on the 31st. In January, Buddy's birthday is on the 12th, and Lorraine's is on the 18th. In February, Mary Ann's birthday is on the 2nd, mine is on the 6th, and Donny's is on the 13th. The only birthdays not in these three months are Mama's in July and Davey's in October. So the winter birthdays were celebrated at the beginning of December, the middle of January, and the end of February.

At the party we each had our own birthday song, our favorite flavor of cake with the appropriate number of tiny candles to be blown out, and a few small gifts.

"What kind of cake do you want this year?" Mama would ask.

"Chocolate," I always said.

"Do you want chocolate or caramel or white icing?"

"Chocolate."

My choice was always the same. I loved chocolate. Sometimes one of my sisters or brothers would ask for a cherry pie, or a chocolate pie, or a lemon meringue pie instead of a cake. And their wish was usually granted. The birthdays were celebrated in order according to birthday date. The candles were lighted and everyone sang, "Happy birthday to you" and "May the dear Lord bless you" to each person individually. After his or her gifts were opened, we went to the next celebrant.

I can remember receiving white tissue wrapped gifts from my parents, grandparents, and godparents. The gifts were modest—paper doll cut out books, coloring books and crayons, a set of ball and jacks, paddle balls, modeling clay, a plastic mirror with matching comb and brush, a diary with a tiny key, a Nancy Drew book, a jewelry box, a Scrabble game, a goldfish in a tiny glass bowl. But the gifts were my very own, exciting to open, and deeply appreciated.

After the singing and gift opening was done, the cakes and pies were cut and distributed. The birthday boys and girls got the first generous pieces. Ice cream was scooped on top of the cake—strawberry, chocolate, vanilla or a combination of all three. I felt special on the day of my shared birthday celebration. I didn't even realize until I was in first grade that other children had birthday parties just for them—and invited friends. I never got to go—we couldn't afford the gifts—but the idea fascinated me.

My school friend, Marcie, had no sisters or brothers. She said she was lonely and always wanted to come over to my house to play. I couldn't imagine being the only child in a family. I didn't think I'd like that—and I felt sorry for her. On the other hand, Marcie was a pretty blue-eyed girl with perfect long blond curls. She wore beautiful dresses with matching ribbons in her hair. I couldn't help but wonder what it would be like to be her.

"I'm going to have a birthday party just for me," I told her. It was late May—just a few weeks before school would be out for the summer. I had already celebrated my birthday in February. "My party is going to be on Saturday."

"Can I come?" she asked.

"Sure. But you have to bring a present."

I don't remember how we set up the time. In fact, I had forgotten about the whole fantasy by Saturday. I was playing outside in front of the house with my brothers and sisters. A blue car pulled up. We stopped playing to watch. The passenger door of the car opened and Marcie stepped out wearing a white organdy dress with a big pink bow at the waist and a matching bow in her hair. In her hands she carried a large brightly wrapped package. She waved to the driver and walked toward me. Her mother must have thought there was a party going on because there were so many of us. The car pulled away.

"When is the birthday party?" Marcie asked. She looked around.

My brothers and sisters stood staring at us. I pulled her by the hand toward the wooden porch steps. We sat down. The sun was warm. My eyes were focused on the birthday gift Marcie held on her lap. She had brought a big beautiful birthday present just for me! Her eyes were on my rumpled dress and stringy hair.

"There's not one," I said. "I made it up. I wanted to have one, but I couldn't."

"No party?" She looked at me with disbelief. She looked at my brothers and sisters. "You lied! You're a big dummy!"

I wasn't sorry. I was 6 years old. It didn't matter if she was mad. The only thing I cared about was opening that present. Unfortunately, I never got a chance. One of my sisters or brothers told Mama what was happening. She came to the screen door.

"You both stay sitting right there while I call Marcie's house," Mama said.

My brother Donny walked Marcie home. She took the present with her. She stopped asking about coming over to my house to play.

"You have to stop making up stories," Mama said. "That was embarrassing."

Chapter 18

As an adult, I'm no longer the naïve, unsophisticated little girl I once was. Life changes you. But I can't help but appreciate the spunk I had as a child—and I hope to never lose it. As a parent, I marvel at the way my parents dealt with life's daily challenges. I hoped to be able to do as well.

Moving to the suburbs opened up a whole new world to me. The families were young. There were lots of children my children's ages. Single family ranch houses, colonials and tri-levels on wide lots filled the neighborhood. There were no businesses scattered about. Only the schools were within easy walking distance. Shopping required long walks to major intersections or driving to the bright new shopping centers. Even our parish church was new and modern—in keeping with the latest changes from Vatican II.

Women my age—or close to my age—lived all around me. They were housewives like me. I had made friends quickly and easily. Jerry, Jeffrey and Cheryl had playmates their own ages. Our yard became a favorite gathering place. I learned a lot from the other mothers. We traded child rearing tips, favorite recipes, housekeeping shortcuts, sewing and craft tricks. We met for coffee at each other's houses while our older children were in school. Our little ones played together while we visited. My children were invited to birthday parties.

"I can't believe Jerry is going to be 7 years old," I said to my husband. "I want to have a birthday party for him. I mean a separate one just for his friends."

"How many kids are you thinking of inviting?"

"Most kids have six or eight. I thought he could invite some from the neighborhood and some from school."

"It's a good idea. What's involved?"

"I picked him up last Saturday from Ricky's party. I saw what that was like. I can ask Jerry about what they did at the party—what kind of games they played. And what they ate. It shouldn't cost too much. We'll probably just need a cake, ice cream, some balloons..." I started a list.

The party was a huge success. Jerry was so excited. He received lots of small gifts. It felt good to give him something I had always wanted. And he still would have a second party with his grandmas and his godparents and cousins.

Suddenly, it struck me. Our children were being raised in a totally different environment than I was. I'm changing, too. I'm becoming more aware of what other people think. Is that good or bad?

***

Often I have wondered how I must have appeared to others as a child. I wasn't dirty looking. I washed my face and neck and combed my hair each morning. But I probably was unclean and messy compared to some. It's hard to tell. Mornings were chaotic at our house. Everybody was trying to get cleaned up and dressed at the same time. I don't remember how I decided what to wear for school. And it was rare for anybody to check me over before I left.

I can remember awakening some mornings with wet underpants. It was cold in my bedroom. Instead of changing clothes, I'd run downstairs to stand by the heater. The warm air from the furnace would slowly dry my underpants. I'd decide not to change. My pants were dry. Nobody would know the difference. It was too much trouble to find a clean pair that fit. Besides, if I changed, everyone in the family would know I wet the bed.

Underwear was communal property in our family. I didn't even realize there were distinct underpants for boys and girls until the age of about 12. It was difficult enough to find something that fit. Everything was too big for me. The elastic in the white cotton pants was usually stretched to fit my older siblings. Most times, I had to fold the fabric at the waist and use a large metal safety pin to hold my pants up. And still they slipped down. I had to keep pulling them up.

One morning on the way to school, I walked right out of my underpants! I was carrying my books. I was wearing a dress. I felt my underpants slipping down. I knew I should stop, put my books down, and pull them up. But I was with friends. I was too embarrassed to have anyone see me pulling my pants up. So I didn't stop. And my pants fell right down to my ankles. I stepped out of them and I kept on walking. I don't know if anyone noticed. Nobody said anything.

Stockings were also communal property. They were washed and tossed in a box that was kept in the pantry. In the morning, one had to search for two socks that matched—and hopefully fit. We called it "the sock box". It seemed perfectly logical at the time. A sock box required no effort be spent sorting and pairing colors and sizes. As a child, half of my time walking and running included stopping to pull up stretched out, too large anklets.

We took baths on Saturday nights.

Water was never hot and available in our house. The tiny hot water tank in the basement was gas-fired and had to be hand lit with long wooden matches. There was no thermostat on the tank. Once the tank was lit, it just kept heating until it was turned off. Daddy said the tank would explode if it got too hot.

Water for washing dishes was heated in pots on the stove in the kitchen. We used cold tap water for washing up during the week. Mama lit the tank for washing clothes so sometimes hot water was unexpectedly available. But on Saturday nights, Daddy always lit the tank for our once a week baths. It took what seemed like hours for the water to get hot enough to fill the bathtub—especially on cold winter nights.

Once the tub was filled, baths were done production line style— oldest to youngest. We were not allowed the luxury of soaking. There was not the room or the time. Generally at least two of us younger kids were in the tub together—Colette and Karen, Billy and Davey, Janet and Judy. And the water never stayed hot for very long. When we were small, Daddy usually supervised our Saturday night baths.

"Hop in and get your hair wet," Daddy told us.

Getting your hair wet meant having to lay back and duck your head under the water. Daddy would toss a bar of white Ivory soap into the tub and hand each of us a washcloth. The soap would float along the top of the water, ducking and bobbing between us. As soon as our hair was wet, Daddy would squirt a dot of Breck shampoo on each of our heads and begin scrubbing. Meanwhile, we'd take turns capturing the soap and rubbing it against the washcloths to make foam to wash our arms, chests, backs and legs.

"Stand up and clean your bottoms real good," Daddy instructed. "And be sure to wash between your toes."

While Daddy supervised our cleaning up, Mama would be warming clean water for rinsing in silver pots on the electric stove in the kitchen.

"Okay!" Daddy would holler into the kitchen. "Victim number one is ready for rinsing and wrapping."

Mama would bring a warm pot of water and pour it over our heads and bodies to rinse off the soap.

As soon as we were rinsed, Daddy would lift us out of the tub one by one. He would wrap a thin cotton towel around our skinny bodies. Then he would carry us across the kitchen into our parent's bedroom to snuggle under the thick feather comforter until Mama could bring our clean underwear and warm flannel pajamas and robes.

Mama would dry us thoroughly, rubbing our hair with the damp towel. After we were dressed, she would comb our wet hair. If it were cold outside, she would send us into the kitchen to sit by the open electric oven to dry our hair. When we were old enough to care, Karen and I would sit there wrapping each other's long hair in tiny round metal curling rods. The idea was to keep the rods in the hair overnight, so that we would have springy curls in the morning when our hair dried.

Once I outgrew communal baths, I learned to light the gas tank and time my baths for late Saturday nights when there was likely to be the least number of family members around who had to use the bathroom. The youngest family members were in bed and the oldest siblings were out of the house. Generally, I washed my hair at the kitchen sink while I filled the tub. As soon as the tub was filled, I ran down to the basement to turn off the hot water tank so I wouldn't forget. But no matter how well I planned it, with one bathroom in the house, there was always someone knocking on the door.

One of my greatest pleasures after leaving home has been the pleasure of being able to take a long hot shower or bath without having to light the hot water tank, wait for hot water, or having someone knocking on the door to use the bathroom just as I get into the tub.

Taking care of our teeth was not a priority. Brushing wasn't talked about at home or at school, and preventive dentistry was unknown to us. When you had a toothache, you treated it with home remedies like aspirin, cloves and ice packs or used over-the-counter toothache kits to numb the pain. You went to the dentist only when your toothache was unbearable because you knew it usually meant the dentist would pull the tooth.

Most adults had all their teeth pulled and false teeth molded for them by the time they reached their late 20s or early 30s. Both Mama and Daddy had false teeth for as long as I can remember. Daddy had a white porcelain cup he kept on a shelf inset in the wall behind the hinged mirror of the medicine cabinet in the bathroom. He set the cup on the sink and soaked his pink-gummed white enamel teeth in baking soda while he washed up and shaved in the morning.

I was fascinated with those false teeth floating in the cup. On Saturday mornings, I sat on the closed toilet seat and watched Daddy shaving. I kept poking at the teeth with my finger. They bobbed up and down in the cup.

"Be careful with those," Daddy warned. "They'll break if you drop them."

I pictured little teeth rolling all around on the linoleum.

You rarely saw Mama or Daddy without their teeth. I don't know whether or not they wore them at night, but they seldom talked or smiled without them. Sometimes Daddy would make silly "monster faces" at us by pushing his upper teeth an inch or so out of his mouth with his tongue—but the glaring effect was offset by his laughter. Mama hated when he did that.

"Stop it, Frank!" she said. "You're going to loosen those teeth and they're going to fall out!"

When we did brush our teeth, we used baking soda. One day, I found my brother Donny sprinkling Ajax cleansing powder onto a toothbrush over the bathroom sink. He was 14.

"What are you doing?" I asked.

"I'm going to brush my teeth with Ajax."

"Yuck! Why?"

"It'll make them whiter." He smiled. He brushed his front upper teeth up and down with the white paste, rinsed with water, and bared his teeth to show me. "See how shiny?"

"That's disgusting." I tried to imagine how terrible the sink cleaner must taste. "But your teeth sure are white and shiny!" Despite the sparkle of my brother's smile, I was never tempted to brush with Ajax.

When one of my "baby" teeth would be loose and ready to fall out, Daddy would notice. He would see me wriggling the loose tooth around with my tongue or moving it back and forth with a finger in my mouth.

It bugged him to see me struggle when he had a simple solution.

"I can take care of that for you," he said. "I could pull it. It won't even hurt. Then you can get some money from the tooth fairy."

One trick Daddy had to pull a tooth was to tie the end of a string to the loose tooth. He would have me sit in a kitchen chair he set by the pantry. He'd tie the other end of the string to the round handle of the open pantry door. Once I was seated, he would quickly shut the pantry door. The taunt string would usually yank the loose tooth out easily and painlessly. I wasn't scared. I knew it might bleed a little, but Daddy wouldn't hurt me.

If that didn't work, Daddy offered the next solution.

"Want me to pull it for you?" he asked. "Remember, you can have a visit from the tooth fairy tonight!"

If I agreed, he'd sit me in the chair, wrap a clean dish towel around a pair of pliers, tell me to open my mouth wide, and reach in with the towel-wrapped pliers to gently wiggle the tooth until it came out.

"Got it. Hold your hand out."

He would drop the small bloody tooth into my open palm. I would examine it with interest as I moved my tongue around the tiny hole in my gum. I could feel the next tooth coming up just beneath. It amazed me that the tooth he pulled always looked so white and perfect.

"What made my tooth decide to come out?" I asked.

"It's time for you to have bigger teeth. Your body knows that. Open your mouth. Let me see your new tooth that's started to grow."

"Not yet. I want to get this tooth ready for the tooth fairy."

Daddy would hand me a clear glass half filled with water. I would carefully drop the tooth inside. Then I would take the glass of water upstairs to my bedroom and set it on the windowsill. When bedtime came, I would check to make sure the tooth was still in the glass. I would try to stay awake to see the tooth fairy come—but I was never successful. The next morning there would always be 25 cents in the bottom of the glass and the tooth would be gone.

Any problem with a permanent tooth was much more serious. When I was only 11 years old, I had a terrible toothache. It was a tooth on the lower right side of my mouth. No home remedy helped. Daddy took me to a dentist near our house to see what the problem was, and what could be done. It was my first visit to a dentist. I sat in a padded black chair with my head back and my mouth hanging open. I shivered at the sight of all the shiny instruments and the unfamiliar chemical smells. Daddy stood next to me.

"It's going to have to come out," the dentist said. "You go into the waiting room, Mr. Taube. We'll take care of this in no time."

"It'll be all right," Daddy told me. He squeezed my hand. "I'll be right outside."

My frightened eyes followed Daddy as he left the room. The dentist did not speak one word to comfort me or to let me know what he was planning to do. He talked only to his white-jacketed assistant as I sat there trembling with my mouth still opened wide, my stomach tight with fear. She stood next to a tray of implements.

"Numb it up," he instructed.

The assistant picked up a long needle and injected it into a cylinder. She walked toward me. I whimpered as she brought the needle towards my open mouth and injected it into my gum. After waiting a few moments, the dentist reached into my mouth with long silver-nosed pliers. He began yanking on the tooth.

"Owwww!" I cried. The gum was not numbed enough. It hurt. "Owwww, stop!"

The dentist ignored my cry. He began to pull with greater and greater force. The tooth was not coming out. The assistant leaned over me, peering into my mouth. Her brown eyes were opened wide. "Maybe you should wait," she said. "Maybe the tooth isn't numbed enough."

"Dang," the dentist mumbled. He ignored her. He braced himself against the chair and put two hands on the pliers to get more leverage. Suddenly there was a loud "pop" as the tooth broke. He finally removed the pliers from my mouth.

"Daddy!" I screamed. I began to sob. "Daddy, help! It hurts."

"What in God's name are you doing to my daughter," Daddy hollered as he ran into the room. "What's going on?"

"She moved and I broke the tooth. We're going to have to cut the pieces out now."

"And I'm standing right here while you do it!" Daddy took my hand. "I'm not moving from this spot."

Daddy stood in front of me where I could see him as the dentist injected more numbing substance into my gum. He then removed the tooth piece by piece.

"All done," he said. He smiled at Daddy.

"Yes, you are," he said. "And you're a butcher." He tugged my hand and pulled me up out of the chair. "Let's go, Colette." As we walked through the open doorway into the hall, Daddy stopped and turned toward the dentist. "You're not getting a dime for all the pain you've caused my daughter today. And I'm telling everyone I know what a hack you are."

Daddy held my hand as we walked out of the dentist's office. His whole body was trembling. I had never seen him so angry!

"I didn't move, Daddy." I sniffled. "Even though it hurt a lot. I sat really, really still."

Daddy stopped, bent over, put his arms around me, and pulled me tightly against him in a hug. "I know you did, honey. It wasn't your fault. It was the dentist's fault. You were very brave. I'm proud of you."

***

The practice of dental hygiene changed a lot during the late 1950s. Gradually we learned how important it is to take care of our teeth. To brush regularly, to floss, and to take advantage of preventive dentistry. Now we visit the dentist once a year. X-rays are commonly used. Teeth are filled instead of being pulled. There are more options for tooth replacement. Fewer people expect to wear full dentures in their lifetime. And we began taking our children to the dentist as soon as their permanent teeth came in.

Chapter 19

Over the months, I gradually acclimated to living away from the city. I kept busy.

In the winter while the boys were in school and Cheryl napped, I sewed drapes and curtains for most of the windows. I wallpapered the bathroom. In the spring, we sodded the front lawn and seeded the back. We planted junipers under the front windows, and some annuals in our newly shaped flower beds—purple petunias, yellow marigolds, and mixed color impatiens.

In the summer, Jerry laid patio blocks outside the sliding glass doors next to the family room. He installed a black coach light lamp post on the front lawn. He built a wooden storage shed along the back of the house. We bought a metal swing and slide set for the kids. The house was shaping up inside and out. Now I was planning the bulbs I'd plant in the fall—daffodils, tulips, and crocuses.

In May, Mama had sold the house on Mt. Olivet to a young couple who had grown up in the neighborhood. Her move to Utica seemed to happen overnight. She spent the summer settling in. She planted a rose garden and a wildflower rock garden against a hill behind the cottage-sized house. She combed the woods and roadsides for plants. She rarely stopped by. When she did, she always took time to notice what we had done to the house since her last visit.

"The living room drapes are beautiful," she said. "Where did you get that fabric?"

"At Penney's," I said. "It was on sale."

"What are you working on now?"

"I'm making some dresses for Cheryl. She's going to be starting kindergarten in a few weeks."

"That's right. I can hardly believe it. Kids grow up so fast! What are you going to do when they're all in school?"

I'd been thinking about that a lot lately. What would I do to keep myself busy once all the kids were in school? At first it wouldn't be too bad. This year Cheryl would only be in kindergarten for half days. But after that...

"Oh, I'll keep myself busy. With three kids there's always something to keep me going."

Shoot. I shouldn't have brought up the kids. I held my breath. I hoped Mama wouldn't ask me about any plans for more babies. I looked at her warily. She glanced at my face, and looked away. There must have been something in my eyes that stopped her from saying anything more.

"I'm sure you'll find plenty to do. You always find something to keep you busy. By the way. You were talking about making a roman shade for your bedroom. I saw a pattern in last month's Good Housekeeping. I still have the magazine if you're interested."

"Thanks, Mama. I'd like to take a look at it."

And that was that. For now.

***

A few days later, Jerry came home from work with surprising news. We were sitting on the patio with our after dinner coffee. The kids were playing on the swing set in our backyard.

"Guess what?" he said. "I was talking to Walter Goulet. I don't know if you remember him. I went to high school with him. He was at our wedding. Anyhow, he's been taking college classes. The Veteran's Administration is paying for it."

"I remember him and his wife, Janet," I said. "Isn't he working at Ford Motor?"

"He's been working there and going to school nights. He finished his bachelor's degree last spring. Now he's quitting his job to go to school full time in the fall. He eventually wants to get a doctorate degree so he can teach college."

"Wow, that's great."

"But the really great thing is he told me I could get the VA to cover me going to college part time, too. So I decided to check into it. And it's true!"

I looked at him. His blue eyes sparkled with excitement.

"I didn't know you wanted to go to college. You've never talked about it."

"I never thought too much about it. I guess I assumed it was something out of my reach. A lot of my friends in high school had parents who could afford to send them to college. Walt and I went into the service instead. He was smart in school, and I was pretty good. We studied together. Maybe that's why he thought to bring it up."

"Where would you go? What would you take?"

"I can start at Macomb County Community College. That's where your brother, Bill, goes. It's close to home. I can take a couple of classes a semester. I'd start out just getting a general associate's degree. That's a two-year program. Later, if I want to continue, I'd take business management classes. The classes would be interesting—and relate to my job. They'll cover me through a bachelor's degree. It'd take a long time. But I can do it. I know I can. What do you think?"

He was so excited he stumbled over his words. But he was clearly looking for my approval. I stood up and walked over to him. I bent down and put my arms around his neck. I hugged him to me.

"I think it's great! It's exciting. I'm really happy for you. You're a smart man. And determined. I know you can do it. There's no doubt in my mind."

"It would mean I'd be gone a couple of evenings a week. And I'll have homework to do. It'll take away some family time."

"But you're doing it for the family, too. Won't the extra education increase your chances for promotions?"

"Probably. It's hard to say for sure."

"In any case, it'll improve your marketability if you ever decide to change jobs. Don't worry about me and the kids. We'll cope. When would you start?"

"I called college admissions this afternoon. I have to take some placement tests but they said I can expect to be enrolled for the fall. I wanted to talk with you before I committed to anything."

"You've got my support—my blessing, actually. I'm happy you have such a great opportunity. And I'll be so proud of you. Imagine—having a college degree!"

I was happy for Jerry. How could I help it when he was so excited? I'd miss him the evenings he'd be at school, but I would deal with that. It'd be good for the kids seeing their father going to school. It'd emphasize the importance of learning—and the importance of getting a college education. But I was surprised to find that I was also a little envious. I'd love to be able to go to college.

***

Fall came and everyone started school.

The neighborhood school our children attended was only 2-1/2 blocks away. You reached Charwood Elementary by crossing our street and walking along Sutherland for a short way. Then you use a cut-through between houses to come up behind the school building. I'd been walking Cheryl each morning—as I had done at first with the boys—and meeting her at lunchtime to walk her home. Now the weeks had passed and she was growing comfortable with school.

"Mama," Cheryl said. "You don't have to walk me anymore. I'm a big girl. I can walk with Jerry and Jeffrey and the other kids now. Nobody's Mama walks them to school."

It was true. Other mothers did not walk their children. The kids went to and from school in groups. They came home each day for lunch. There was a Neighborhood Watch program in the subdivision. All along the route were families that had been investigated and their dwellings authorized by the local police department as safe houses. There were signs in the front windows. The mothers in these homes kept their eyes on the children walking to and from school. The children knew if there was ever a problem, they were to run to these specially marked homes.

I looked at my second grader. "Jerry," I said. "Are you ready to take responsibility for walking Cheryl to and from school every day?"

"I can do it, Mama," he said.

"She can walk with me, too," Jeffrey said.

"I'm not a baby," Cheryl fumed.

I looked at her. I looked at my boys. They were so young. I knew they only had one subdivision street to cross—besides the one in front of our house. And there were safety patrol boys stationed at the crossing. It was a short, protected walk to school. For the last two years, a sixth grade neighbor girl had been walking with the boys. What was so different about letting Cheryl be more independent? But I knew. She was my baby.

"Okay, "I said. "But you'll still have to walk with the older kids."

It would be a while before I'd be comfortable letting them walk all alone.

***

I was Jerry's age the year my twin sisters were almost kidnapped. It was early fall. I was in second grade, Karen in first. Janet and Judy were not quite 3 years old. It would have been less than a month before Davey was born. Karen and I had come home from school for lunch. There wasn't much time for dawdling. We had an hour from when we left school to walk the four blocks home, eat our lunch, and get back.

Demerits were doled out for being late.

We were getting ready to return to school when Janet and Judy raised a fuss. They wanted to go with us.

"We go to school," Janet said.

"School, school!" Judy cried.

"You can't go to school with us," I told them. "You're too small."

"Just let them walk to the corner with you," Mama said. "You can go the Van Dyke way. It's just half a block to the corner."

"No, Mama. They're too slow. It'll take too much time. We'll be late for school. We'll get in trouble."

"You have plenty of time."

"But the Van Dyke way takes a lot longer."

"Just before you get to the corner, tell them to turn around and go back. But make sure you watch them until they get to Ma and Pa's house." Ma and Pa lived three houses from the alley that ran behind the stores along Van Dyke.

Mama leaned down and put her arms around Janet and Judy. "You make sure you turn around when Colette tells you to," she told them. "I'll be standing right here watching for you."

Karen took Judy's hand, and I took Janet's. We started down the long street. It was a sunny day. The leaves on the trees were just starting to change. We tried to hurry our little sisters along, but they were out for a walk and wouldn't be rushed. It seemed to take forever to reach the end of the block. We stopped.

"Okay," I said, as I let go of Janet's hand. "It's time to go back." I turned her around. I started walking backwards. "You two have to go back right now!"

"I go to school!" Janet cried.

"No! Go back!"

Karen was having the same problem with Judy. We looked at each other in frustration. We kept walking. They followed. It was getting later and later. We had only a few minutes to get to school. We threatened dire punishment from Mama and Daddy. We tried to force them to turn around. But no matter what we did, they kept coming. We turned the corner and started down Van Dyke.

"You have to go back. If you go back now, I'll give you gum after school."

Still they followed us. Finally, in desperation, Karen and I decided to speed ahead and leave our twin sisters behind. We figured they'd get scared and go home. We didn't know what else to do. We were afraid of being late. We kept walking backwards, calling for our little sisters to go home. We were about a half block ahead of them when a car suddenly pulled up at the side of the road next to Janet and Judy. The passenger door opened, and the girls stopped to look.

Karen and I started running back. We were yelling and screaming. I don't know what would have happened if one of our neighbors, Mrs. Weisenhofer, didn't happen to be driving by. She knew us. We played at her house with her daughters sometimes. We had stayed with her family the night of the fire. She saw the car; she saw the twins; she saw Karen and me running and hollering. She pulled up behind the stopped car and began tooting the horn. Immediately, the passenger door was shut and the car peeled away.

Mrs. Weisenhofer got out of the car and stood by the twins until Karen and I arrived. We were crying as I explained what had happened.

"All of you get in the car," she said. She touched my shoulder. "I'll drive you to school. Then I'll take your little sisters home."

I don't know the rest of the story. I assume Mama must have been frantic when she watched from a distance as my sisters turned the corner. She didn't have a car. She was heavily pregnant and couldn't move fast enough to go after them. I don't know what Mrs. Weisenhofer said to Mama when she drove the twins home. I don't know if the police were called. When Karen and I got home from school, Mama wouldn't talk about it. She just shook her head when I tried. But she never blamed us for what had happened.

***

The following summer, Karen and I decided to take a walk. We told Mama where we were going, but she was busy and didn't seem to pay too much attention. We wanted to see if we could make it down French Road, around the old gas tank, and up Van Dyke back to Mt. Olivet—a distance of at least a mile. City airport ran along French Road so the area was fenced. There were no houses along the way, and the curve around the tank had narrow sidewalks and was little traveled.

As we rounded the curve, we saw a blue car had stopped along the road. It had its passenger door open—completely blocking the sidewalk.

"Let's turn around and go back," I whispered to Karen.

"No! I want to go around the tank. You said we could!"

"There could be a bad person in that car. We better not take a chance."

We turned around and headed back the way we had come. The car made a u-turn and now sat next to the sidewalk in front of us. Again, with the car door open and blocking the sidewalk. I could see the outline of a man inside the shadowy interior. We turned around again. Each time we changed directions, the car was there. I was petrified, and didn't know what to do. There were no other cars going by, and no houses or businesses to go to for help.

We had turned back the way we had come for the third time, when I saw my brothers walking towards us.

"Buddy, Donny, help!" I yelled. We ran toward them. "A bad man is trying to get us!"

"Sure," Donny said. "A boogeyman."

"Look around the curve! His car is there." Tears ran down my cheeks. I turned around and looked. There was no car.

"Mama made us come and get you," Buddy said. "We were playing ball in the alley. You know you're not supposed to walk this far. Now let's get home. You're in big trouble."

We walked ahead of our brothers. They were big boys to us—12 and 14. We felt safe with them. We weren't worried about getting in trouble. We were anxious to get home and report what had happened.

"Don't ever walk around that area by yourselves," Mama said. "You should know better than that. It could be dangerous!"

"But, Mama," I said. "That man…"

"You girls have a good imagination. I don't want to hear anymore about it!"

The two of us looked at each other and shrugged.

***

A couple of years later, Karen and I were walking down the tree-shaded sidewalk, across the street, about three or four houses from home. A car with all its windows open stopped by the curb next to where we were walking.

"Hey," the man inside the car called. He beckoned us over to the passenger door with his hand. "Can you give me directions?"

We stopped. I turned to Karen. "Wait here," I said.

I walked toward the car. Karen stayed on the sidewalk. I stood on the grassy patch between the sidewalk and street, and bent down to look inside the car. A dark-haired, mustached man in his mid-forties looked me in the eye. His penis was exposed, standing erect outside his unzipped pants. He drew attention to it by tapping it back and forth.

"Where are you going?" I asked.

"I need to get to Mt. Olivet cemetery."

"Sure," I said. I was careful to keep my face free of expression. I turned to Karen and whispered. "Get his license plate number." I turned back to the man and started giving him directions. Out of the corner of my eye, I saw Karen walk to the back of the car.

"Where do you live?"

I quickly pointed to the house we were in front of.

"Thanks for the directions." He peeled away.

The most amazing thing to me is that my sister and I never told anyone about the incident. We had the license plate number and could

easily have described the pervert. But what would Mama have said?
What would she have done? We didn't even try to talk to her about it.

As a parent, I shuddered to remember these incidents. To think
what could have happened. I vowed to keep the lines of communication
open with my children.

Chapter 20

After Thanksgiving, my preparations for Christmas began. I spent weeks getting ready. I made shopping lists and to-do lists. My projects included sewing, knitting and crocheting gifts. I was creating a wardrobe for the Barbie doll Cheryl would get from Santa. I was knitting an afghan for Mama's couch. I was decorating Christmas stockings for each of us to hang on the fireplace. I was planning what kinds of cookies I'd bake.

Also, I tried to come up with projects for the whole family to work on together. This year, I'd bought some flat wooden ornaments in various holiday shapes and figures—angels, Santa Claus, the three kings, stars, snowmen, reindeer, Christmas trees, wreathes. The kids and I would spend evenings painting them while my husband was in school or doing his homework. Closer to Christmas, we'd decorate cut-out cookies in these same shapes. I wanted holidays to be as special to my children, as they had always been to me.

***

Growing up, Christmas was my favorite holiday of the year. Daddy would buy a 7-foot fresh cut evergreen from the church lot. He mounted it in a three-legged stand centered in front of the living room windows. The stand was nailed to a 2-1/2-foot square, 3/4-inch thick plywood board so it wouldn't tip over. We loaded the tree with multi-colored lights, golden ropes of tinsel, exotic glass ornaments, and spiky silver icicles.

When the decorations were complete, Daddy topped the tree with the angel—imported from Germany—that had been a gift from Ma and Pa for my parents first Christmas. It was a beautiful 8-inch porcelain figure dressed in flowing lace robes with golden hair and delicate silver wings.

"Be careful, Frank," Mama would warn. She held the ladder as Daddy stood atop it leaning toward the tree. "You don't want to fall—and you don't want to break anything!"

At the base of the tree, Mama spread the green felt skirt she had embroidered, appliquéd and beaded with Christmas symbols. Atop the skirt, my parents set up the nativity scene. First, a rustic 12-inch wooden stable was set down. Inside, were placed the 6-inch hand-painted ceramic figurines of Mary and Joseph, and the tiny infant Jesus in a manger. The donkey, cow and sheep were arranged around the manger. The bottom of the stable was lined with loose straw. The two shepherds and three kings were set outside the stable; the golden-winged angel was mounted at the peak of the roof. The figurines were also imported from Germany and gifts from Ma and Pa.

For days before Christmas, Mama spent hours making huge batches of butter cookies cut in holiday shapes. We helped decorate them with blue, green, red and yellow frostings and multi-colored sprinkles. She also made gingerbread men and chocolate chip cookies, date bars, Russian tea cakes and Chrusciki (Polish angel wing cookies). All of the goodies were packed away in empty potato chip tins to be kept fresh until Christmas Eve. The house was filled with the pungent smells of vanilla, ginger and chocolate. We could hardly wait for the magic day when we could eat our fill of the delicious baked treats!

Christmas Eve was the one day of the year that we all went to church together. We would attend midnight Mass as a family. Daddy sang in the choir. Mama would put the Kielbasa and Kieszka in the oven to cook while we were at church. We came home to the spicy aroma of cooked sausage wafting throughout the house. We sat around the kitchen table and filled our plates with the sausages, sauerkraut and thick pumpernickel bread.

After we had eaten our fill, we moved into the living room where we gathered around the piano to sing Christmas carols: Silent Night, O Come All Ye Faithful, Jingle Bells, Away in a Manger, The First Noel, Santa Claus Is Coming to Town. Daddy played the piano by ear. He never had lessons and couldn't read musical notes, but he was able to pick keys close enough to make a melody recognizable. None of us had very good singing voices. But when Daddy played, we would stand around the piano and belt out the words to the songs as he pecked at the old ivory keyboard.

Soon it'd be late, and we could barely keep our eyes open. Our singing would become less and less enthusiastic. Daddy would look at Mama and wink. "Time for bed," he'd shout. "I think I hear sleigh bells! I better hurry and put out the cookies and milk for Santa Claus." We didn't stop to watch him. Instead, we'd rush up the steps to our bedrooms, put on our nightclothes, and jump into bed. Sleep would come quickly.

When we climbed down the steps the next morning, rubbing our sleepy eyes, the living room would be piled high with gifts. Those from Santa were unwrapped, lying under the tree, and bearing large tags with our names hand-printed on them. Only the presents from Mama and Daddy and our gifts for each other were wrapped. The room was charged with excitement as we each searched for our own gifts. By the time everything was unwrapped and exclaimed over, ripped paper was scattered throughout the room.

Somehow, we each received our most wished for gift at Christmas. When we were small, the gifts came from Santa Claus, later from our parents. Even in the leanest years, Mama and Daddy managed to make

Christmas special. I don't know how they knew what we wanted, how they managed to shop for all of us, or how they paid for everything, but they rarely disappointed us. And there was always a stocking loaded with candy for each of us!

The gifts were not expensive or exotic. Our wishes were modest. Some of my most memorable gifts include a Betsy Wetsy doll with baby bottles and layette; an easel complete with finger paints; a tiny metal sewing machine that really stitched and came with a wicker sewing basket loaded with multi-colored spools of thread, tiny scissors, needles, patterns and fabric; a doll with golden hair that could be combed and styled.

One holiday season particularly stands out in my memory. It was a Saturday afternoon, the weekend before Christmas. Mama and Daddy were out shopping. I heard a car pull up in front of the house. I looked out the living room window. Two strange men opened the doors and trunk and began pulling boxes out of the car. They climbed the steps and stacked the boxes on the porch next to the door. I ran to get Mary Ann from the kitchen.

By the time she arrived in the living room, looked out the window, and decided what to do, the men had returned to their car. She opened the front door just as they pulled away. We ran outside to look at the tall stack of boxes. Each colorfully wrapped box was uniform in size: 3 feet long by 2 feet wide, by 1 foot deep. Mary Ann lifted the top box and examined the markings. Then she looked at the next box.

"Look," she said. "Each of the boxes is marked with one of our names."

"What are they for?" I asked.

"I don't know. Let's take them inside."

My sisters and brothers rushed into the living room. I found the box marked "Colette" and tore it open. Inside, was a pink dress, matching stockings, underwear, flannel pajamas, red mittens and scarf, a striped wool hat, a doll, a Monopoly game, and a Sear's gift certificate from the Goodfellows for a pair of shoes. I watched my sisters and brothers as they tore open their packages. Each had received an individualized supply of clothes, as well as toys or games, wallets or purses. We were so excited! To us, Santa Claus had visited early.

"Put everything back in the boxes, Mary Ann said. "Don't open the toys or anything else. We'd better wait until Mama and Daddy get home."

When Mama and Daddy arrived home, they were not thrilled.

"I'm so embarrassed," Mama said. "Who would put our names in for these?"

"Charity is for those less fortunate than us," Daddy explained. "Other people need it more."

"But, Daddy," I started to say. "I need..."

"Shhh," he said. "Mama and I have to figure out what to do."

Eventually, Mama and Daddy decided to swallow their pride and accept charity for the first time. They realized that each gift was personalized and radiated the love that was put into it by a generous group of volunteers—people who didn't even know our family. And we were so excited! How could they take away the presents—and how could they return them?

"I'll call and thank them," Daddy said. He looked at Mama. "And I'll tell them to take our name off the list for next year."

"All right then," Mama said. She looked at us. "But I want all of you to remember that we don't need charity! We're not poor. And I don't want you going around telling anyone where you got this stuff!"

Easter Sunday was also a special holiday. On Saturday night, Mama would set out the Easter outfits she had prepared for each of the girls. The new dresses she had sewn, the straw hats with matching ribbons, the white anklets and patent-leathered shoes. The first thing we'd have to do in the morning is go to Mass. We'd each go in pairs when we were ready—wearing our beautiful new Easter finery. After that, we'd have our breakfast—Kielbasa and ham, pumpernickel bread and butter, pineapple upside down cake and cinnamon rolls. Next, we'd change out of our good clothes. Only then could we begin to search for our Easter baskets.

The evening before, we'd each have taped a tag with our name hand-printed on it to the handle of a 6-inch square wicker basket. We'd fill the bottom of the basket with a little bit of green synthetic "straw", and set it on the dining room table. Not too much straw; there had to be plenty of room for the treats. Next to the ten baskets, we'd set a plate of carrots "for the Easter bunny". We believed that this mythical bunny would come to our house, eat the carrots, fill our baskets with candy, and hide them for us to find.

Sure enough, on Easter morning the table would be empty and the search for our baskets would begin! The most important rule in searching was that you couldn't tell anyone if you found a basket that wasn't your own. Everyone had to find his or her own basket. It must have taken Mama and Daddy hours to fill all the baskets and find the hiding places. They were experts at concealing the candy-filled baskets. They came up with the most ingenious places—with the degree of difficulty depending on the age of the searcher.

Baskets were hidden behind stacks of cans on the pantry shelves, in clothes hampers, on closet floors, behind the sofas and chairs, in the cedar chest, under the dining room table, in the sock box, under the glider on the front porch, in the attic, in the coal bin, behind jars in the fruit cellar, and even in the rafters of the garage. It would sometimes take my older brothers most of the day to locate their baskets.

Once you found your basket, the candy was all your own. You didn't have to share. There were yellow marshmallow chicks, multi-colored jelly beans, maple filled eggs, solid chocolate bunnies and malted milk balls. Some of us would eat the candy quickly—in a day or two. Others rationed it out over days, even weeks. I always saved mine for as long as I could. Candy was a great way to bribe younger brothers and sisters into doing chores for me.

***

This Christmas, I'd been a little distracted. I had more than baby Jesus on my mind. It had been thoughts of another baby altogether. It started with a visit to my neighbor, Sally White. She and her husband lived across the street, a few houses down. They adopted a little girl last month. The baby was only 8 weeks old when they got her. She was adorable! The family already had a 3-year old biological son.

I'd never known anyone who adopted a child. No friends. No relatives. My sister Mary Ann was a foster mother through Catholic Social Services before she had my nieces. She'd wanted a baby and it wasn't happening. So she took in the newborns. Each of the babies was with her for only a few weeks before their adoptions took place. It was always traumatic when she had to give them up. That was my only association with the adoption process.

I hadn't known you could adopt a child when you already had biological children. More importantly, I didn't know you could adopt if you were physically capable of conceiving more children. I thought adoption was an alternative only for childless or infertile couples. I'd begun to wonder. Could we adopt a child? Is it possible?

Sally assured me that adoption was more open now. They had been approved as adoptive parents. If they could be, she thought most anyone could—as long as the reasons for adopting were acceptable. Those who would be adoptive parents would have to have the capacity to love, to encourage, to nurture a child not born of them. And, of course, the couple would have to meet the rigid guidelines for stability— economically, psychologically and financially. She said there was a long process of investigation and approval.

Thinking about my own children, I couldn't imagine how very difficult it would be for a birth mother to give up her baby for adoption. How awful it would be to have to make that choice. After weeks and months of careful consideration, to decide it was the best solution for both her and her child. She wouldn't be rejecting her child, but deliberately—and with much heartbreak and pain—she'd be limiting her role to giving birth. She'd sign her baby over to the adoption agency with the hope the child would have a better chance in life with both a mother and father to love and care for him or her.

Would I feel guilty about taking someone else's baby?

***

I remembered a scene from my childhood. It was Christmastime. Mama's cousin, Helen, was sitting on the Queen Anne style armchair in the living room next to the Christmas tree. I was sitting on her lap, playing with a sparkly necklace she wore around her neck. Janet and Judy were a few weeks old. She had brought matching pink crocheted wool blankets as gifts for the newborn babies. They were sleeping in bassinets in the dining room. She'd been standing over them, watching them sleep, and had just moved into the living room.

"Anne, you have so many beautiful children," Helen said. She touched my cheek. "You are so fortunate."

"I am lucky," Mama said. "It's hard sometimes, but I do consider myself lucky."

"We just had the one. I can't have any more. We've tried and tried. The doctor said it's not going to happen."

"I'm so sorry. I know you love children. It was so awful...you losing Chester when he was just a toddler."

"What would you and Frank think about me taking your twin girls, raising them as my own? They're so adorable..."

"What? What are you saying? Are you..."

"Wait! Don't be mad. Let me finish. I'd treasure them. They'd have everything you can't provide. Roger and I are quite wealthy, you know. But we can't have children. And you have so many..."

When Daddy got home from work that afternoon, Mama had dinner on the table.

"Can you imagine her nerve?" she said. "What can she be thinking? How could she believe that we'd just turn our babies over to her? Does she imagine that love is like a pie that you cut up into only so many pieces? That the pieces get smaller with each child you have? That you could possibly care less for your babies just because you have more than one child?"

"Shhh," Daddy said. He looked around the table. "She just doesn't know any better. How can she? We've been fortunate. We really have. You have to feel sorry for her."

As a child, it was reassuring to hear that Mama and Daddy valued us so highly. I always felt loved, but this was the closest I can ever remember to hearing in words that our parents treasured each and every one of us. That it didn't matter how many children were in the family.

**

I longed for another baby. Not to replace Mark, but to mother. I knew I could love an adopted child as much as I loved my own biological children. A daughter would be perfect. Cheryl would have a sister. I wanted so badly for her to have a little sister! Would this be a way to fulfill my dream?

How would Jerry feel about it? Would he be open to the idea? Was he ready for another baby? He loved our children. Would he be willing to parent a child not born of him? We wouldn't have trouble getting approved—would we? I'm a good mother. Jerry is an excellent father. What would it cost? Could we even afford to go through the process? Would it take a lot of money?

All of these thoughts were going through my mind. I was excited about the prospect at one moment. The next, I was thinking it was impossible. Just a dream. I decided to wait until Jerry had a break from school before I'd bring it up to him. At Christmastime. In the meantime, I'd try to get as many answers as I could. From Sally—without letting her know I was thinking about adopting. I'd act as though I was getting information for someone else.

Chapter 21

I waited until late Christmas Day to bring the subject of adoption up. We were sitting in the family room on the couch in front of the fireplace having coffee, a plate of cookies on the table in front of us. The children were tucked in their beds. The room was lighted from the glow of the fire and the twinkle of the multi-colored bulbs on the decorated tree. Piled around the tree were mounds of opened gifts—stuffed animals, Play-Doh, magnetic cut-outs, fire and tow trucks, Matchbox cars, TinkerToys, a doll house, Etch A Sketch drawing boards, and assorted books, games and puzzles.

"What a great Christmas," Jerry said. "The kids really seemed to enjoy it!"

"I'm happy they still believe in Santa Claus!"

"It does make it more fun."

"They're getting so big. I wonder how much longer they'll believe."

"Hard to know." He took a sip of his coffee and reached for the plate of decorated cookies. "Mmmm. These are great."

"I wanted to talk to you about something I've been thinking a lot about."

He turned to look at me. "Sounds serious."

"It is serious. But it's something that could be really good—really good for us. It's about adopting a child." His eyes widened in surprise. He opened his mouth to speak, but I held up my hand. "Wait. I just need you to listen for a minute."

I talked fast, stumbling over my words. I told him about the Whites adopting their baby—their little girl—that they had adopted her when they already had a son. I talked about how adorable she is. I explained that adoption had changed, that families that have other children—even biological children—can adopt now, and that there are babies available for adoption. Finally, I stopped talking. I looked into his eyes. I waited for him to say something.

"Are you asking me if I'd consider adoption?"

I smiled nervously. "Yes, I am." I hesitated. "Would you?"

"I don't know. It's not something I've ever thought about."

"But would you consider it?"

He sat quietly. Finally he spoke. "Probably. It's something I'd have to learn a lot more about. Then we could talk seriously."

"A baby." I whispered. "I'd want a little baby. A girl, if possible. But I don't know if they'd let us adopt."

He smiled. "We're such a nice family—why wouldn't they let us?"

"I don't know. I thought maybe I could do some research—call a few agencies, find out what's involved, what it would cost."

"You do that." He put his arm around my shoulder, and squeezed gently. "It's really a great idea," he whispered. "Adoption is definitely something I'd consider."

I smiled happily. "We probably shouldn't say anything to anybody until we find out more about the process—about our chances."

"Probably not. Other people might not understand—and it's not really anybody else's business. But I think this is something we might be able to do. I like the idea. I'm excited!"

"Me, too." I laughed. "And you're right. It's nobody else's business until we figure out what we want to do."

***

It didn't take long to find an agency. I looked in our local telephone directory under "adoption", and talked to social workers at several public and voluntary agencies. Michigan Department of Human Services only placed older children. Catholic Family Services only placed babies with infertile couples. But Children's Aid and Family Service of Macomb County had babies available and was much more flexible.

"Adoption is for anyone who can provide a warm, loving home for a child in need," the social worker said.

I told her about our situation and the possibility we might be interested in adopting. "I'd like a baby," I said. "Preferably a baby girl." Considering the circumstances, I asked whether or not the agency would accept our application for the kind of child we had in mind—and, if so, how to apply.

"I don't see any problem," she said. "And we are accepting new applications right now. I'm in the process of setting up preliminary meetings. They'll be group meetings just to provide general information. Then if you decide to continue, there will be private consultations. Give me your address and telephone number, Mrs. Dywasuk, and I'll contact you when I have the dates of our next meetings."

Setting up the appointment only took a few days. Soon we found ourselves in a meeting along with eight other prospective adopters being given general information about adoption. We were told about the things we might consider while we were still trying to decide if adoption was for us. At the close of the meeting we were given application forms. We were invited to fill out the forms at home if we were still interested in adopting.

"Completing the forms and submitting them to the agency is a way of demonstrating your real interest in adoption," the social worker said. "But you will not be committed. You can still change you minds and bow out of the process at any time."

***

Before we decided to do anything, Jerry and I spent a lot of time talking about all the implications of adopting. We asked ourselves and each other question after question: Do we really want to adopt a child? Are we willing and able to become parents to a child born of somebody else? Will adoption satisfy our desire to raise another child? Could we love a child not born of our own flesh and blood as much as we love our biological children? Can we be, feel like, consider ourselves, see ourselves as parents to a child not born of us?

Because we'd be adopting after the death of Mark, would we be able to accept the adopted child for herself? Could we adapt easily to a child who turned out to be greatly different from us in temperament, talents, and appearance? Would we be adopting in a futile attempt to replace our lost child? Would we resent an adopted baby for surviving when our biological child did not? Had we waited long enough to make such a decision?

At some point we knew we'd have to talk the adoption over with our children—before we got too far along with our plan. They'd need time to adjust. But it would be difficult because of the death of Mark. They still asked why they didn't get their baby brother.

"We've got to do this exactly right," Jerry said. "Especially the timing. We don't want the kids to get their hopes up and then crush them again. The loss of Mark was devastating to them—even though they never met him."

"I know," I said. "I guess we should put off talking to them until it's pretty certain we'll be accepted—and we feel confident we want to go through with the adoption."

Finally we decided to just fill out the forms and send them to the agency. We were as certain at this point as we could be. The next steps would be up to the agency. From the general meeting we had learned that once the initial forms were returned to the agency, we would be notified by telephone of the date and time of our next visit to the agency. By mid-February we were assigned a social worker. Mrs. Cavanaugh would be the person who got to know us during the "adoption study".

Over the next few weeks, we met with Mrs. Cavanaugh in a series of interviews at the agency office. The meetings were not question-and-answer sessions. Instead, they were informal conversations designed to help us to determine whether or not we wished to become adoptive parents; to discuss our capabilities for and feelings about being parents of a child not born to us; and to assist us in preparing for this unique parenthood. We talked about adoption itself—what it would mean to us, to our family, to our future. We tried to picture ourselves as parents of an adopted child.

"The more you communicate your feelings and ideas about adoption," Mrs. Cavanaugh said, "the more comfortable you'll be about adopting." She encouraged us to voice any concerns so she could help us recognize and resolve any uncertainties or misconceptions we might have about adoption or the child to be adopted. "You need not worry that I will think there is something wrong with you—and turn you down for adoption—because you have doubts. We're just as eager as you are for one of the agency's children to find a place in your home. I want very much to help you."

As we came to understand the characteristics presumed to indicate our capacity for adoptive parenthood, we were asked to state our preferences as to the kind of child we wanted—and the kind of child we could accept. "Since you have a handicapped sister," Mrs. Cavanaugh said, "it seems you might be the perfect couple to consider taking a physically challenged child."

I looked at her. My heart started pounding. My face flushed. "Excuse me a minute," I said. "I...I need to use the ladies room." I walked into the ladies room and splashed my face with cool water. What was this reaction? Why did I feel threatened? I loved my sister. And I admired her. She was an amazing woman who, despite her physical challenges, had accomplished a lot.

***

Lorraine was born in January 1930—three months after the crash of the stock market. By the time she was 2 years old, The Great Depression had spread throughout the country. "1932 was the worst year of our marriage," Mama said. "Daddy struggled to find work. In January, Lorraine was diagnosed with cerebral palsy. We were told she was physically handicapped and would never walk. In October Marvin died of spinal meningitis. I was 5 months pregnant with Mary Ann."

'But how could you cope with all of that?" I asked her.

"What alternative did we have? When you're faced with hardship, you only have two choices: accept and deal with the circumstances or give up and have a nervous breakdown. In either case, it's not going to change what's happening."

Lorraine inherited Mama and Daddy's positive attitude and strong will. She was intent on learning to walk and wasn't about to give up. She bugged the doctors and tried anything they suggested to make her legs stronger—exercises, surgery, braces, shoe lifts. Eventually she succeeded. It was mostly with the aid of crutches, but she was able to take a few steps unaided and could walk around rooms bracing herself on furniture. To get outdoors, she managed to climb up and down the front porch steps using the handrail Daddy installed for her.

When she was 15 years old, she decided to walk to Ma and Pa's house—half a city block away. She was nearly there—walking with her crutches—when Mama found out. She sent Buddy with the wagon to bring her back home. "I could have made it, Mama," Lorraine said. She was angry and crying. "You never even let me try."

"You probably could have," Mama said. "But I was too scared. I'm sorry. I was just so afraid you'd fall."

As young as I was, I remember thinking how sorry I felt for both of them. For Lorraine who wanted so little and for Mama, who couldn't give it to her no matter how hard she tried. But Lorraine didn't argue with Mama. She only smiled and gave her a hug.

Lorraine has always been the heart and soul of our family.

Unassuming, grateful for what she has, loving unconditionally, as spiritual as a saint, and always ready to listen. She is highly intelligent, loves to read, and is the least worldly person I have ever known. Politics is her passion. And she has spread political awareness to everyone who comes in contact with her—inside and outside the family—from as early as I can remember.

When we got our first television set in 1952, Lorraine stayed glued to it throughout the Republican and Democratic conventions. She was rooting for Eisenhower and ecstatic when he won the nomination for President. Since the 1950s, she had worked at the 14th Congressional District Republican headquarters as an active volunteer—rooting for her candidates, stuffing envelopes, and answering phones.

When Karen and I were in grade school and wanted to be Girl Scouts, Lorraine started a troop at our parish church with the help of an assistant leader. Many of our friends joined and we soon had a large troop with lots of adult participation. We went to the camp in Metamora where we stayed overnight in rustic cabins. And she arranged countless activities for the troop like touring a television station, a newspaper, a bread factory; appearing on popular television shows including American Band Stand; and inspiring everyone to work feverishly to earn merit badges.

Lorraine remained the Girl Scout leader until Karen and I lost interest as young teens. By that time, my green uniform sash was loaded with merit badges. Thanks to her leadership, the Girl Scout Promise "to serve God and my country" remains embedded in my consciousness. She has been there for me since I was a small child—inspiring me to try harder, boosting my self confidence, doing whatever she can to help out. In a crisis, she is the one the family asks for prayers—she seems to have a special connection to heaven. Lorraine has been an inspiration to everyone who knows her.

Mama and Daddy told us that Lorraine was not to be treated any differently than anyone else in the family. And I had always accepted that. Now, I recognized the fact that a handicapped child takes special parents. Parents who can look beyond a physical limitation and love the child for herself—the person she is. If I were to adopt a child, I must be able to see her unique place in the family totally undiminished by any special needs. I would have to see a handicap as something that can be overcome or compensated for.

Was I strong enough to be a parent to a handicapped child? Did I have the endurance to meet such a child's needs—not only today, or next month, but for the rest of her life? A handicapped child, especially a severely handicapped child, may have to endure a great deal in life. She will have to work harder, against greater odds than normal, for all of her achievements. She needs parents and a family who are especially capable of giving an abundance of love, security, support, and comfort. But the thought of raising a handicapped child made me feel sad. Wouldn't that sadness be a burden to a child?

I realized I was not generous enough to knowingly take on the challenge of a special needs child. If a child we adopted turned out to have a mental or physical illness, I could deal with it—just as I would deal with a disability in a child born to me. That child would be mine and I would love her no matter what. But I could not make the choice to consciously adopt such a child. I doubted that I had the strength, the determination, the ability to assume the added responsibility, to help the child—and I'd be afraid to try.

"It's not a problem," the social worker said. "It's more important that you feel confident enough to understand and discuss your feelings—and to admit any reservations you have about taking certain kinds of children."

"And it would be unjust of us to try unless we were 100 percent sure," Jerry said. "Every child deserves to be loved unconditionally."

***

As the weeks passed, we became more and more comfortable with the idea of adopting a child. Now it was time for the home visit. "The home visit will offer me a view of how you live—and where your adoptive child will live, Mrs. Cavanaugh said. "It'll also give me an opportunity to get acquainted with your other children, and to see how family members relate to each other in the friendly atmosphere of your home."

Next, our case worker would contact the references whose names we submitted. These references would help her see us through the eyes of other people who know us and would introduce her to people who would be important to our adopted child. "References don't as a rule provide me with new information about you," she said. "Usually they substantiate what I already know. They can confirm my impression, change the emphasis of my thinking, deepen my understanding of you, and sometimes throw new light on any uncertain factors in a case study."

After our latest interview, Jerry and I sat in the car in front of the agency's offices. We had just had an emotional session where we'd discussed what raising children means to us. We had talked about Mark and how devastating his death was to each of us. Mrs. Cavanaugh had advised us—assuming the home study and references were as good as she expected them to be—that she could see no problems going forward with placing a child in our home. It was time to make our final decision, time to talk to our children, time to let our friends and relatives know what we were doing.

I wiped my eyes. "Well, what do you think?" I said. "Any reservations?"

Jerry was teary-eyed. He wiped his eyes with his handkerchief, and then put his arm around my neck. He pulled me to him. "None whatsoever," he said. "You?"

"None." I smiled.

"Then let's go home and talk to the kids."

Chapter 22

The children were ecstatic about the news. They all started talking at once.

"Are we going to get a boy or a girl?" Jerry, Jr., asked. "Will it be a tiny baby?"

"I want a little sister!" Cheryl said.

"Can I tell at show-and-tell?" Jeffrey asked.

"Here's the thing," Jerry said. "It's not absolutely, positively for sure. It might not happen. You need to understand that."

"There's going to be what's called a home visit," I said. "The social worker is going to come and meet all of you. She'll ask you what you think about having a new brother or sister."

"And then it'll be a little while before we find out what happens next."

"Will she bring the baby with her?"

"No. Remember we said it's only a 'maybe' right now?"

"Where is the baby? When can we go get him?"

"Can I tell Aunt Mary Ann we're getting a new baby?"

We explained the adoption process as best we could to children who were just 8 years old and not quite 6 and 7. But it soon became obvious that all they had in mind was getting a new brother or sister as soon as possible. And we knew that everyone they came into contact with would hear about the upcoming adoption.

"You'd better start calling people tomorrow," Jerry said. "Especially our references."

"Especially my mother," I said.

"Are you concerned about what she's going to say?"

"I'm more worried that she'll be mad if she hears about it from someone else."

He laughed. "I get your point."

"But I wish Daddy were here. He'd understand. He'd be so happy for us."

***

Daddy's illness was the saddest part of my childhood. I remember clearly when it began. It was a hot day in the spring of 1951. I was 10 years old. Daddy and my uncles had been replacing the shingles on the roof of Ma and Pa's two-story house on Mt. Olivet. Daddy was climbing down the ladder when he lost his balance and fell down the last few rungs. As soon as they made sure he wasn't hurt, my uncles began to tease him.

"Can't hold your liquor, Frankie?" they taunted good naturedly.

Pa had bought some beer for the men as a special treat—a reward for their hard work on a hot day. As they were finishing up, they had mixed the beer with shots of whiskey from a flask Uncle Harold had hidden in his pocket. Mama and Daddy were not drinkers. They did not serve alcohol in our home—even for special occasions. If alcoholic beverages were served at a wedding, Mama might have a high ball—ginger ale with a shot of whiskey. Daddy might have a beer, two at the most.

"I only had one," Daddy said.

"A shot and a beer—that'll do it." They laughed.

Mama was not amused. "You know you're not used to drinking," she said. "And you shouldn't be up on that roof in this heat!"

Mama was not criticizing Daddy for drinking. She had gotten a scare when she saw him fall. Even at my age, I knew how much more serious the fall could have been. What none of us knew at the time was that this was an early symptom of something far more serious. It would be another year—and many more instances of lost balance—before Daddy's problem was diagnosed as multiple sclerosis (MS)—a little recognized disease at the time.

Over the next months Daddy had episodes of stumbling, shuffling, weaving, lack of coordination, and double vision. Our family doctor could find nothing wrong. The symptoms came and went, but grew steadily worse and more frequent. People stared at Daddy when we were out. Neighbors began to ask, "Is your Daddy a drinker?"

"They asked me again at the plant if I'd been drinking," Daddy said. We'd just sat down at the table for supper. "They're threatening to change my job. They're worried I'll lose my balance and fall into one of the furnaces." Daddy was an inspector in the heat treat area of the plant—a choice position he had worked his way up to. Changing his job meant less money.

"We have to find out what's going on with you," Mama said. "I guess we'll need to go to see the neurologist at Harper Hospital like Dr. Zabinski suggested."

It was the spring of 1952 when Daddy was diagnosed. Our parents told us about the disease at supper one evening. Being children, we didn't understand the implications. Mary Ann had been married at 18 years old in the fall of 1951. Davey, the baby of the family, was 2-1/2 years old. We knew Daddy was sick, but he wasn't going to die soon. For us, life went on. Meanwhile, our parents began to prepare as best they could for an uncertain future.

The first noticeable change came when Daddy began giving Mama driving instructions. On family outings that summer, Mary Ann and her new husband transported some of the family in their car. When we arrived at our picnic spots at country schoolhouses, Daddy and Mama would leave us while they went off "to teach Mama how to drive". It was a shock the first time they came back with Mama at the wheel. We all pretended to run and hide so she wouldn't hit us with the car.

By winter Mama began driving Daddy to and from work. He had been working at his company for 24-1/2 years. He needed 6 months more to qualify for retirement and a pension. As his staggering became worse, he began to use a cane to try to keep his balance. The day came when a company official called him into the office and told him he was done—no job, no pension. Daddy was devastated. He begged to work for a few more months. He would do anything—nothing would be too menial. But the answer from the company was "No" and "Good-bye."

Daddy appealed to the union. He had been a union member since the union was initiated—and a steady reliable worker for his whole career. They refused to help. My parents had no familiarity with lawyers or lawsuits. I don't know whether or not in that day and age they could have sued. Times were different. Instead, he lost everything: his health, his income, and his pride. It would have cost the company so little to provide Daddy with the pension he had earned—and it would have meant so very much to our family.

That summer was the first time Daddy didn't have some kind of a job since he was 14 years old—the year he had graduated from eighth grade and was sent to work in a factory. He hated being home. He was like a caged bird. For the first time in his adult years, he had time on his hands. He wasn't supposed to drive because his reaction time had slowed, and Mama was afraid he'd get in an accident. But there was no holding Daddy down.

Mama was attending classes downtown to brush up on her shorthand and typing skills. She planned to find a secretarial job in the fall. Buddy and Donny were working summer jobs. As soon as Mama got on the bus to go to school, Daddy would pack the six youngest of us into the car for an excursion. Lorraine stayed at home. Although I knew Mama didn't want Daddy to drive, I also knew how important it was to him to be able to get out of the house.

We didn't go far—to Belle Isle, to the Detroit Zoo, to Metropolitan

Beach. Places he knew he could get around. Daddy had difficulty walking and realized his limitations. He planned our excursions carefully. He was in charge; I was a 12-year-old surrogate mother. I minded the younger children and worried about Daddy. But we still had great times. When we got home, I knew Mama would be waiting.

"You know you shouldn't be driving!" she said. "How can you endanger your kids like that? I've been so worried..."

"Stop it," Daddy said. "I'm not an invalid yet. It's one of my good days. I wouldn't have taken them if I thought there would be a problem."

And Mama would stop. Her heart wasn't in scolding Daddy. She knew how significant those outings were to him. I didn't say a word. I would think about how Daddy had staggered and tripped—and about how worried I'd been while we were out. I was torn between Mama who was right and Daddy who had a desperate need to preserve some freedom.

That summer we still went on Sunday outings—with Mama driving. But they weren't the freewheeling adventures we had experienced when Daddy was at the wheel. There were always specific destinations and much shorter distances. We'd drive to Ma and Pa's cottage, to visit relatives, and occasionally to a beach close to home. And it was rarely the whole family now, as my older brothers frequently had to work.

Without an adequate income or pension, money was always a concern. My brothers' summer jobs supplemented the small disability check Daddy received. Ma and Pa helped with the property taxes. But there were doctor bills and experimental medicines and no money in the bank. I don't know how my parents managed. They wouldn't accept charity from anyone outside of the family—and they didn't believe in welfare. Somehow, we never starved.

By the fall of 1953, Mama found a job with Kelly Services—a temporary placement agency for clerical workers. Daddy became the stay-at-home parent. Both hated this arrangement. Up until this time, Daddy had kept his positive outlook. He had always been an easy-going, good-humored man with an optimistic personality. But he had been the provider and family protector. Now Mama had to go out into the world every day to bring back a paycheck. He had a difficult time accepting that.

Mama had loved office work—but that was before she had a family. Now she worried constantly about how Daddy and Lorraine were managing without her. And about Davey who was not yet in school. During the day, Karen, Billy, Janet, Judy and I were in class. We came home for lunch, but were back in school until 3:00 in the afternoon. After school, I was there to help. Lorraine usually started supper.

But Daddy kept calling the office—wherever Mama was working— with one emergency or another. It was a concern for her on her temporary job assignments, and it was a problem for her emotionally. As much as she had been through during her lifetime, this was a strain that was just too much for her to handle. Mama was an extremely competent stenographer and typist. Kelly Services wanted to keep her on the job. They offered to find a place for her within the agency itself. But Mama declined. By the following June, she resigned.

"I just can't do it anymore," she told Daddy. "I worry all the time about what is happening at home. I worry about you falling. I worry about what would happen if a fire started. I worry about something happening to Davey. Lorraine is having a difficult time managing a 5-year-old. I worry about the kids having an accident going to or from school. It's just not right for me to be gone."

By then, Daddy had begun using a wheelchair. He could still get around with a cane, but his lack of coordination was becoming more and more of a problem. It was obvious he soon would be needing help. "I agree you should quit your job," he said. "We need you at home. Financially, we'll manage somehow. Things always have a way of working out."

My parents celebrated their 25th wedding anniversary in May. The extended family gave them a huge party at the house. Despite medical concerns, Mama and Daddy were so happy. All of their friends and relatives were there. They were proud of their children and the family they had created. Early in the afternoon, Mary Ann pulled Mama's wedding dress and veil from the storage closet. At 13 years old, I was the only one it fit.

"I weighed 90 pounds when we got married," Mama said. "Look at me now!" Mama thought she looked fat. Everyone knew she was wearing a size 16 dress because she had lamented the fact over and over since returning from purchasing the new dress with Mary Ann. After having twelve children, it was the heaviest she had ever been. But for having so many children, she looked amazing.

"I think you look beautiful, Mama," I said. And I meant it. She was glowing.

I put the wedding dress on over my slip. We went out into the back yard where the family was gathered for pictures. My sisters arranged the lace cap and spread the 15-foot veil out over the lawn behind me. Davey ran into the house to get Mama's white high-heeled sandals for my feet.

"You look like me in that outfit." Mama smiled. "I never realized how much you look like me. It seems like yesterday that we got married."

Daddy came up behind Mama. He wrapped his arms around her waist and pulled her against him. "It was yesterday, he said.

"Right." Mama laughed. She pointed to Buddy who is 6 feet 3 inches tall and towered over Daddy. "Then he would be pretty hard to explain." She waved her arms over all of us. "So would all of these children."

Mary Ann's husband took pictures of me in the dress. He took some of Mama and Daddy. I changed back into my party dress. He took moving pictures, then arranged the twelve of us in a group in front of the garage and snapped a family photo. But the images from that day remain embedded in my mind's eye. It was a day to celebrate family—and love.

Mama used her last paycheck to pay for a first and only vacation trip for her and Daddy. It was the month after they celebrated their 25th wedding anniversary. He was 49 years old, she was 45. They traveled by car through Canada to Finger Lakes in New York by way of Niagara Falls. Mary Ann and her husband came to stay with us while our parents were gone. Daddy finally fulfilled his dream to travel—and to see all five of the Great Lakes.

***

Buddy had graduated from high school in the spring of 1953. He was attending college at the University of Detroit on a scholarship—while holding a 40-hour per week job to help support the family. Donny worked after school and during the summers. Lorraine sold greeting cards from home to friends, relatives and neighbors for Mitchell Greetings Company. Mama did day care for neighborhood children whose parents worked outside the home. Along with the small monthly disability check Daddy received, that was our family income. But everyone was much happier with Mama at home.

Meanwhile, Daddy's condition kept worsening. He went from doctor to doctor trying to find a cure—or at least some relief from the symptoms. When the experimental drugs didn't work, he tried physical therapy. He spent hours lying on the living room floor doing leg lifts with sand bags on his legs. "You got to use it or lose it," he said. "That's true about your body—and it's true about your mind."

Next, he spent several weeks in a rehabilitation center. But nothing worked. Gradually, he became more and more confined to a wheelchair. He had to be helped in and out of bed. His speech had begun to be seriously affected. He spoke with a slur and became increasingly difficult to understand. We began to understand that Daddy was not going to get any better. Today was the best we had.

But he did not let himself get depressed. He had always been curious and ready to learn new things. He studied the Book of Knowledge and the dictionary. He listened to sports on the radio and read the daily newspaper. When his eyes grew tired, or his vision blurred, he picked our brains. "What new did you learn in school today? What book are you reading right now?"

He was always ready and waiting to play a game of Scrabble. You couldn't beat him. He was constantly learning new words, and we were afraid to challenge him. He would put down a word like "aadvark". If you challenged him, he would pull out the dictionary and read the meaning: "It's an African ant-eating mammal; groundhog," he said. Sometimes we wouldn't challenge a word and he would laugh until tears streamed down his cheeks. "That's not a word. I fooled you this time!"

Daddy's dream of sending his children to college ended by the time Donny graduated in 1955. Although he had been accepted by Michigan State University, he took a full-time job instead. Buddy dropped out of engineering school. Daddy was sad, but philosophical. "You have to do what you have to do," he said. "The family needs the income. One day the boys will be repaid for their sacrifices." As we got old enough, each of us took part time jobs, finished high school, and took our turn supporting the family.

Over the next few years, Daddy became less able to take care of himself. Eventually he became confined to bed. At first, Mama took care of him without nursing help. As he became more and more incapacitated, a visiting nurse came once a day for an hour. She taught Mama to irrigate the catheter and use a machine to clear the phlegm from his throat. Mama fed and bathed him, kept his lungs clear, and attended to all his physical needs. She had a lift installed over Daddy's bed so she could change the sheets and shift his position to make him more comfortable. Her main concern was preventing pneumonia and bedsores.

Daddy never complained about his own circumstances. He watched the birds and changing seasons outside his bedroom window. He listened to the Detroit Tigers baseball games on the radio and always kept up with the latest news. Over time, his words became more and more difficult to understand. It took patience to decipher what he was saying. But his mind remained clear and alert. The French doors to his bedroom opened to the dining room and he always watched for company.

I still lived in the city—within a mile of our family home on Mt. Olivet. I tried to visit him every day. I didn't have a car, but—when weather allowed—I'd put my babies in a stroller and walk over to spend time with Daddy. I got to talk to him one-on-one to my heart's content. I knew he counted on me. As soon as he heard me come in the front door, he'd call out. "Hey, Colette, I've been waiting for you. I want to hear what's new." And I always tried to come up with something interesting.

My toddlers would rush into the bedroom and climb up on the side rails of his high hospital bed. "Hi, Grandpa!" they'd cry. They talked over each other. "We walked over here. We saw some squirrels by the big tree. It's raining out. We got wet, but Mama said it was okay because it wasn't thundering or lightening. A little rain won't hurt you. I lost my tooth but I got 50 cents from the tooth fairy. Last time I only got 25 cents."

I laughed as I followed them into the bedroom. "Hey, one at a time," I said.

Daddy reached out and grabbed my hand. He smiled at the kids. "Hi Jerry. Hi Jeffrey. Hi Cheryl. You're full of news today. How has your Mama been treating you? Has she been good to you today? Who's got a new joke? "

No matter how silly the joke or how many times he'd heard it, Daddy always responded to the pre-school humor. He would laugh until tears rolled down his cheeks. "I'll have to remember that one," he'd chortle. All of his grandchildren loved him. I was happy that my children got to know their Grandpa a little bit. But Jerry, Jr. is the only one of my three that can still clearly remember him.

If Daddy hadn't eaten, I would feed him his lunch. It was a scary procedure because sometimes he would eat too fast and choke on his food. When that happened, Mama would have to rush over to suction him out so he could breath. Mama never allowed any of us to nurse Daddy. "It's not proper," she said. "Daddy would be embarrassed and so would I." But she was always happy when anyone came to keep him company. After Daddy ate, I would sit with him while Mama did chores or ran errands.

His mind was always working. "I've been thinking," he said. "Why do you think birds can't fly backwards? This is my theory…" and he'd be off. Or he'd ask, "What are you reading right now? Did you bring your book along? Read me a bit." After a chapter or so, he'd say "Okay, that's enough. That will give me something new to think about for a while."

One day I was sitting with him while Mama did the wash. By that time, we had all pitched in to buy her an automatic washer and dryer. "You know, Colette," he said. "It's time for me to die. I'm such a burden to your Mama."

"Do you want to die, Daddy?" I asked. "Are you ready?"

"It's not that. God is the only one who decides when we're ready. I just feel so useless—and it's so hard on your Mama."

"I know it's hard on Mama. But you're not useless, Daddy. Every day I come here I learn something new from you. And that's just me. If you multiply what I've learned over the years you've been sick, times all of your children and grandchildren, just think of all the important contributions you're making!"

Daddy reached over to touch my hand resting on the bed rail. "You're a good girl, Colette." He smiled. "I'll have to think about that for a while."

The doctor came to the house weekly to check on Daddy during his declining years. He also made house calls—day or night—if Mama thought there might be a problem. "Your mother is an amazing woman," he said. "I've never seen such devoted home care."

"Yes, she is." I smiled proudly. "She is determined to make sure Daddy has the very best of care. But I worry about her. She's not young.

How can she keep doing this?"

"I've talked to her about that. She's determined to keep taking care of him."

"I know. 'I can't let your Daddy end up in a nursing home,' she says. 'No matter how good a place might be, the people there don't love him like I do. I'll keep doing this just as long as I can. When we got married we committed to loving each other in sickness and in health. Your Daddy has kept his part of the bargain and I intend to keep mine—even if it kills me. I know he would do the same for me.'"

As Daddy grew weaker and weaker he frequently developed infections and pneumonia—despite Mama's vigilance—and had to be hospitalized. But he always returned home. Mama was in her 50s. It was getting harder and harder for her to take care of Daddy, but she insisted on struggling on. Then, in May 1967, just before their 38th wedding anniversary, Daddy was hospitalized for the last time. It didn't seem any different than any other time Daddy was taken to the hospital.

I was pregnant with Mark. It was a month before he was due to be born. I had stopped at the hospital to visit Daddy. He had been sleeping the whole time I was there. I was getting ready to leave. I leaned over the hospital bed to kiss his forehead. "I have to go now, Daddy. I'll be back to see you tomorrow evening. It'll be no time before you're home again. I love you." I started to turn away.

"Wait," he whispered. He opened his eyes and smiled at me. "No, it's time. Don't worry. I'm ready. But I don't want you to ever forget how much I love you." Then he closed his eyes.

"Daddy? Daddy!"

The nurse walked over and checked his pulse. "Don't worry," she said. "He's just sleeping. It's all the medication. You take your Mama and go home for a while. He'll sleep through the night now."

"You go ahead," Mama said. "You need to get your rest. I'm going to stay. I'll just doze in the chair here next to Daddy's bed. I'll be fine. Billy will be here after he gets off work."

I said good night to Mama and left. It was the last time I saw Daddy alive. He died peacefully in his sleep a few hours later—with Mama sleeping at his side.

***

It has been almost two years since Daddy's death. I miss him terribly. I could talk to him. He seemed to understand everything. And he was always open to new ideas. I knew he would love the idea of us adopting a baby. It would be a great adventure to him. He would enjoy getting to know a grandchild with a totally unique and different background; he'd be intrigued. I wasn't sure how Mama would feel—about what she'd say.

Chapter 23

I called Mama first thing in the morning. Pa had been ailing and she was busy running back and forth to Uncle Stanley and Aunt Coalletta's where he was staying. I had only spoken with Mama briefly over the last few weeks—mostly to ask about Pa's health and to see how she was doing. Things did not look good. Cancer had spread to his lungs and he was not expected to live much longer. Mama was distraught.

"We'll be sure to get over to see Pa again this weekend," I said. I took a deep breath. "But I wanted to talk to you about something else that's going on. I don't want you to hear about it from someone else in the family." I told her about our plans to adopt.

"You're thinking about adopting?" she said. "Why? Why not just have your own baby?"

"It would be our own baby, Mama, our very own. He or she would just come into our family in a different way."

"Hmm. You know my friend, Mrs. Bielski? Her son and daughter are adopted."

"Carol and Bobby are adopted? I didn't know that."

"I guess it's something nobody ever talks about. I think it's got to do with Mrs. Bielski being embarrassed because she couldn't have kids."

"It's so sad she feels that way. Do they know they're adopted?"

"I assume they do. Everyone knew. Besides, they're adults now and have their own children."

"They must know then. Nowadays the agency thinks it's vital to raise your adopted child with the knowledge that he or she's adopted. It's something that's discussed in the interviews."

"You've been meeting with the adoption agency already?"

"We've had lots of meetings. Now we're ready for the home study. We wanted to wait to tell the kids and everybody else until we were pretty certain of going forward."

She didn't say anything. I sat quietly. I wanted to give her time to think over what I had told her. Finally, she spoke. "I guess you'd be giving a poor orphan a loving home. That would be good."

"It would be a blessing for us, Mama. To have a beautiful new baby... to love, to raise. We'd be so fortunate."

"And the other kids?"

"Are excited! They don't care how a new baby comes into the family."

"No, they wouldn't. I hope it works out for you. I've got to go. I'll expect to see you this weekend."

***

The official acceptance letter from the adoption agency arrived in mid April. My fingers shook as I opened the envelope. "This is to advise that the home study and reference checks relative to your case file have been completed," the letter stated. "We are pleased to advise that you have been approved as potential adoptive parents."

I screamed in delight. I ran to the telephone to call Jerry at work.

"That's great!" he said. "What else does the letter say? Is there any indication of when we can expect to get a child?"

"It says: 'the agency will keep in touch with you in regard to the children who are available for adoption'. That's it. There is no indication of when that might be."

"Why don't you call Mrs. Cavanaugh? Maybe she can give us a better idea of how long we have to wait."

"I can only give you a rough idea," she told me. "It is impossible to say precisely how long it will be before a child is placed with you. It's sufficient to say it can now be any time—possibly even a few weeks."

"Should we start getting ready then?"

"I would. You can at least get the bedroom set up. You don't know the exact age of the child who'll be placed with you, but you have asked for an infant."

"Oh, my God! This is really happening. It's like a dream come true."

She laughed. "It's nice to hear your excitement. By the way—I wouldn't buy too much in baby clothes until you know the exact age and sex of your child. You'll have enough time to gather the things you need before you bring your baby home."

**

While we waited to hear from the agency, we began to prepare for our new family member. The bedroom next to ours would be the baby's room. We painted and papered the walls—using colors and patterns that would be suitable for either a boy or a girl. The kids helped with the choices and the preparations as best they could. Jerry fitted new blinds on the windows; I made new curtains. He brought the crib and changing table down from the attic and set them up. We bought a new mattress and bumper pads, a matching quilt, a chest of drawers, a lamp and a diaper pail.

I unpacked the boxes of baby clothes and bedding that had been carefully stored after each of our older children outgrew them. I sorted through sheets, blankets, changing pads, diapers, tiny undershirts, kimonos, and sweater sets to make sure they were still serviceable. Then I washed and folded everything. I sorted the clothing and arranged the items in piles by size and color. I stacked the diapers on the shelf of the changing table. I made a list of stock items we'd need to buy—rubber pants; baby powder, oil and shampoo; cotton swabs and cotton balls; baby bottles and formula.

I tried to imagine the tiny life that would soon be joined with ours.

Although a boy would be fine, I felt certain it would be a girl. Was she born yet? Maybe she'd be born today. If she was already born, where was she right now? Did her biological mother know she'd be giving her up for adoption? Maybe today was the day she'd sign her away forever. I tried to picture myself with another child. But how could I? I didn't know what he or she would look like—physical characteristics, coloring, his or her sex, or even the age of the child.

As the days passed, we eagerly awaited our social worker's call to tell us that a baby had been found for placement in our family. Suddenly, one day, the full significance of what we'd done—what we were about to do—swept over me. For the first time it really hit me. We were about to bring a new child—a stranger into our home, into our life. He or she would be part of our family. Nothing would ever be the same. What if the child didn't like us? What if he or she came to resent the fact that he or she's adopted? Were we doing the right thing?

Then I remembered that I went through the same kind of self-questioning just before each of my children had been born. Mixed up feelings were to be expected. They're only natural. Parenthood, adoptive or biological, is a big step in any person's life. Those soon to be parents by birth have times of feeling worried and apprehensive, too. But biological parents are already totally committed to having a child. They have no opportunity to change their minds. The baby is already present in their lives—soon to be born. There are no choices left to make. With adoption we could always change our minds. But deep inside I knew that adopting a baby was what I truly wanted to do—that it was right for me and our family.

***

Pa passed away on April 26, 1969—just 11 days before his 86th birthday. The family held a wake and funeral to remember him and honor his life; he was buried in Mt. Olivet cemetery next to Ma. It was one of the few times I had ever seen Mama cry. "He was such a good father," she said. "And such a good man. I'll miss him. But I know he's better off. I hated to see him suffering. He was in so much pain."

A few days later, Mrs. Cavanaugh called to tell us she had a child for us to consider. "It's a little girl that was born on March 7," she said. "The baby is being offered for adoption through our affiliate agency in Kalamazoo. If you're interested, you'll have to travel to the office there to hear more about her background. You'll be able to make a decision whether or not to consider her for adoption while you're there. If you decide to go forward, you can actually meet her the same day—so you won't have to drive back another time."

We decided not to tell our children anything yet—in case for some reason we weren't going to adopt this particular baby. We scheduled the meeting for May 8, the day after our ninth wedding anniversary. On the 135-mile trip from our home to the agency office, Jerry and I talked excitedly. About how amazing it was that we were actually going to adopt a baby. How some things in life seem almost inevitable— obviously the birth and death of Mark influenced our decision to adopt. How the timing was so right—had we tried to adopt a few years earlier, we would have been turned away. How strange it was to have the choice of hearing all about a child before making any decisions—to meet or adopt her.

"This feels so much like the times we were on the way to the hospital to have one of our babies," I said. "It's exciting—and a little scary!"

"Well it certainly has to be easier for you," he said. "You don't have to go through the physical pain and trauma of birthing a baby. For me, it's kind of the same—minus the worry about something going wrong with the delivery."

"That's right. You weren't allowed in the delivery room so you never witnessed the birth of our babies. You never saw them until they were all cleaned up."

"That's how it'll be for you this time. Somebody else did all the hard work."

"Yes. It's kind of sad to think about the birth mother."

"I know. It would be so hard to give a child up for adoption."

We were both quiet for a few minutes, then I asked: "Have you thought about any names for a new daughter?"

"Not really. You know me. I always put if off until I meet the baby."

"I like the name Linda."

"That's a pretty name. We'll have to see if it fits her."

***

When we arrived at the Children's Aid offices, the social worker was waiting. She was a slim, gray-haired woman who introduced herself and shook our hands. We were so excited; neither of us remembered her name. She invited us into her office and offered us a cup of coffee. We refused and nervously took the chairs she pointed to in front of her desk. Finally she sat down and opened a manila file that lay on the desk in front of her. "I can see you're anxious to get started," she said. "So let's go."

The worker proceeded to tell us what was known about the baby being offered to us for adoption. "I want to make sure that you know, understand and can accept everything significant about her background before you make a decision to consider this child," she said. "So if you have any questions, ask them. I'll be happy to answer those that I can."

Based on all the information we received, she told us that we were expected to decide whether or not we wanted to meet the baby. Because of the distance we had traveled, the foster mother had already brought her to the office. She was waiting in another room—so we could see her immediately.

"Although the decision you are making now is only to consider the child, it is still a very important one. Once you see the baby, your final decision is bound to be influenced by your feelings. Emotions rather than reason will tend to rule. I'll leave the two of you alone for a few minutes so you can talk." She left the room and closed the door softly behind her.

Jerry and I turned to look at each other. Then we stood up and hugged. We understood each other. We were about to make a momentous decision—but neither of us had any question about considering this baby. We opened the door immediately. The social worker was standing by her secretary's desk. She smiled, nodded, and beckoned us to follow her. We held hands as we walked to the door of the room where the baby was waiting. Would she be our child? This was our final—and most significant—decision in the entire adoptive process.

The baby was lying in a crib, her deep blue eyes open wide. She had dark brown hair with red highlights. She was sucking contentedly on a pacifier. Her blanket had been kicked aside; she wore a pink dress and tiny knit slipper socks. The social worker leaned over and picked her up. She turned to me. No matter how well I felt I had prepared myself, seeing for the first time this child who might become mine was a shocking, tender, unforgettable experience. At this moment, I realized the full significance of taking someone else's child. I felt like laughing and crying at the same time.

I found myself immediately drawn toward this baby—my arms automatically stretched out for her. I knew she was mine as soon as I held her quivering little body against me. All doubt and apprehension about adopting vanished when she snuggled up against my shoulder. I was ready to love this beautiful baby unconditionally. Jerry reached over and put his arms around both of us. I looked into his eyes. The tears ran down both of our faces. We were ready to take this baby home—to make her our own.

The social worker smiled at us. "You take your time," she said. "There's absolutely no need to hurry. When you're ready to talk, just open the door a crack to let me know. If the baby needs changing or whatever, you'll find everything in the diaper bag that's hanging there on the crib." She turned and left the room.

Jerry and I spent the next hour talking and taking turns holding the baby. She had spit the pacifier out as soon as the social worker left the room. She seemed content just to cuddle. Whenever I looked into her eyes, she was staring right back at me as though she was checking me out. We knew we had found the little baby girl that God had meant to be in our family. We were both happy and excited.

"What do you think about the name Janette?" Jerry asked. He was sitting on a wooden side chair, his elbows resting on the arms. The baby was on his lap facing me; her head leaned back contentedly against his chest.

I smiled as I studied her features. "I like it. It seems to fit her. Where did you get the name?"

"I don't know. I just thought of it. She looks like a Janette."

"Would you spell it the French way?"

"No, I don't think so. I'd spell it J-a-n-e-t-t-e."

"That's unusual, but I do like it. Could we add my middle name so it's Janette Marie?"

"That would be perfect."

I knelt on the floor in front of the chair and put my index fingers inside the baby's cupped hands. "What do you think about the name young lady? And what do you think about being part of our family?"

She just looked back at me with those piercing blue eyes as though she understood everything.

Once we decided that this child was the right one for us, everything moved quickly. The social worker set May 13 as the date for us to come and get the baby. We provided her with the name we had decided upon; it would appear on all the legal documents. She gave us a list of the items that would be needed that first day including the clothing—with sizes indicated, a car bed, the baby's formula for feedings, and everything else we needed to know before the day arrived.

"Here is my card in case you have any questions between now and then," she said. "Your daughter's foster mother will provide a full, detailed schedule of feeding times and so forth so you'll know her usual daily routine. She'll also write some notes about the baby's personality, her likes and dislikes, what might be the problem when she cries, what to do to quiet and satisfy her, and what to expect from her. But you're both experienced parents. You can anticipate that it'll take a few days for all of you to adjust to the change."

On the drive home we talked about how fortunate we were to be adopting this child. We recognized what an awesome sacrifice the biological mother had made so that her baby would have a better chance in life. How letting a child go for adoption would be worse than experiencing the death of a child. We felt a little guilty that we were in a position to take the baby when the birth mother couldn't keep her. We wondered if she would be pleased when the agency worker told her some general facts about our family. And we realized what a tremendous responsibility we'd have to live up to in parenting this child.

We decided that the first thing we'd do when we got home was take the time to sit down with our older children and talk about the adoption so they had time to get used to the idea of a new sister. We talked about what we would answer if our children asked questions like "Why doesn't her 'real' mother want to keep her?" We also decided to let our children be the ones to announce to all our neighbors, their friends, their teachers—to whomever they liked—that they were going to have a new sister. And we decided that we would take them along the day we bring the baby home. It would be a significant day for the entire family.

We knew that the flurry and excitement of the final preparations for our new baby would keep us busy now. We would try to include the older children in helping us to get ready. We'd take them shopping with us, and allow each of them to select a little gift to present to Janette when they first meet her. In these ways, they'd be able to express their welcome to their new little sister.

We talked about what we would tell family and friends about our child's background. We knew people would be curious about this; we might be asked very personal questions—even from strangers. We decided that the less anyone knew about her background the better. We would not disclose this information to anyone—not even our closest friends and relatives. What we might say—for instance, the version we tell now of why her mother gave her up—could come back to us years from now completely distorted. If we didn't tell anyone anything about Janette's background, we'd never have to worry about her hearing distorted stories from others.

If someone pressed us for details, we'd say that we have thought it all out very carefully and that we feel the information about our child's background should stay between us and her. It's not because her background is terrible—it's just that we feel it shouldn't be important to anyone else. She is a person—an individual in her own right—and she should be accepted as she is. We expected that the questions would stop after a while. People would soon forget our child is adopted. And that's the way it should be.

***

As Jerry drove, I closed my eyes to rest for a little while. The day had been filled with emotion. I thought about the feeling I had about this child being the one intended for our family. It reminded me of how I felt when I first met my husband. I was 17 years old and had just started my senior year at Dominican High School. Karen and I were attending a meeting of a lay fraternity for young adult men and women called the Third Order of St. Francis. Buddy and Donny both belonged. The group, which gathered at St. Bonaventure Monastery's Third Order Hall on Mt. Elliott in Detroit, had a lot of social events for young Catholics.

Most of the members were in their late teens and mid to late 20s, but there was no age restriction. Jerry was 23 years old when we first met; he had recently returned home from serving in the U.S. Navy. I was attracted by his gentle manner and his sharp mind. He was tall—6 feet 2 inches to my 5 feet 6 inches—and thin with broad shoulders. He was a nice looking man with light brown hair and a dry sense of humor. But, as young as I was, I was not attracted by his looks. Instead, I recognized the intelligence, the compassion, the goodness in this man. He felt comfortable to me.

Jerry grew up in Cathedral of the Most Blessed Sacrament Parish in Detroit, and had attended the parish's grade school before going on to Catholic Central—an all-boys high school. He was the second oldest of four children. He'd parlayed his Navy electronics training into a career with a business machines firm. His friend, Joe Ricard, had gotten him involved in a bowling league sponsored by the Third Order.

The first time Jerry looked at me, really looked into my eyes, my heart actually fluttered. His bright blue eyes captivated me. What he saw in the skinny little kid smiling up at him through unevenly cut bangs, I can't say. But we became friends. We sought each other out at social events. We laughed and talked together. We might have just remained friends if I hadn't decided to ask him to be my date for the Anniversary Ball—a formal dance which was held each November at my all-girls high school.

He accepted the invitation, and then asked me to go with him to the Ice Capades in Detroit—a week before the dance. From that day forward, there has never been anyone else for either of us. We continued to date throughout my senior year in high school. The first time Jerry visited our house on Mt. Olivet, it was Halloween. With so many people around and so much activity, he thought we were having a block party. He loved the openness and hubbub of our large family. And my family loved him right from the start.

By the spring of 1959, Daddy called Jerry into the kitchen to ask him what his intentions were. "I would be honored to marry Colette if she'll have me," Jerry said. "And I would like to ask for your approval."

"You're a good man," Daddy said. "I give you my wholehearted blessing. I know you'll make her a fine husband. But she's young— only 18. I want her to be sure of you. If she says yes, I'd want your engagement to last at least a year."

But about that conversation, I only heard later. The two of us had never talked about marriage. It was a total surprise to me when for my senior prom that May, Jerry brought me a beautiful corsage—and an engagement ring. In the living room, with Mama and Daddy and my sisters and brothers present, he formally asked me to marry him.

"Yes," I said. I did not hesitate. My eyes sparkled as I looked deep into his warm blue eyes. "I'll marry you. I'd be proud to be your wife." Both of us trembled as he slipped the ring on my finger—and we kissed. The family clapped excitedly.

Later I learned that Jerry had consulted with Daddy before he bought my engagement ring. He'd asked where Daddy had purchased Mama's ring in 1929, and he went downtown to the same jeweler to purchase my ring. His sensitivity in seeking Daddy's approval and his kindness in making him a part of this special time in our lives meant everything to me.

Mama had some doubts. Or she was just upset about me marrying so young. Two weeks before the wedding she called me into her bedroom. "I want you to know that I'm having some health problems—fibroid tumors in my uterus," she said.

"Oh, no," I said. "Is it serious?"

"I could have them surgically removed, but the doctor said they might just shrink on their own after menopause."

"That would be good."

"I also wanted to tell you that if you go through with this wedding, you're on your own. You can't come back home if it doesn't work out. Jerry's always welcome here, but you're not. You can never come back home to live once you leave."

I looked at her in disbelief. Why was she saying these things? I knew she liked Jerry. And I believed she loved me. Then I understood that it must be a combination of emotions she wasn't used to dealing with. She was 52 years old and probably menopausal. Combined with her concern about the tumors, Daddy's illness, the perceived loss of another daughter, and the excitement of the wedding—it was all too much for her. I put my arms around her and gave her a hug. "Don't worry, Mama. Everything will work out fine."

When we married on May 7, 1960, Daddy was in a wheelchair. Buddy walked me down the aisle and Donny pushed Daddy's chair to wait for me next to Jerry by the altar. My eyes were on both Daddy and Jerry. When I reached them, Daddy stood up and gave me a hug. "You've got a wonderful man there," he whispered. "Be good to him." Then he turned and placed my hand in Jerry's. "Love each other always." As I looked into my bridegroom's eyes, I knew marrying him was exactly right.

And it has been. The intense passion came after the wedding. We have been fortunate to have it all. My husband is a good man—the best! Over the years, we have worked at keeping our marriage strong—through all the good times and the sad, the trials and the challenges. We have stood by each other, supported each other, and continue to love each other deeply. And with each passing year our love grows. How could I have been so lucky—and so wise at 17?

＊

I opened my eyes. I looked at my husband driving beside me. "Oh, you're awake," he said. "I thought you were sleeping."

"No, just daydreaming." I smiled. "And thinking—about how lucky I am to have you for a husband."

"How lucky we are to have each other—and our family."

"I was also thinking about the baby. She seems so familiar—like I already know her. I have such a strong feeling that she was always meant to be ours."

"I know what you mean. While you were dozing, I was thinking the very same thing."

Chapter 24

The next four days were hectic. We spent hours talking with Jerry, Jr., Jeffrey and Cheryl about their new sister, made calls to family members to tell them the good news, and shopped for the items we still needed. Each of the children carefully selected a special gift for Janette—a cuddly brown teddy bear, a bright multi-colored crib mobile, a squeaky yellow rubber duck. We picked up a new pink outfit to bring our baby home in, ordered special adoption announcements, and bought a keepsake memory book. The memory book would be used to tell the story in words and pictures of how Janette came to be part of our family.

The first photos to be pasted in the book were snapshots of Janette's sister and brothers—and how they looked when she came into our family. The book would include pictures of the older children meeting her, bringing her home, her Baptism, and other important events; it would be used to list pounds gained, first tooth, first step, and all the important markers in her growing up years. In addition to the regular entries, we would ask friends and relatives to write down what their thoughts and feelings were when they saw our baby for the first time.

Finally the day came to pick our daughter up! She was just over 2 months old. We were all so excited; it seemed to take forever to get to Kalamazoo. When we arrived at the agency, Janette was already waiting for us. The social worker introduced herself to the children, and led us into the room where she lay asleep in a crib. I picked her up. She stretched and opened her eyes. She looked at me sleepily. The children swarmed around us—touching the baby and chattering as I re-dressed her in the clothes we had brought.

The social worker handed Jerry the preliminary adoption papers. "Mrs. Cavanaugh will take it from here," she said. "She'll get in touch with you over the next few days. If you have any questions—or if there are any problems—don't hesitate to call her. She'll be doing the follow-up during the 12-month probationary period." She smiled. "You have a very nice family. Enjoy your new baby."

I couldn't believe it when we were allowed to walk out of the agency office with Janette. It felt like we were kidnapping her. As I held her in my arms on the long ride home, I marveled at the miracle that had made this particular child ours. We were now responsible for her. She was a vulnerable human being. We did not know her. She did not know us. Yet from now on our lives would be permanently fused. Whatever happened—whatever the future held—this child would be part of it.

***

I am a believer in Divine Providence. We are born when we're meant to be born—to whom—and surrounded by those who were intended to love us. Its way beyond my capabilities to understand the why and how of what's meant to be, but I do recognize that being in the right place at the right time is significant in God's overall plan. And I would assume that since life is so orchestrated, we die when we're meant to die. I have experienced two incidents in my childhood that make me a believer.

The first happened when Karen and I were returning to school from lunch one afternoon. Usually we walked along Gilbo, a side street east of our house which ran north and south parallel to Van Dyke. This particular day we had some pennies to spend so we decided to go west to Van Dyke in order to stop at Klatt's grocery store. The store had an entire display case filled with penny candies. We were talking about our favorites—Mary Janes, Snaps, Bit O'Honeys, Candy Pills, Circus Peanuts—and deciding which to choose and share.

We were 20 feet from the store when I noticed my shoe had become untied. "Wait Karen, stop," I said. "I need to tie this stupid shoe. I don't know how it got untied."

Karen stopped and turned around. "Hurry up," she said. "We don't want to be late for school. And you're not supposed to say, 'stupid.'"

Just as I bent to tie my shoe, a car came from behind us along Van Dyke, swerved across our path, and crashed into the storefront—shattering the huge glass display window. I jumped up. Karen and I stood there stunned as Mr. Klatt ran out of the store to pull a bloody, staggering driver from the car. If we hadn't stopped for me to tie my shoe, we would have been in front of the store—exactly where the car had crashed!

The second incident was even more miraculous. It was a hot, muggy afternoon in August. Karen and I had gone shopping with Mama who was driving the car. We were returning home. The wide back seat where Karen was sitting was stacked with the bags of brightly colored fabrics, dress patterns, and sewing notions we had purchased at Penney's. Mama was teaching us to sew. She had shown us how to choose patterns, examine the characteristics of fabrics, and visualize combinations of colors and prints. We were talking excitedly about the school outfits we would help her create for the two of us and for Janet and Judy.

I was sitting in the front seat. The car windows were open. Mama smiled and nodded her head as we talked. Her gray hair, topped with a new white straw hat with bobbing yellow and white daisies, blew in the breeze flowing in through the open window. Horns blasted and brakes squealed as we swung in and out of the lanes of traffic homeward bound from the offices and factories of our busy city. We were driving west on McNichols, a five-lane highway, approaching Outer Drive, a four-lane north/south boulevard. The light was green for us.

Suddenly, Mama gasped. A double trailer truck had run the red light and stopped right in the middle of the intersection, completely blocking our path. In that split second, I saw there was no way around the truck and we were traveling too fast to stop in time. My mouth flew open in a silent scream. As I turned to look at Mama, the wind lifted her hat and it flew into the back seat. She made a grab for her hat as she applied the brakes. For an instant we were distracted. She retrieved her hat and flashed a triumphant smile as she jammed the dancing daisies on her head. Then her face went white.

I jerked my head quickly around as I remembered the truck. To my astonishment, we were on the other side of the boulevard. Our car had come to rest next to the curb in the far right lane. The truck was still across the intersection. Nothing was moving. It was as though time had frozen, like a movie stopped on one frame. Then suddenly, like the click of a switch, the traffic started to move as though nothing had happened. The truck completed a left turn onto McNichols and drove past us.

"Mama!" I gasped. "How did we get around that truck? How come everything was so still?"

"I don't know," she said. "I just...don't know." Tears ran down her cheeks as she leaned her forehead on the steering wheel. The passing drivers were gaping at us. I realized they didn't even know what had happened. They were staring because Mama was blocking traffic—and she was crying. After a few minutes, Mama raised her head, wiped her cheeks with the back of her hands, and started the car. "It's a miracle," she said over and over as we drove home. "What would the kids and Frank have done without me? Who would have taken care of them?"

Ten minutes later, we were safely home. I leaned against the passenger door. My eyes were on Mama's shaking hands still on the steering wheel. I rubbed the "goose bumps" up and down my arms. I looked back at Karen. Her blue eyes were open wide. She looked as stunned as I still felt.

"Listen," Mama said. "We won't tell Daddy or anybody about what happened today. It would only upset everyone. If you want to talk about it, talk to me. Please?" She looked to Karen in the back seat. Her eyes searched mine. We both nodded.

"But Mama," I asked. "Why didn't we hit that truck? What happened?"

"It was a miracle. There is no other explanation for it. It was simply a miracle. It wasn't our time to die."

And it truly was miraculous. I've replayed the incident countless times in my mind. There was no way around that truck. Traffic blocked all of the lanes. There is no logical explanation for what happened. God works in many strange ways and there's a purpose to everything that happens. Who knows why this strange incident occurred? Obviously, He had other plans for each of us. Daddy was already sick and Mama was needed at home; the family couldn't have survived without her. Karen and I were witnesses to the fact that it wasn't our time either.

I've spent the years since then living with the awareness that I'm here for a reason—that my actions and accomplishments have meaning. Throughout my life I've wondered for what special purposes I was spared. I knew in my heart that adopting Janette was an important part of God's plan for me and my family. I wondered how this strange incident had impacted Mama and Karen's lives. We've never talked about it. Certainly they remembered it happening. I made a note to myself to bring the subject up to each of them.

***

When we returned home, one of the first things I did—after Janette had settled down for a nap—was ask the other children what they had to say about their new sister. I took the memory book out to write their thoughts down.

"I think she is cute," Jerry, Jr. said. "It was worth going to Kalamazoo and going 160 miles home."

"I think she is cute and I like her," Jeffrey said.

"I love her," Cheryl said. "She cries a lot. But she's cute. I like her. And I love her."

And Janette did cry a lot as she adjusted to us—to her new home. As with any new baby, the first few days were rough. The foster mother obviously had her own way of holding and handling her. Tiny as she was, she seemed to sense the change. The strangeness caused her not to follow any schedule. It took a great deal of loving patience, warmth and cuddling to quiet and satisfy her. One advantage I had as an adoptive mother—over any new biological mother—was that I was strong and vigorous and emotionally and physically able to cope with a fussy baby.

Although we sent out the adoption announcements immediately, we had asked neighbors, friends and relatives to wait a few days before coming to see our new daughter. She needed time to settle down before being exposed to the strains and distractions of meeting so many strangers. And it gave us time to get to know our child. People understood and respected our request for a little while by ourselves. They knew there was nothing more frustrating than trying to remain calm, patient, and gracious to guests while attempting to cope with a crying baby.

Mama was the first to meet Janette. She didn't say much, but she wrote in the memory book. "What a cutie, with all the hair and pretty auburn color. A beautiful bundle of joy." I was so glad I had thought of this special book for our baby. Mama was not sentimental and rarely expressed how she felt. This way her thoughts were captured. Other relatives also wrote their feelings. The welcoming notes were something our daughter would always have to look back on when she was old enough to wonder how she was received into the family.

"You are beautiful to hold, such a lovely girl and such a lovely personality. Glad to have you in the family. With very much love, Aunt Judy."

"To a chubby faced little girl who already is very strong. You are indeed a very lucky little girl, with luckier parents. Uncle Bill."

"Wow! Are you ever small. You have a nose just like your daddy. You sure are cute! Uncle Dave."

"Such bright eyes and so alert! A darling baby so lucky to have such wonderful parents. They're lucky to have you too. Aunt Lorraine."

"The most delicate darling I have ever seen. I loved you from the first. Aunt Mary Ann."

"To a little bundle of joy that looks like a real Dywasuk. You will be as pretty as your mother. I am proud to have you as my niece. Love, Aunt Janet."

To us Janette was ours from the day we brought her home from the adoption agency. It took a while for our older children to realize the full significance of a new sister in their lives. At first, they treated Janette like a new toy. They didn't want to leave her alone—even to sleep. They wanted everyone they knew to meet and admire her. Jeffrey begged and begged until I agreed to take Janette to school for "show-and-tell". He wanted to "show" his first grade class his "new 'dopted baby sister." Of course, I had to also take her to Jerry's second grade class and Cheryl's kindergarten class.

But gradually the newness and fascination died down. In its place began to develop a much deeper, more meaningful relationship. We found that brothers and sisters interact and grow together in the same way whether they're adoptive or biological. They'll learn to love and respect each other as persons. They'll argue and fight, defend each other, and compete with each other for attention. Eventually, they'll come to be so much a part of each other's life that they'll never think or care about the fact that they're not related by blood.

Chapter 25

Once the first excitement of the adoption was over, everyone seemed to forget Janette was adopted. She was taken for granted—just as our other children were. We meant to keep it that way. At first it was difficult not to announce spontaneously to every stranger who remarked on how cute our baby was, that "We adopted her!" It was tempting to share the happiness and joy of having her in our family. We were still amazed at our good fortune. But we soon realized it would probably make our child feel uncomfortable as she grows older.

This doesn't mean, of course, that we avoided discussing adoption. We felt free and easy about it. But we realized that mentioning adoption should serve some purpose. Otherwise there was no more reason for bringing it up than to go around announcing to everyone that you are married, a Catholic, or belong to the Altar Society or Knights of Columbus. On the other hand, we knew it was important that Janette grow up with the knowledge she's adopted. The key was to be natural about it—and to strike the right balance.

Whenever I was feeling especially tender and loving, I'd say: "I'm so glad we adopted you! You're my special adopted girl." Gradually she'll learn the word "adopted" and come to associate nice, loving, good feelings with it. Although she doesn't yet understand what it means, she'll feel it must be something good. We wouldn't remind her about it too often, yet we'll remind her often enough so that she knows she's adopted—as we promised the agency. The important thing to remember is that any child wants more than anything else in the world to be special—yet at the same time she wants to be exactly the same as everyone else.

During the probationary period, Mrs. Cavanaugh made several appointments to visit our home. Janette was still under the legal guardianship of the adoption agency. It was her job to make sure everything was going all right for all of us. The year before the adoption petition is granted by the court is in some ways an extension of the home study—yet it is quite different. Now we were acting as adoptive parents rather than just talking about it.

"The agency expressed its confidence in you when Janette was placed in your home," Mrs. Cavanaugh said. "We want the adoption to work out well just as much as you do. No matter how many problems you are struggling with in mutual adjustment, if you love and accept your child—and she loves you—the adoption agency will be ready to approve your application for the final adoption decree."

But there were no problems. As the months passed, our daughter became totally and completely ours. We grew to know and love her in the same way we loved each of our children—for the special and unique individuals they are. We loved her as much as we loved our older children, as much as it is humanly possible to love another. Each child—biological or adopted—is loved equally. Each is loved in his or her own special way—not more than, nor less than the others, but for him or herself.

We would never forget she's adopted—we wouldn't want to. That is part of her specialness. She was entrusted to our care. We were chosen not only by society but by Divine Providence to raise this particular child. She was meant to be with us. We couldn't imagine her being with anyone else. She is also special because she's so different from a child that we could conceive—a child that I could bear. I imagined us growing ever more pleased and enchanted by this difference as the years pass. Although I'm sure she'll pick up family traits, it'll be thrilling and fascinating to watch her developing her own separate, individual personality.

***

At a wedding a number of years ago, I watched a 4-year-old girl on the dance floor—swaying and spinning slowly to the music. She had long, medium brown hair and wore a pink ribbed top. On her head she wore a wide-brimmed purple felt hat with a feather. She held her arms out from her body horizontal to the floor. She danced alone her eyes half closed moving to the music—oblivious to what was going on around her. The little girl brought tears to my eyes for I recognized in her the free spirit I once was.

The pressure to conform is one disadvantage of growing up in a large family. In my case, it came not so much from my parents as from my older brothers. If I was out there alone swaying and spinning, one of my brothers would surely have come out to the dance floor. He would have poked me and said: "Why are you wearing that dumb hat? What are you doing dancing by yourself? People are looking at you. Stop putting on a show." And I would have opened my eyes, looked around to see people watching me, been embarrassed, and left the dance floor.

Maybe it's common for older siblings to critique and comment on the behavior of younger ones. I don't know. In our family, it could have been the four-year gap between the older and younger halves of our family because I don't believe I tried so hard to shape or influence my younger sisters and brothers. Perhaps my brothers were self-conscious about the size of our family and cared too much about what other people thought. Whatever the reason, the younger members of the family were taught that standing out or "making a spectacle of yourself" was to be avoided at all cost.

My older siblings also insisted there are inescapable family traits—

like not having any musical ability. Yet Daddy played the piano "by ear". He never had lessons and couldn't read musical notes. But he was able to pick keys well enough to make a melody recognizable. He loved music, and he loved to sing. He sang in the church choir at 9:00 a.m. Mass on Sundays. Whether he was good or not, I don't know. Mama used to tease him about his off-key singing. But he would just smile and keep on singing. Soon it became family lore that "Taubes can't sing. We're not musical. We have terrible voices." Anyone that tried was teased mercilessly.

I still did my best to develop my uniqueness. I pursued music even though I didn't think I was very good at it. In grade school I learned to twirl a baton and marched with the band, took piano lessons, and played the clarinet. Although I never mastered any of them, I did learn to read music and find the right keys. In sixth grade, I joined the children's choir. We sang in church at Christmas and Easter and on-stage in the auditorium for special school-sponsored performances. I continued with the choir through eighth grade where, as a soprano, I was chosen to sing a solo of Beautiful Dreamer. I was not outstanding, but I managed.

I've always liked to perform. Karen and I would put together plays in the garage and recruit neighborhood kids to come and watch. We dressed up in odd bits of clothing and made up the script as we went along. The older we got, the more elaborate our efforts became. I checked out books of plays from the library, improvised them, assigned parts to friends, and made up costumes. After joining the Girl Scouts, I took the bus to audition for parts at churches and schools that were hosting regional performances. I never got a part, but I kept trying.

In high school I joined the voice group. We were taught by the drama teacher to project our voices and enunciate words in alliterations. I loved that after school class and looked forward to performing with the group on stage at the spring talent show. Unfortunately, my after school jobs interfered. Try as I might to be there, I had to miss too many practices. Sister told me I had to choose between the voice group and my after school jobs. As our family counted on the money I earned, I was forced to drop the extracurricular activity.

Artistic talent is another area my older siblings insisted we are lacking in our family. I grew up believing that "Taubes can't draw or paint. We're definitely not gifted." I have no idea where that family tale originated as I have a beautiful chalk drawing of a sailboat that Daddy created when he was in eighth grade. He obviously had some artistic talent as he drew the picture freehand and won first place in an art competition at his school.

I was never much interested in drawing or painting. One Christmas I asked for and received an easel and paints—but art was never something I actively pursued. Creative expression was not encouraged at the grade school I attended. Instead, we were taught to "color inside the lines". I never questioned the directive. I followed instructions. And I believed I didn't have much artistic talent.

Creative writing was altogether different. I loved playing with words and making up stories before I even learned how to write. I never shared my stories. I was too smart for that. My brothers would have had a field day! Instead, when I learned to write, I wrote in my diary and locked up the words with a tiny key. The only exception was re-writing and performing the plays I found in library books. But nobody else knew or cared that they had been modified.

In school I wrote assignments to please the teachers and received my "A+s". The one exception I made was a disaster. As a high school senior, I researched and wrote my final term paper on multiple sclerosis—which was a little known and difficult to diagnose disease at the time. My curiosity was sparked and I spent hours at the downtown Detroit library tracking down information in medical journals. I turned the paper in, filled with excitement and a sense of accomplishment. I knew I had done an excellent job. When the grades were handed out, I received an "F" for failure.

The nun who taught my senior English class was intimidating.

Sister Eileen Therese never smiled and everyone was afraid of her. But I couldn't believe I deserved the poor grade I had received on my term paper. I thought I had done exceptionally well. For my own peace of mind, I had to find out where I had gone wrong. So I worked up my nerve and approached her after class. "Sister," I said. I stammered nervously. "What was wrong with my paper?"

She turned and glared at me. "Do you think I'm stupid?" she said. "You should have copied something less obvious. How in the world could you even imagine that I would believe you wrote that paper?"

My mouth dropped open as I stared at Sister in disbelief. "But I didn't copy it. I wrote it. I worked really hard..."

"Get out of here or I'm not only going to fail you, I'm going to get you suspended from school. You won't graduate!"

I walked out of the classroom mystified. I wasn't a student who excelled, but I had never cheated, never been in trouble of any kind. Why would Sister assume that at the end of my senior year in high school, I would change my ways? And why was she so angry? In the end, I failed my senior English class because of that term paper.

I chose not to appeal the decision. I didn't need the credit to graduate. I didn't even bother to tell Mama what had happened. She had problems enough coping with Daddy's sickness and everything going on at home. I knew I had written the paper. Obviously it was exceptional. Trying to prove my authorship was pointless. My only regret was that Sister refused to return the term paper to me and I didn't have a copy.

***

As a parent, I'm determined to raise our children without the restrictions on individuality that I had experienced. Although I managed to experiment with various creative endeavors, I felt repressed—by both my family and my schooling. I planned to make sure that our children were free to express themselves—to develop their unique personalities. And even for myself, I felt there was still time to explore my own individuality—to become all that I could be. I was still very much interested in writing. Perhaps this was a direction I could take.

For now, my focus was on finalizing the adoption. When that day came, Janette would legally be ours. A new birth certificate would be issued listing us as her parents—with no indication of adoption. The original birth certificate and all the papers and documents concerning the adoption would be sealed and filed in court. In the eyes of the law we would be a family. We'd legally belong to each other—forever. It would be a memorable day—a day to rejoice in—a day to celebrate.

Chapter 26

As Janette settled into a routine, I began to find time on my hands to think. I was pleased with the size of our family. I couldn't imagine wanting any more children. But I was now only 28 years old. Three of my children were already in school. What would I do with the rest of my life—especially as my baby got older? What did women do? For Mama, it was different. She had children until she was 40 years old. There were no perma-press clothes, electric dryers, automatic washing machines, dishwashers, even freezers.

Being a wife and mother had always been my greatest ambition. But I only had four children to raise and I was a highly efficient homemaker. I could always fill my time with sewing, baking, cooking, canning, washing, ironing, and volunteering. But I was beginning to realize that I wanted more. I wanted to explore who I am as an individual— yet still be a good wife and mother. Then I came upon a way that I could do both. It was through my writing. I was so excited. It was like remembering a long forgotten dream. I had always kept a journal— since I was a child. Not every day. Just when I felt the urge. Now I wanted to pursue writing to publish.

I was interested in factual writing—not fiction or poetry. In a magazine, I found an advertisement for a ten session nonfiction writing

course that I could take by mail. It was offered through the Famous
Writers School and cost $400. The course was designed in segments
and provided how-to instruction on magazine article and book writing.
Published authors were the instructors. They reviewed assignments
and offered critiques. The course was self-paced. I could read the
instructions and work on the assignments during my free time. It
would not interfere with family time.

The only problem was getting the money to pay for the course. I
could take it out of household funds, but I didn't want to do that.
Exploring a career in writing was something I wanted to do entirely on
my own. If I was successful, it would be my own personal success. If I
failed, it wouldn't cost anyone else anything. And I would have at least
tried my hand at being a professional writer.

"I'm behind you 100 percent," Jerry said. "The course sounds
really good. And we can afford it. The company will take installment
payments."

I smiled. "I appreciate your support," I said. "But this is something I
want to do on my own. I'll figure out a way to pay for it."

***

In my family, we were raised to be hard workers. We had chores
at home from as early as I can remember. Though our house was
cluttered—that was unavoidable with so many people living in such a
small space—it was clean. Every Saturday, we scoured the main rooms
of the house—living room, dining room, kitchen and bathroom. Jobs
were assigned and rotated according to age and any outside work
responsibilities. But I can remember Karen and I being responsible
each week for cleaning the living room, dining room, and staircase to
the upstairs bedrooms.

These were not simple jobs. We had to move all of the furniture to
vacuum underneath. We had to lift off the cushions of the couch and
side chairs, sweep the side pockets and underlining, and take the pillows
outside to the front porch for beating and fluffing. Wooden furniture

had to be waxed and glass surfaces polished. The steps had to be dusted and vacuumed. Glassware had to be removed from the china cabinet in the dining room for cleaning as well. And Mama's silver coffee set on the buffet had to be polished—so did the silverware.

The boys—first my older brothers Buddy and Donny, then Billy and Davey—were responsible for washing the kitchen and bathroom floors. This was a long process that required using hot water and Fels Naptha soap and scrubbing on hands and knees with an oblong wooden backed brush. Once the floors were washed, they had to be rinsed with a hot wet mop. Newspapers were then spread across the floor to absorb any excess water and allow traffic in the rooms while the floors dried. Venturing off the newspapers was considered a major offense as it would track dirt on the clean linoleum.

Everyone did chores at home including Lorraine. Being physically handicapped didn't exempt her from carrying her share of family responsibility. Her every day job was washing the dishes. I can see her leaning against the wide porcelain kitchen sink with her hands up to the elbows in hot water—talking, washing and rinsing. We each took turns wiping the dishes and putting them away. Lorraine was a great listener—the one in the family who usually took the time and interest to hear what a younger sibling had to say. And, with her tremendous store of knowledge, I thought she was the smartest of my older sisters and brothers. If she didn't know the answer to a small child's question, she'd take the time to find it.

Lorraine's weekly chore was sorting the magazines and newspapers that accumulated in the mahogany magazine rack that stood in the corner of the dining room next to the table. Our black dial telephone stood atop on a white doily. Lorraine would sit on the floor hidden from view by the table—supposedly sorting the contents. Invariably, you'd find her reading everything that came into her hands. It was the perfect job for her—but she was so engrossed in what she read it took her hours to complete.

Other chores during my early years included "watching" my younger brothers and sisters, folding and sorting laundry, and running errands. Eventually, I learned to iron, sew and help with the mending. In addition, everyone was expected to take outside jobs whenever possible "to help support the family". Any money collected had to be turned over to Mama. We started young, sacrificed, and worked hard for what we earned for our family's well being.

"Mrs. Witkowski wants you to go to the store for her," Mama said. She called out to Karen and me through the screened bedroom window. We were playing in the backyard.

"Awe, Mama." I said. "We don't want to go. It's too hot."

"You don't have a choice. She's waiting for you. Stop at her house and get the money. She'll tell you what she needs."

Mrs. Witkowski lived near the corner of the street, right next door to Ma and Pa's. Karen and I were afraid of her. She made us feel uncomfortable. She was so stern. She always wore a long black dress and head scarf. She never smiled, and she spoke very broken English— so it was difficult to understand her. And she was not a patient woman. She almost always ended up yelling at us.

But Karen and I would trudge dutifully down the street pulling our red wagon, climb up the high concrete steps of her porch, and ring the doorbell. Mrs. Witkowski would come to the door, hand me her black coin purse, and begin to recite her list. She was unable to write it down because her English was not good enough. And we were unable to write it down because we were very young and our written vocabulary was not extensive enough.

"I want ugs," Mrs. Witkowski said.

"Eggs?" I said.

She would nod her head. "And cum."

"Cream?"

"No, no! Cum." She demonstrated by spreading her finger across her palm.

"Butter?"

She would nod emphatically.

And so it went—guessing what she needed and trying to memorize the items—until she completed her list.

After walking six blocks to the store in the hot sun, reciting the list to the grocer as best we could remember it, and returning with the groceries carefully packed in the wagon, Mrs. Witkowski would do her inspection. We stood there nervously while she checked each egg for cracks and took inventory of the items. Next, she poured the change from her coin purse into the palm of her hand and counted it. If anything was wrong—like we missed an item or the bananas were too ripe—we had to trudge back to the store. No matter how many times we had to go back and forth, the payment for our hard work was always the same—5 cents for each of us.

Even in the 1940s when first class stamps were 3 cents, 10 cents was small payment for the amount of work involved. We would hand Mama the money when we returned home. "Is that all she gave you?" she said. "That's not very much!" Mama wasn't questioning our honesty. She was just amazed that we had been paid so little.

"That's all she ever gives us," I whined. "It's always the same. And we had to go back because one egg was cracked. The grocer said it was our fault but we were really, really careful. It's not fair! Why do we have to keep going to the store for her?"

"Because I said so. Mrs. Witkowski can't go to the store herself. It doesn't hurt you one bit to do her errands!" But mostly Mama was embarrassed to turn the woman down. She was Ma and Pa's neighbor so Mama felt obliged. Also, she wanted other neighbors to know the Taubes were hard workers and willing to do odd jobs.

Coming from such a large family, I learned to iron clothes at a young age. It was one of my assigned chores at home, and I was exceptionally good at it. So occasionally I would be hired to iron at Mrs. Patulski's house. I didn't mind it because I was paid well—a dollar for a large basket of clothes. But for me it was also a peek into someone else's life—and a way of getting individual attention.

When I knocked at the side door of her house, Mrs. Patulski would be waiting for me. Her ironing board would already be set up on the back screened porch and she would be sitting out there on a leather recliner with the basket of clothes by her feet. She'd smile and wave me into the house. "I'm ready if you are," she said. "But first, we need to sprinkle the clothes."

I would fill a small glass Coca-Cola bottle with warm water and plug it with a metal sprinkling cap. Next, I would take the items to be ironed—stiffly starched shirts and blouses, table clothes and napkins, hankies and pants--sprinkle each lightly to dampen the fabric, then fold and roll the cloth tightly so that each piece was about the shape of a rolling pin. There were no steam irons then and lightly dampening created the steam needed to remove wrinkles when the hot iron was pressed against the cloth. While I sprinkled, the electric iron would be heating.

Mrs. Patulski sat with me and visited while I worked. "So what's new in the neighborhood?" she asked. She wasn't looking for gossip. She was just interested in anything I had to tell her. She was a kind lady and made me feel that what I had to say was important. The time flew by. And she always complimented me on what a good job I was doing as I hung or folded each ironed item.

Karen and I also did some babysitting. Jobs were few and far between because people in our neighborhood generally didn't socialize without their children. And, if they did, they mostly had older daughters to watch the younger children. But we loved to babysit whenever we had the opportunity. We were paid 25 cents an hour and, most importantly, we could eat whatever we wanted in the houses where we were babysitting. We were amazed at the assortment of treats other people had in their houses. We gorged ourselves with assorted fruits, candy bars, chips and soda pop. But nobody ever complained about the amount of food we ate.

My older brothers and sisters had part-time jobs from the time they were in their early teens. I can remember Mary Ann working at a concession stand on Belle Isle, Buddy working at a gas station, and Donny working at a grocery store. They also worked as janitorial and cafeteria helpers at their high schools to help pay for their Catholic education tuition. Everyone in the family contributed with outside jobs to the best of their ability.

I particularly remember when Lorraine decided to start selling greeting cards. A large brown cardboard box arrived at the house. Inside, were boxes of birthday and all-occasion cards, elegant stationary, colorful gift wrapping paper and ribbons, and a wide variety of both religious and secular Christmas greeting cards. The samples were so beautiful; I couldn't imagine anyone refusing to buy them.

Karen and I went door to door in the neighborhood—pushing Lorraine in her wheelchair. She held the cardboard sample case on her lap. We would stop in front of each house and one of us would go up the steps to ring the doorbell. Then we would walk back down to the sidewalk and wait for someone to answer the door. Lorraine sat in her chair with the order blanks. When the door was pushed open, she would start her spiel, show the samples, and take the orders. It was difficult for people to refuse to buy.

The summer before I started high school, I found a job as a clerk at Kresge dime store in downtown Detroit. I was 14 years old and had to get a special worker's permit. I made 55 cents per hour. Every Friday I collected my pay envelope filled with cash and proudly turned it over to Mama. She counted out enough money to pay for bus fare for the following week. For lunch I took a sandwich from home. The rest went into the family coffers.

When I started high school, I also worked in the cafeteria at lunchtime and sold candy in the snack bar after school. These jobs helped pay for my all-girls Catholic high school tuition—and provided a free hot lunch. After school I took a bus to my job downtown. Karen started at Dominican High School the following year. She also worked in the cafeteria for tuition and a hot lunch. Her first after school job was as a clerk in a drug store.

Billy started a paper route when he was 10 years old and worked at it for many years—well into his early teens. The Detroit News was an afternoon edition during the work week and morning edition on Saturdays and Sundays. Rain or shine, snow or sleet, hot or cold, winter or summer, Billy had to deliver the papers. He would ride his bike to the station—which was ten blocks from home—fold the newspapers so they could be thrown onto porches, load as many as his canvas bag would hold, and pedal through the neighborhoods. Then he would go back for more. The size of his route increased as he grew older. On Saturdays he knocked on the doors of his customers to collect the money, turned it over to the station manager, and pocketed his weekly tips. People liked him—he was reliable.

I remember seeing Billy one freezing winter day riding his bicycle down the snow covered street. The white canvas bag on his handlebars was overflowing with newspapers. He was standing on the pedals putting all his strength into forcing the bike to move. His face was red from the cold and his nose was running. He was wearing wide-ribbed corduroy pants and a brown wool jacket with buttons missing. The front was fastened with a large silver safety pin to keep it closed. He had a plaid hat with earflaps, but the buckle was broken and the ties were flapping against his chin as he pedaled toward me smiling and waving. At that moment, I felt both sorry for my younger brother—and proud of him. He was such a hard worker.

By the time I was in high school, I was an accomplished seamstress. Although we wore uniforms to school, I sewed most of my own casual clothes including skirts, blouses and dresses. Before graduation, I sewed a navy blue linen suit with matching blue and white polka dot blouse for my upcoming job interviews. The suit jacket was lined with the polka dot fabric. I wore the suit with wrist length white cotton gloves and a tiny white hat to the meetings. The attorneys, who hired me as their legal secretary in their "one girl" office, later told me that they were as impressed with the outfit I wore as they were with my shorthand and typing skills. Mama taught me well.

After graduating from high school, I worked as the lone secretary in the downtown Detroit law offices of three attorneys for a salary of $55 per week. I typed all of their legal documents, set up appointments with clients, and handled incoming telephone calls. Of my total salary, I was to give Mama $35 per week, and keep the rest of the money to pay for my expenses like bus fare, lunches and clothes—as well as to save for my upcoming wedding. It didn't quite work out that way. I was thrifty. I took a sandwich from home and made coffee at work. But I barely had money to cover transportation to and from the office.

Although I set money aside every payday, there was always a family emergency and my money was needed at home. In the end, Jerry paid for all the upfront costs of our wedding—like the hall rental, invitations, flowers and deposits for food and drinks. I paid for the material for my wedding gown, which Aunt Evelyn designed and sewed. Jerry and I used the money we received as wedding gifts to pay for the rest of the day's expenses, and our honeymoon.

I worked in the law offices until after I was married. When I was pregnant with our first child, I had to resign because morning sickness totally incapacitated me. "We really hate to see you go," the attorneys said. "You're very good at what you do. It'll be hard to replace you." Ultimately, I learned to work hard, to be determined, and to persevere from master teachers—my parents. Combined with my thirst for knowledge and the desire to be the very best at doing whatever interests me, I have been able to be successful. And I hoped I would always be.

＊

After much thought and exploration, I finally found a way to pay for the Famous Writers School course. One of our neighbors was a

Beauty Counselor regional manager. She worked out of her home. She recruited housewives like me to put on makeup demonstrations—similar to Tupperware parties. "You learn about our products and how to apply them," she said. "Then you gather women in your home or theirs, show them the benefits of the products, and get them to buy. You earn a commission on everything you sell."

I thought about all my family and friends. I certainly had enough potential customers. If I could get each of them to put on a party with their friends, I'd soon earn all I needed to pay for the course. I didn't hesitate. "Sign me up," I said. We worked out the details of the training, the commissions, and I received my demonstration kit. Soon I was an official Beauty Counselor—able to show everyone I knew how to improve their looks. I started bugging my sisters, cousins, neighbors and friends to host a party in their homes.

"You're doing what?" Mama said. "Selling makeup! People will think you have to work. How does Jerry feel about that?"

I explained that I would only do the makeup demonstrations until I paid for my writing course. "Jerry is supportive," I said. "He knows I love to write. And he'd pay for the course if I let him. But I wanted to do it myself."

"I don't understand you. What about your new baby—and the other kids. You'll be taking time away from them. And the adoption isn't even final yet. What will the social worker think?"

"It's not an issue with the adoption. Why would it be? Social workers have children—and they work. Besides, I'm not taking anything away from anybody. I'm just trying to fulfill a dream for myself—on my own time."

"What's so important about writing? I thought you were happy being a wife and mother. Isn't that good enough for you?"

"I love being a wife and mother. But I want more. I want to use all of my talents and abilities. I know you don't understand—and I'm sorry. But this is something I need to do."

"You sound like one of those women's libbers."

"It's just a different time, Mama. But you know what? I guess I come by my desire for independence naturally. You've told the story over and over about how excited Ma was when women got the right to vote. And Grandma Taube always worked out of the house."

"Well I'm not having any makeup demonstrations for you at my house."

"That's fine. I don't expect you to. I just wanted to let you know what I was doing."

The makeup demonstrations were going well. Most people were receptive—and they were easy to do. I was surprised at how much I enjoyed sharing my new skill. And I was pleased to find the work didn't interfere with family time. If a one-on-one demonstration was scheduled during the day, I asked the potential customer to come to my home while Janette was napping. On other occasions, I biked or walked to a customer's home with Janette in a stroller or on the back of my bike. She happily entertained herself while I visited.

I didn't have a car available during the day, so the group parties were scheduled in the evenings after dinner. Jerry was home studying for his classes and the children were all ready for bed when I left. It felt good to be earning my own money. I was surprised at how quickly I accumulated $400. I signed up for the writing course, sent in the tuition, and continued to schedule makeup sessions while I awaited the packet of materials to start my classes. I was amazed at how quickly I'd become proficient at low key selling. I had twice the amount I'd targeted when I resigned as a Beauty Counselor. I set the extra money aside to use for some future dream.

Finally the course materials arrived. I was so excited. A new part of my life was just beginning. In taking this writing course, I was going to be doing something just for me—something I'd dreamed about doing. It felt so good!

Chapter 27

Over the next months, I began to study the course materials and complete my writing assignments. Reading a wide variety of authors and looking for subjects to write about made me super-sensitive to world events. The 1960s had been witness to so many phenomenal changes. Although I've always paid attention to current events—we were raised to read the daily newspaper—my family and home life was so much more day-to-day, mundane, and controllable. I've been aware of what was happening—and had opinions and concerns—but I'd not been individually involved.

It was a sad decade in so many ways. The assassinations of President Kennedy and Robert Kennedy; civil rights workers Medger Evers, Dr. Martin Luther King, Jr., and James Meredith; and the shootings of other prominent activists. The race and anti-war riots throughout the country. Sit-ins, the Bay of Pigs invasion, the Cuban missile crisis, the cold war and the construction of the Berlin Wall, the U.S. involvement in Vietnam. Yet it was an exciting and innovative decade, too. The invention of pacemakers and the artificial heart; the breaking of the genetic code; the surgeon general's report linking smoking to lung cancer; the introduction of the birth control pill.

And then there was the first man to orbit the earth, the space walks and the moon landing; the establishment of the Peace Corps, Medicare, the Head Start program and the War on Poverty; the enactment of the Civil Rights law; the banning of school prayers by the Supreme Court; the Miranda decision curbing police interrogation powers; the invention of Polaroid color film, the microwave oven, dishwashers and garbage disposals; the Beatles, hippies and flower children, LSD, and rock festivals. Finally, there was the publication of Betty Friedan's Feminine Mystique and the women's rights movement.

There was plenty for me to think about—and to write about. Although I haven't been an activist, I've been witness to all of these changes and events. Life in this country has been fundamentally altered by them. And they have and will continue to have a strong impact on me and my family. Especially the women's rights movement. It can potentially change the way women work, live, love and play. I've been spending a great deal of time wondering how and why a woman's traditional role has become what it is—and how I feel about that. I wasn't sure yet.

***

I'd been a non-participating witness to other important historical events before in my life. I was born ten months before the attack on Pearl Harbor. I don't remember anything about the war years except this: you were supposed to save foils—the kind in which cigarettes and gum were wrapped. Karen and I would walk up and down the tree-shaded sidewalks looking for the tossed wrappers. We would carefully strip the papers from the foil, discard the paper and roll the foil pieces into a ball which grew larger as we added more foil. What we did with the balls remains a mystery to me. Perhaps our older siblings took them to a collection center for recycling.

My first real awareness of the larger outside world was after the Presidential race of 1948—when I was 7 years old. I can clearly visualize the headline of The Detroit News proclaiming "TRUMAN WINS". I knew my parents were disappointed. They had been Roosevelt

Democrats until Daddy was compelled to join the union at his plant. "I don't like the idea of having to pay dues for other men to tell me what I want or what I should do," he said. The experience changed family politics. Daddy and Mama became more and more conservative—and two of only a few scattered Republicans in our largely blue collar neighborhood.

They often commented on world events—it was part of the discussions at the supper table. Daddy had also grown disenchanted with some of President Roosevelt's social reforms. "The country's becoming too socialistic," he said. The civics lessons we learned at home have carried each of us forward throughout our lives. I've never known any of my sisters or brothers to miss voting in an election.

But Lorraine was the family politician. She read incessantly and shared with all of us what was happening on the national scene. She could store information and cite facts like a vocal encyclopedia. Walking with crutches and speaking with a slight impediment never kept her from expressing her viewpoint to whomever would listen. She eventually ran for the office of Republican Precinct Delegate in our neighborhood—and was elected. She volunteered at the 14th District Republican Party headquarters and was active in getting Dwight Eisenhower elected. "I like Ike," she said. "He knows what he's doing."

But Mama and Daddy weren't political activists. They didn't have the time or inclination. Mama was a homebody and Daddy's participation in the outside world was limited to church-related activities. Other than an occasional choir practice or usher's club meeting, he was home every evening. The only other event he participated in was the planning and organizing of the yearly parish picnic. The men in the usher's club were expected to help out.

That changed when the pastor asked Daddy to consider starting a new Boy Scout troop at the parish. My brother, Buddy, was 11 years old. He wanted to be a Boy Scout, but the parish troop had too many boys and not enough Scout leaders. No more boys could join. Mama was proud Daddy had been chosen. "We had a lot of discussions about it," Mama said. "We had seven children at home. I hated the idea of him being away more frequently. But Daddy said he would just get the troop going until someone else could take over. 'It's just one day a week,' he said. 'And I'll quit the choir and usher's club.' So I agreed."

Daddy was the Scoutmaster of Boy Scout Troop 15 for nearly eight years—until he got too sick to continue. He was a model leader. He loved the boys and the boys loved him. He was extremely creative in coming up with projects that held the interest of boys from 11 to 18 years old. The boys started as young scouts, earned countless merit badges, and achieved Eagle Scout status at unprecedented numbers.

In general only 4 percent of Boy Scouts become Eagle Scouts. Each candidate must earn at least 21 merit badges, hold leadership positions in the troop, and successfully complete a service project that benefits the community or an organization. Daddy's scouts accomplished all of this—and several became assistant Scoutmasters when they were 18 years old so they could continue to be part of the troop.

Within the troop, Daddy created a Native American dance group. The boys dressed in leather costumes and feathered headdresses, painted their faces, and learned to step rhythmically to drum beats. They were called on to perform at community events throughout the city—and were featured in local newspapers and on TV.

Each summer Daddy took the boys for a week to the Boy Scout camp in Howell, Michigan. It was the highlight of the year for the troop. Throughout the winter they planned and prepared for the event. With Daddy's supervision and the assistant troop leaders' participation, the boys organized everything themselves—meals, grocery shopping, gear lists and activities. At the camp, the scouts slept in pup tents and prepared their entire meals outdoors over tiny kerosene stoves and the campfire.

Watching Daddy check the supplies spread out on the church lawn the day of departure was a sight to see. The boys could barely contain their excitement. And Daddy was in his element. He was as excited as the boys about spending a week in the outdoors. As part of the troop, Buddy and Donny went camping with Daddy. He took Billy along from the time he was 8 years old.

Buddy, Donny and Billy were all Boy Scouts. Each achieved the rank of Eagle Scout. Although Daddy was no longer the troop leader when Billy joined, the assistant troop leaders he had trained over the years continued with the enthusiasm Daddy had instilled in them. And Billy benefited from the pioneer work Daddy had spearheaded. Even today, more than 20 years after Daddy became Scoutmaster, I run into men who were in Boy Scout Troop 15 when Daddy was the leader. "Oh, you're Mr. Taube's daughter," they say. "I'll never forget your Dad." And they go on to tell me how Daddy had influenced their lives in some positive way.

Daddy's volunteerism cost Mama the most. She was the one who had to take up the slack all the hours and days when he was away from home. But she knew he loved being a part of the Boys Scouts—and she was proud of him. As a child, I never resented Daddy's absences. I knew he was doing something important, something he believed in, something he enjoyed very much. He wore his uniform so proudly. And I am awestruck when I think of the countless lives he touched over the years. Few men can make such an impact.

When Daddy was sick, he constantly had visits from young men who had been in his troop. They came when they were home on leave from the service, from college, from studying for the priesthood. In later years, they visited with their wives and children. These young men went on to touch other lives and make a positive impact that carried forward and will continue to carry forward for generations.

∗∗

I had a rich history to draw from for my writing assignments. The first lessons of the course taught me to observe people and scenes around me—body language, facial expressions, ways of talking, sounds, smells—and to write about what I saw and heard. I was assigned other published authors to study. I learned that settings, description and dialog are key factors in any writing. I mailed the first few assignments—and was delighted to get positive reinforcement from the instructors. I hadn't received any comments on my writing capabilities since the devastating response of my high school English teacher. I incorporated any suggestions for improvements as the lessons progressed.

When I received an analysis of my fourth assignment which I entitled, "Was It a Miracle?" there was a recommendation from the instructor that I explore sending the article to inspirational magazines in an attempt to sell it. The article told the miraculous story about the near accident Mama and Karen and I had experienced when I was a child. I went to the library and studied the Writer's Market—a book that outlined where and how to sell what you write. I followed the instructions carefully and mailed my submission.

Meanwhile I continued to write. For the next assignments, I wrote about Daddy and the way he dealt with his illness which I entitled, "I Remember Dad". I wrote about a Catholic public speaking/leadership course Jerry and I took through the Gabriel Richard Institute and entitled it, "GRI Spells Leadership—A Unique Institute in Michigan Lights a Candle Around the World." Finally, I wrote an article questioning a Catholic woman's traditional role as strictly wife and mother and entitled it, "A Woman's Place." As each piece was critiqued by my instructors and returned to me, I submitted the revised articles to various inspirational magazines.

In researching and writing "A Woman's Place", I found out a lot about myself. I realized that I was definitely looking for a more fulfilling life. I was happy being a wife and mother—but it wasn't enough for me. "For centuries society has characterized the ideal woman as one who marries, has children and dedicates herself to her family and home," I wrote. "This ideal woman, who has chosen the vocation of marriage, theoretically finds true fulfillment in her devotion to her husband and children.

"From earliest childhood woman has been told by her parents, her teachers, her church and by society in general that this is woman's traditional role in society. She is expected to marry. If she does, she is considered successful. When she has children, she truly arrives. If by chance a woman finds she isn't satisfied or feels her intellectual energies aren't being properly stimulated or challenged by the traditional role, it's too bad. If she doesn't feel happy or fulfilled or even busy enough in her push-button kitchen, it's just too bad. She shouldn't have gotten married.

"A woman looks at her children and she knows she loves them. If she feels she has sacrificed her individual human self for them she either considers it worthwhile or keeps it to herself and tries not to feel resentful. She drives her children to scout meetings, play practice, little league and dance lessons. She picks them up from school. She sometimes even fights their battles for them. She is always, always there. She has learned to live her life through her husband and children.

"But why should it be that way? In by-gone days woman's work took all the time and energy a young woman could scrape together. Perhaps a wife and mother was a full-time occupation. But with all of our modern conveniences it's just not anymore. Today women have actually had to learn to fill their time. They try to keep busy staying always within the traditional role that has been imposed on them.

"A woman may work with the PTA or make cancer pads. She may work part-time as long as she's there when her husband and children 'need her.' A job like this may fill some of a woman's time but still leave her feeling unfulfilled and guilty for wanting to get away for even a few hours a week...Meanwhile husband and father struggles to make a decent living at his job. He must consider not only his children but also his wife as dependents. If he finds he hates his work, it's too bad. He has too much financial responsibility to risk a change. When he comes home he may have to face an unhappy, unfulfilled, frustrated wife who takes out her resentment on her husband at being stuck home all day...

"Perhaps, tomorrow, the ideal woman will be characterized as the one who uses her specific talents in doing God's work whether it be in the home or in the world. While serving as an example, women today who are now doing their 'own thing' must speak out and convince others that there is no specific woman's place in the world. Christ called each of us to do His work. Not as a man or as a woman but as an individual."

As rejection slips came in the mail, I re-addressed the submissions and sent them out to other publications. And one day, a check arrived. It was my first sale. Daily Meditation Magazine wanted to publish "Was It a Miracle?" I screamed in delight. I had received payment for something I had created. I would soon realize my dream of becoming a published writer!

The second article to sell was "A Woman's Place", which would appear in Franciscan Message a magazine published by the Franciscan Friars of the Assumption Province in Wisconsin. I was sure this Catholic publication would take some flak for sharing my opinion. And I was also sure my mother wouldn't be too happy about my "liberal" viewpoint. But I felt liberated. My mother would learn to deal with it.

***

During the 1960s my younger sisters and brothers had begun marrying and leaving home. Karen married in 1963 and Janet in 1964. Billy was just married in February 1969 and Judy was married in September. Only Davey and Lorraine remained home with Mama. "I feel like everyone is abandoning me," Mama said. But she kept herself busy—sewing doll clothes and dresses for her granddaughters, hooking rugs, crocheting hankies, doing embroidery and gardening. And she was content—as long as she was kept informed about what was going on in each of her children's lives. "I better be the first to know any news," she warned. "Not the last".

Chapter 28

On May 19, 1970 we went to court to finalize Janette's adoption. It was a memorable day—a day to rejoice, a day to celebrate. All six of us were there—our complete family. The judge asked us individually if we loved Janette. Of course, we each answered, "Yes." I felt tears in my eyes as he announced that we were now legally each other's for life. "You are officially a family," he said. "This child now belongs to you as much as any child can ever belong to her parents—or her brothers or sisters." I already knew that nothing could ever separate us.

Janette was now 14 months old. Jerry had been holding her in his arms, as we looked up to the judge sitting on his bench in his austere black robes. Janette wore a white bonnet with lace trim and a flocked white dress. She looked sweet and adorable. Suddenly—just as the judge made his pronouncement—Janette leaned forward. She looked into the judge's eyes. "Thank you," she said. We were all shocked. It was so appropriate—and so strange for a child her age to say. We couldn't believe it. I realized that she was imitating her parents, but it was the first time she had ever been so outgoing—and so precocious.

Afterwards, we all went to Howard Johnson's for strawberry shortcake to celebrate the occasion. Then we decided to take a ride through our old Detroit neighborhood. To show our baby where I spent my childhood—and to see how much the older children remembered of the neighborhood where they were born. In the short time since Mama had moved to Utica, the neighborhood had already begun to change. Only a few of the old neighbors remained. Some of the houses were vacant.

"It seems like forever since we lived here," I said. "The houses look so small—and they're so close together!"

We drove slowly past the house where I had grown up. "Look kids," Jerry said. "See that little door on the side of the house? That's the coal chute—that's where they used to deliver coal."

"What's coal?" Cheryl asked.

Jerry and I looked at each other and laughed. Coal furnaces were a relic from the past. So were outhouses, hanging clothes on outside lines, neighborhood vendors and ice boxes.

***

When I told my sister Mary Ann that I could remember the iceman bringing ice to our house, she was surprised. "You would have to have been a baby," she said. "If I recall correctly, it wasn't too much longer after you were born that we got our first electric refrigerator." But I have a vivid memory of a man coming up the back steps into the kitchen carrying a square block of ice in silver tongs and bending over to place it in the icebox. And she confirmed that the icebox stood exactly where I remembered it.

Donny clearly remembers the iceman coming. "There was a special card that Mama placed in the front room window to tell the iceman how much ice to deliver to our house—25, 50, 75 or 100 pounds," he said. "In the summer I'd sit on the front porch watching for the ice wagon— hoping to talk the iceman into chopping off a piece of ice for me to suck." When the icebox was replaced with an electric refrigerator, our family still referred to it as "the icebox". The new refrigerator had limited storage capacity, but it included a tiny freezer compartment for making ice cubes—one tray at a time.

Milk was delivered every day. The milk was packaged in round quart sized glass bottles with tapered necks and paper seals. Thick cream stood on top of the milk and the bottles had to be shaken before drinking. The milkman also delivered butter, cottage cheese and sour cream. Butter was packaged in small crocks. Dairy trucks weren't air conditioned or refrigerated. The products were packed in ice. As the ice melted on hot summer days, the truck would leave a trail of water wherever it went.

Some houses had milk chutes. These were 12-inch square compartments built into the wall of the house next to the side door. The compartments had two doors—one opened to the inside of the house, the other opened to the outside for deliveries. Houses that didn't have a milk chute, kept a hinged metal box on the porch next to the front door. We had two metal boxes for our exceptionally large deliveries. Empties were washed and left for the milkman to pick up. The milkman used a sectioned metal rack with a handle to carry the bottles to and from the truck.

As soon as we heard the milk truck coming up the street, Karen and I would run out in front of the house. We would wait by the truck for the milkman to deliver to our house and return with the empties. As soon as he opened the back of the truck to store the empty bottles, I would walk over and tug on his jacket. I'd whisper. "Can I please have a piece of ice, mister?" Karen would wait on the sidewalk.

Sometimes he would use an ice pick to knock a small triangular chunk off an ice block and hand it to me wordlessly. Other times he would just ignore me. I'm sure the requests for ice grew tiresome after a while. When I was lucky, I would take the precious piece of ice in my dirty hands and whisper, "thank you". I knew better than to ask for two pieces—one for me and one for Karen. Instead, we would take turns sucking on the dripping chunk of cold wet ice until it melted away.

Butter was a staple in our house—but it was used sparingly. It came in small crocks and was never refrigerated. When margarine was first introduced, Daddy decided to experiment. He bought a crock of "the new kind of butter" at the grocery store. It was uncolored and came with a tube of yellow food dye. Daddy mixed the yellow food coloring into the white cream, and we all tried it. Margarine was not a hit—it was tasteless. We considered it "artificial butter" and were proud to say we used "real butter" in our house.

The neighborhood ice cream man used a bicycle to peddle his wares. The three-wheeler had a 3-foot square metal cooler mounted on the front. Dairy cups, ice cream bars, and a wide variety of fruit flavored Popsicles were packed inside in dry ice. The chemical ice kept everything frozen and didn't drip; it burned if you touched it. We knew better than to ask for chunks of dry ice to suck. The ice cream man would pedal up and down the streets of our neighborhood ringing a bell mounted on the bicycle's front handlebars to announce his presence.

During the summer months, kids from all around would run outside to see him—and watch the lucky ones buy their ice cream treats. We never had the money to buy ice cream, but we enjoyed the excitement. On occasion, Mrs. Schneeman would buy her son Paul an ice cream. If I happened to be playing at their house when the ice cream man came by, she would buy me one, too. It was a rare and wonderful treat.

One neighborhood vendor that Mama took advantage of was the photographer that came door-to-door. He would distribute handbills a few days in advance to let everyone know he would be in the neighborhood on a certain day. Mama spent the money for each of us to have a formal picture taken at around 5 years old. Mine is taken sitting on our piano bench in the living room. I don't remember the shooting of the portrait, but it is one of my treasures.

My favorite vendor was the knife and scissor sharpener. He came once each summer, pushing a three-wheeled handcart with a grinding wheel on the front. "Get your scissors sharpened! Get your knives sharpened!" He would holler out as he walked down the middle of the street.

"Hurry," Mama said. "Run outside and tell him to stop here." She'd push me out the door as she started running through the house gathering knives and scissors.

I would run outside and wave to the vendor from the curb. He would stop in front of the house, wheel his cart next to the curb, and set up his workshop. Mama would bring all the items to be sharpened to the cart and set them on a shelf next to the grinding wheel. Although the prices for sharpening scissors and various sizes of knives were mounted on the side of his cart, she would negotiate a more satisfactory price. Then the sharpening would begin.

The sharpener took each implement separately, spun the grinding wheel with his foot, and guided the blades along the spinning wheel. Sparks flew everywhere and the grinding noise hurt my ears. But I would stand as close as I could and watch in fascination. When he was finished, he would hand each item to Mama. She would check the blades to be sure she was satisfied with the sharpness. When the job was completed, she carefully counted out the coins to pay him.

There was a junk collector who came to our neighborhood once a month. He drove a horse and buggy in the alley along the back of the garages. The wooden buggy had fence-like sides and was overflowing with worn out and discarded household items. A horse well past its prime pulled it. The man sat on a high bench seat atop the buggy and rode up and down the alleys blowing a loud horn. Mama saved old rags and newspapers to sell to him. We called him, "the junk man or the sheeny man".

When Mama heard his horn blowing, she would call to us through the screen of her bedroom into the yard where Karen and I were playing. "Go tell the sheeny man to stop," she said. "Tell him I have some rags for him." We would grab a couple of green apples from under the tree, run out the back gate into the alley, and stand and wait for the man to reach our garage.

Slowly the horse and buggy plodded toward us down the alley. He stopped his horse when I called out to him. "Whoa," he said. He sat patiently holding the reins while Mama pulled her bags of rags and bundled newspapers out of the garage. After she had everything set on the ground behind the wagon, he would tie the reins to the seat and climb down. "Let's see what you have for me today." He examined the items carefully, weighed them on a silver scale hanging from the back of the cart, and then offered Mama a price.

"That's not enough," she said.

He would smile as they haggled back and forth until they agreed on an amount. Then the man would pull a small black cloth bag out of his pocket and carefully count coins into Mama's outstretched hand. While the process was going on, Karen and I would watch the huge brown horse. He would stand obediently—but his head would be bent and he would paw the ground snorting and sniffling. We were fascinated, but kept our distance from the horse.

"Do you have any apples for Chester today?" the sheeny man asked.

We would nod our heads.

"Chester was hoping that you did. If you want to feed him the apples, you must walk up to him very slowly and hold the apples out in front of you on the flat of your hands."

But we stood there frozen. The horse was so tall! Eventually, Mama would take the apples from our hands, smile down at us, and give them to the man. "Maybe next time," she said. "That horse looks mighty big."

He smiled, took the apples, and held them out in his hand for the horse. "Chester says you needn't be afraid of him. And he thanks you for the apples." We'd watch as he climbed back up into the seat of the buggy. "See you next time, then." He picked up the reins, clicked his tongue, and the horse moved away.

The neighborhood fruit peddler had a big red truck with open display shelves. Fresh vegetables and fruits were set against a plywood backing packed with ice chips. He tooted his horn as he drove up and down the city streets. He had a metal scale hanging from the upper rack of the open bed to weigh the produce. Occasionally, Mama bought lettuce or cabbage or bananas off the truck. Most of the fruits and vegetables we ate were home grown. In the summertime, we ate our fill of fresh fruits, berries and vegetables. In the wintertime, we ate canned or preserved vegetables and fruits.

Daddy had a small vegetable garden in the back yard and a much larger one on Pa's property in Utica. He grew strawberries, corn, potatoes, carrots, lettuce, cabbage, onions, tomatoes, cucumbers, green peppers, pumpkins and melons. We also had apple, pear, and mulberry trees in our yard that provided fresh fruit. During the summer months, Mama canned strawberry preserves, tomatoes, pickles, corn relish, peaches, pears and applesauce. Potatoes, onions and carrots were preserved at the end of the growing season by burying them in the dirt floor of the fruit cellar.

***

But the old neighborhood wasn't the way it had been when I was growing up. Many years had passed since Daddy had planted a garden. Neighborhood vendors had gradually stopped coming by while I was still a teen. Supermarkets and modern technology had replaced the necessity for both. I looked around to see which families were still living here. I'd give a report to Mama when we got home. She'd want to know.

All three of our older children remembered the neighborhood where they had been born, but only Jerry, Jr. had clear memories of Daddy—our daily visits to him. He had just turned 6 years old when his grandpa died. I was happy at least one of my children was old enough to remember and appreciate this special man. The rest would have to come to know him through me—and through my writing. My article about Daddy was still being circulated to inspirational magazines. I hoped it would soon be published so an even wider audience would learn about him.

Chapter 29

Mama called that evening to find out how the finalization of the adoption went. I told her about Janette thanking the judge. "Cute," Mama said. "She's a smart little cookie."

"It feels so good to know she's legally ours—no matter what happens," I said.

"I'm happy for all of you. Now you won't have to put up with that nosy caseworker."

I decided to ignore that remark. Mama had just been leaving our house one day when Mrs. Cavanaugh arrived. She had taken an instant dislike to her. I didn't think it was personal. Mama just didn't like anyone she perceived to be an authority figure. So I changed the subject. I told her about driving through the old neighborhood. And about Cheryl not knowing what coal is. "It makes me feel old."

She laughed. "If you're old, I must be an antique. Who's still living on our block?"

"It looks like the Farwells and Mrs. Cratchet are still there. So are the Rhiens, Griglaks, Meehans, Klikuses and Mrs. Witkowski. I couldn't tell about the Weisenhofers. The house was all closed up." Then I went on to name some other former neighbors who were still living there.

"What does our old house look like?"

"It looks the same except they planted some shrubs next to the steps and took down the handrail."

"I don't think I'd like to go back and see all the changes. So many people moved away even before I did. The neighborhood was never the same after they all left."

***

The Angelines moved out of the lower flat of the house next door when I was still in grade school. They rented their place to the Farwells, a couple with a daughter in her late teens and a son 3 years old. They were exceptionally nice people, although a little unorthodox for the neighborhood. There was drinking, card playing and loud parties late into the night. Sometimes the daughter, Joanne, had male overnight guests. But the family never complained about any noise or loud activities that took place at our house.

Mama considered the "goings on" next door quite scandalous, but Joanne was so sweet to my sister Lorraine that she overlooked her "immoral" behavior. Joanne would spend hours sitting on the porch just talking to Lorraine, or pushing her around the neighborhood in her wheelchair. Eventually, she married and moved away. Still, Joanne made it a point to come over and see Lorraine whenever she visited her mother. Now she had bought the Patulski's house, and was once again living in the neighborhood.

The only neighbor that did complain lived directly across the street from us. It was Mrs. Cratchet. Her husband was a mild mannered man who always had a smile on his face. I can remember Mr. Cratchet walking down the street from Van Dyke carrying his black lunch pail, his dark clothes coated with grease, his black cap pulled low over his forehead. I knew he worked in a factory, took the bus every day—even though he had a car—and returned home mid-afternoon. He always waved and called "hello" when he saw me playing by the front steps. And then he was gone. It wasn't until years later that I understood that Mr. Cratchet had died suddenly of a heart attack at work.

Mrs. Cratchet was the direct opposite. She had always been unfriendly and unapproachable, but she became the neighborhood crab after Mr. Cratchet died and her older daughter and son each married and moved away. Mrs. Cratchet continued to live in the house with her youngest daughter, Bernadette, who was a year younger than I.

Bernadette had been blind since birth. She went to a special school and had no friends in the neighborhood. Many warm days when school was out for the summer, she would sit on the front porch glider and just rock back and forth. Her eyelids were always closed, but she was able to discern light and vague shapes. So she would have her head tipped back looking towards the sky and the sunlight. If something moved in front of her, she would twist her head quickly around to try to follow the shadow.

I felt Bernadette's boredom and loneliness and asked Mama if I could go and play with her. But when I knocked on the door, I found that the world across the street was an alien place. Mrs. Cratchet guided Bernadette to a white wooden platform swing in the perfectly manicured back yard, and instructed her not to move from there. She provided us with a set of Braille playing cards and told us to play "go fish" or "war". Bernadette barely said two words throughout the games, and I soon grew restless and bored.

"Do you want us to read one of your special books—or maybe we can go for a walk?"

"You have to ask my mother," she said.

I was fascinated by the Braille cards and would have loved to watch Bernadette move her fingers across the page and hear the stories she would read from any books she might have. Equally, I would have enjoyed sharing with her whatever books I had the ability to read at that young age. I loved books and assumed everyone did. But Mrs. Cratchet wouldn't let her daughter read to me, or me to her. And she wouldn't let me take her for a walk—even around the yard.

All the while we were playing cards, Mrs. Cratchet kept coming to the back door and checking on us. Her constant hovering made me afraid to move from the swing—afraid I would do something to displease her. I felt sorry for Bernadette, not because she was blind but because her life was so restricted by her mother. After a few visits, I stopped going across the street. I felt confined. "Playing" was too much effort.

And Mrs. Cratchet not only hovered over her daughter. As kids, we couldn't play hide and go seek, kick the can, or curb ball in front of our own house without doing something to displease Mrs. Cratchet. Someone was always either stepping on her grass or being too loud. Heaven forbid if a ball accidentally bumped up against her front steps. Even if we were just sitting on our own front porch, rocking on the glider or talking with friends, Mrs. Cratchet would yell out the door to complain about the noise. No matter how quiet and careful we would try to be, it was never enough. With so many kids in and around our house, it was impossible to please her.

Mrs. Weisenhofer was also the opposite of Mrs. Cratchet. The Weisenhofers lived halfway down the block—about midway between us and Ma and Pa. They had two daughters—Mary Anne a year older than I, and Nancy a year younger than Karen. Their well-manicured, lot-sized side yard was perfect for playing outside games and we always felt welcome there. I remember Mrs. Weisenhofer calling us to the house on hot summer days to give each of us a Coca Cola bottle filled with ice cold Kool-Aid. And it was the Weisenhofers that invited Karen and me to sleep over for a few nights when our family had the house fire.

Another neighbor that was especially kind to me was Mrs. Nowak. The Nowaks lived about six houses west of us. Lawrence, the only child, attended first grade with me at Holy Name. Although I knew who Mrs. Nowak was, she rarely left her house. For whatever reason, she stayed inside and kept to herself. As an adult, I realize she might have been suffering from depression or some other illness. I know the neighborhood ladies whispered about her.

One cold winter day, Lawrence and I were building a snowman on their front lawn. My legs were bare and my nose was running. Mrs. Nowak opened the front door and called to me. "Here," she said. "Put these on." She held out a pair of black wool leggings. "You look cold and Lawrence has outgrown them." She held out a handful of Kleenex. "And keep these in your coat pocket."

Now I knew I was never supposed to take charity from anyone—that was pounded into our heads by Mama. But I was freezing and my nose was running. And it wasn't exactly a handout—it was a hand-me-down. The leggings were just going to waste because they were too small for Lawrence. I was familiar with hand-me-downs; it was a common occurrence in our family. Gratefully I took the leggings, sat on the porch step to take off my boots, and pulled the leggings up under my dress. They felt good and warm. I put the Kleenex in my pocket. "Thank you," I whispered.

But when I arrived home wearing the leggings, I was in trouble. "Where did you get those pants?" Mama said. As I explained, she got redder and redder. "In the first place, those are boy's pants. You have no business wearing them. In the second place, we're not accepting charity from anyone. You know better than that. Take them off and take them back right now." I didn't mention anything about the Kleenex.

As young as I was, it embarrassed me to return the leggings that Mrs. Nowak had given to me. I knew that she had only meant to be kind. And I sensed that a lot more was involved in the lack of acceptance on Mama's part. But I took the leggings back and gave them to Lawrence. "Mama says I can't wear boy's pants," I said.

One day not too long after that, I watched as Mrs. Nowak was wheeled out of her house on a long white stretcher and loaded into an ambulance with flashing red lights. Later, I learned that she had died. Mama told me that Mrs. Nowak had committed suicide—a grievous sin according to the Catholic Church. I never saw Lawrence again. He and his father moved away. But I always wondered about the harm neighborhood gossip and rejection of kindness must do.

In our neighborhood, it was rare to see the inside of our friend's houses. We played outside—on the street, in yards, or on porches. When you went to call a friend to play, you literally called: "Johanna, Johanna" while standing at the bottom of the front porch steps. You were not allowed to ring the doorbell, knock on the door, or call on the telephone.

In warm weather, inside doors were open and you would be calling up through the screen door so you could easily be heard inside. During the winter when inside doors were closed, it often took a lot longer to get a response. If nobody came to the door after a reasonable time, you walked away. It meant the family was busy or your friend couldn't come out to play. You didn't wait for or expect any explanation.

The only time I saw the inside of most houses on our street was during the years of the block rosary sometime in the early 1950s, just at the start of the Korean War. One evening a week Catholics in our neighborhood would gather together in each other's living rooms to recite the rosary along with a program broadcast on the radio. The purpose was to pray for peace and the conversion of Russia. Neighbors took turns hosting the weekly event. Children and adults knelt together and quietly recited the prayers. Most families on the block participated. To see neighbors praying together was powerful.

***

"I know what you mean about the neighborhood not being the same without everyone we knew living there," I said. "But it still looks the same."

"I'm just glad I moved when I did," Mama said. "The change was difficult to get used to, but I'm adjusted now."

"Talking about change. I've got some more exciting news." I told her about the two articles I had sold and explained what they were about. She was quiet for a few moments. I waited to see what she would say.

"They're going to print those stories in magazines and anyone will be able to read them?"

"That time we almost got in an accident was a long time ago, Mama."

"I don't care about everyone knowing about that. It was a miracle. I eventually told Daddy about it—and Father Graeber. They both agreed. What happened gave me hope during a lot of bad times. I'm happy you've shared that story. I'm more concerned about this women's libber article."

"It's not a women's libber article. Even Pope Pius XII said: 'Women must have an ideal that attracts them and transmits to them a vital, irresistible force. Such an ideal is the truth that woman has a dignity which was given her by God.' That's a quote I use in the article and that's what it's about. It's got to do with a changing world—and a woman's role in it. Besides, what could possibly be wrong with an article that'll be appearing in a Catholic magazine published by Franciscan friars?"

"Huh!" She grunted. "Just let me know when you get copies of the magazines. I'm anxious to read those articles."

I felt deflated. Mama wasn't excited for me. She was more concerned about my viewpoint and what other people would think about it. She'd totally missed the point about what I had accomplished. But what did I expect? She'd rarely been supportive at significant times in my life. For some reason, I thought about the day I learned about the facts of life. It could have been a bonding moment. Instead, she brushed the opportunity aside.

My cousin Marilyn is Aunt Bea's oldest daughter. She was in the same grade as me in school. Maybe it's because she's the oldest child in her family—or maybe it's because Aunt Bea is more progressive—but Marilyn was always a step ahead of me when it came to finding out important things. I hated that, and did my best not to let her know.

One day when we were about 11 years old, Marilyn brought over a pamphlet entitled, What Every Girl Should Know. "Look at this," she said. She waved a glossy 7-by-9 inch booklet in my face. "You think you're so smart. I bet you don't know anything about what's in here."

"Let me see it," I said. I pulled the booklet out of her hands and began leafing quickly through the pages. It contained a detailed explanation of menstrual periods: what they were, why they happened, and when girls could expect to start having them—along with black and white illustrations. Modess—a company that produced sanitary napkins—published the booklet. I was speechless. I hadn't even known where babies came from, let alone that a woman's body functions played such an integral part in having them. My cousin certainly had the best of me this time.

Countless times Mama had sent Karen and me to the grocery store to buy Modess, but we didn't know what we were buying. She would give us a folded note. The grocer would hand us a rectangular shaped box wrapped in plain brown paper. Karen and I often speculated on what might be inside. We called the boxes, "the surprise packages". "What's in here, Mama?" I said. "Is it a surprise?" I asked each time we were sent to the store.

"Never you mind," she said. "Don't be so nosy. If I thought you should know, I'd tell you." She would take the package and put it away.

Of course, as kids will, Karen and I rummaged through Mama's bedroom closet when she wasn't around. We found the box and opened it to find white bandage-like pads. We looked at each other, shook our heads, and put everything back. We couldn't figure out what they were. It was a mystery. But we couldn't ask anyone because we were snooping and this was something that we knew was supposed to be a secret. Now it was clear. While I sat there—stunned by my discovery—Mama walked into the living room where Marilyn and I sat on the couch.

"What do you have there?" Mama asked. She walked over to the couch and pulled the booklet from my hands. She turned the pages slowly. "Where did you get this? From Marilyn?" I nodded. She looked sternly at Marilyn, and then handed the booklet back to her. "This is private and you should keep that booklet at home."

Meanwhile, Aunt Bea walked into the room. "Give me that," she said. She took the booklet and put it into her purse. "You two go on outside and play. We won't be staying much longer."

Embarrassed, I looked at Marilyn. She avoided looking at me. "Let's go out in front," I said. "Everyone is playing kick the can."

"Okay," she said. She headed for the front door making a wide arc around Mama.

Aunt Bea must have had a talk with Mama—or maybe she took matters into her own hands. In any case, a few weeks later I received my very own copy of What Every Girl Should Know in the mail. I didn't tell Mama. She never brought the subject up again—and neither did I. Of course, I shared my booklet with Karen. But the two of us didn't talk about this hush-hush subject until a long time later.

I always felt a little bit guilty whenever I pulled that booklet out. Not because it was secret stuff—but because of what I was thinking the day I had learned about the facts of life. For a few moments, I had wondered what it would be like to have Aunt Bea for a mother instead of Mama. I thought it might be nice. She seemed so supportive. My mother lacked the ability to share anyone else's emotions, thoughts, or feelings. Or so it seemed to me then.

Chapter 30

Aunt Bea has always been the aunt I feel most comfortable with. She's very different than Mama. I'm sure it's partly due to their ages and birth order—Mama being the oldest and Aunt Bea the youngest with 11 years between them. But she is warm, mellow, earthy and "with it". There is not a pretentious bone in her body. What you see is what you get. Although not at all religious, she has a good and generous heart.

Mama says it has to do with the difference in Pa's financial circumstances during Aunt Bea's growing up years. She was only 10 years old when the stock market crashed the year Mama and Daddy were married. Up until that time, Pa was considered to be pretty well off. He owned several buildings and businesses. Like so many during that time, the Great Depression eventually wiped him out financially. He had to file for bankruptcy. For Aunt Bea, there was no private schooling. Through most of the years she remembers growing up, she lived in the flat above the funeral home—across the hall from Mama and Daddy.

Mama infers that Aunt Bea had hung around with "a rough crowd" in high school. I take it to mean that she hasn't learned the social graces that Mama thinks are important. For example, Aunt Bea not only drinks beer—she drinks it straight from the bottle. And she swears sometimes.

Mama loves Aunt Bea as much as I always have—they've just lived in different worlds.

"What was Mama like growing up?" I asked Aunt Bea one day—trying to understand how their personalities could be so different.

"I really don't remember much," she said. "I was so young when your Mama got married. To me, she was always an adult."

"Do you think part of the difference between you is because she went to a Catholic high school?"

She laughed. "Could be. The schools your Mama attended certainly were a lot different than the public schools I went to."

Aunt Bea also brings up the hard life Mama and Daddy had in the early years of their marriage—a time none of my older sisters or brothers remembers. They were too young. She's the one who told me about Lorraine's birth and diagnosis, Marvin's death, and Johnny's birth and death. She talks about Mama's difficult pregnancies. "Your Mama and Daddy never complained," she said. "They suffered their losses and their hardships—and went on. I have always admired their courage. I think maybe it's made your Mama a little tougher than me."

Aunt Bea has five children—two born later in life. Her second oldest daughter, Geraldine, is the same age and grade as Karen and her oldest son, Tommy, is close to Billy in age. With three small children and no jobs, Aunt Bea and Uncle Harold drove out to California in the late 1940s. We kids thought that was so adventurous! They towed a silver trailer—and that was their home. When they returned some months later, their family lived at Ma and Pa's cottage while they started building their house on the lake.

Uncle Harold dug an open basement, built a cinder block foundation, poured a cement floor, and installed electricity and plumbing. For many years, the family lived in Lake Orion during the summer and spent the winter in Utica. The summer before Marilyn started the sixth grade, they moved to Lake Orion permanently. Over the years, Daddy and my uncles helped Uncle Harold with some of the building. So our family spent an occasional summer Sunday on the lake while the men worked on the house.

Uncle Harold took a job at the Ford Motor plant by Seventeen Mile Road and Van Dyke in Utica. Once the family moved, Karen and I were invited most summers to spend a few days with them in Lake Orion. Uncle Harold would drive down to Detroit to pick us up after work. Karen and I never told Mama or Aunt Bea that he always stopped at the bar "for a couple of drinks" on the way home—while we waited in the car.

We knew Mama would never let us go with Uncle Harold if she knew about the drinking. And we knew Aunt Bea would say something to Uncle Harold if she knew. We certainly didn't want our uncle to be mad at us. He was our ticket to a glorious vacation on the lake with our cousins.

At the lake there were always lots of visitors during the summer, but Aunt Bea took it in stride. She cooked and served and enjoyed the company. It was a different lifestyle—swimming, boating, and fishing during the day, campfires at night, and occasionally roller skating at the local rink. But it was a lifestyle that Karen and I loved. We were allowed to sleep in the trailer with our cousins and we were never expected to help out. If there was ever any problem, we felt comfortable talking about it with Aunt Bea. She was like a second mother to us—a mother you could talk to about anything.

And she paid attention. As a child, I had shoulder length medium brown hair with a natural part on the left side. My hair was poker straight and very fine. I would constantly be pulling it behind my right ear to keep it off my face. When I ran, my hair would fall across my right eye blocking my vision. To keep it out of the way, I had gotten in the habit of sucking a piece into my mouth and holding it with my lips.

"You better stop sucking on your hair," Aunt Bea warned me one day when I was staying at her house. "I know a little girl that used to suck on her hair. She had to have her appendix out. When the doctor opened her up, her appendix was all wrapped around with gobs of the hair she had sucked in."

I looked at her, my eyes open wide with concern. "Would she have had to get her appendix out if she didn't suck on her hair?"

"Nope. It was all caused by her sucking on her hair."

"If I stop now will I still have to get my appendix out?"

"Not if you stop now."

"I will then." I never sucked on my hair again—and I still have my appendix.

Mama had a different approach. I was a small-boned little girl of average height—but scrawny. Part of the reason was genetic, part the lack of rich food and sugary treats, and part was a highly active life style. I played hard outside every day, year round, and walked wherever I wanted to go. But skinny as I was, I learned to stand straight and tall. Posture was important to Mama. She watched to make sure I didn't slouch.

"You don't want to grow up with rounded shoulders," she said. She would poke me between the shoulder blades as I passed her. "Stand tall if you want people to respect you. Be proud of who you are. Remember, you're just as good as anyone else. Think of yourself as a princess."

Mama always carried herself well. She held her head high and never slouched. She had the presence of royalty. I was proud of how she looked—and I wanted to be like her. So I would automatically thrust my shoulders back and continue with whatever I was doing. I was a natural slouch. If Mama wasn't constantly after me to straighten up, I'm sure I'd have grown up to be round-shouldered.

But I never dared talk to Mama about things that bothered me. As a young teen, I thought something was wrong with me—that I'd never grow breasts or start my period. I was skinny and flat-chested. There was a popular song of the day by Teresa Brewer that was called, "Skinnie Minnie Fish Tail". One day at Aunt Bea's I heard some older teenage boys taunting one of the girls with that song. I lived in fear that one of my brothers—or any boy—would start calling me that. If one of my brothers had heard it, or thought of it, I believe they would have.

So Karen and I talked about it. I was 14, she was 12. But she was already concerned about being skinny and flat-chested, too. We were too embarrassed to talk to anyone—even Aunt Bea about this. Instead, we confiscated a couple of our older sister's bras and started wearing them under our blouses stuffed with toilet paper. If any of our family members noticed our sudden blossoming, they didn't say anything.

Later, we found "falsies" at the dime store. These were foam mounds shaped like breasts that could be inserted in a bra. The falsies worked better than toilet paper because they were spongy, waterproof, and could also be used in bathing suits. I can't imagine how we looked or whom we fooled, but in our minds it solved the "skinnie minnie fish tail" problem. Unfortunately, one day I had a bad experience.

We were on a family beach outing at Bishop Lake State Park in Howell. My younger brothers and sisters and I were swimming in about 3 or 4 feet of water. It was a hot July Sunday and the sun was beating down. Although there was a lifeguard, I was trying to keep an eye on my siblings as I paddled around in the cool water. The lake was crowded with swimmers of all ages and shapes.

As I raised my right arm to dip into the water, the soggy sponge falsie popped out of my bathing suit. I stared in frozen horror as I watched it float—nipple up—on top of the water. I made a grab for it as I looked quickly around to see if anyone had noticed—right into the bright blue eyes of a boy who was smirking at me. Luckily, he was only a kid—10 years old or so, and not related. It was embarrassing, but not the catastrophe it could have been.

And I did fool a couple of perverts. The first incident occurred when Karen and I were walking down Van Dyke with a group of our grade school friends. I was wearing my toilet paper or falsie filled bra and a pale blue wool crew neck sweater. We were looking for boys to toot their car horns at us as they passed. It was something entertaining and inexpensive to do on a warm Friday evening in autumn.

There were six of us walking along the sidewalk in two groups of three. I was on the inside toward the buildings, furthest away from the street. We were giggling and laughing and waving at cars as they passed by. I didn't notice a man walking toward us along the sidewalk until he started to pass. Suddenly, he made a lunge toward me, grabbed my left fake breast, and squeezed. "Hey!" I hollered as he started to run. "He just grabbed my breast!"

My friends stopped. We all turned to watch the man's black-clothed back disappearing down the street. "Ah, well," Karen said. She smirked. "Did he hurt you?" We exchanged a grin. Then we all turned back around and started walking. Obviously, my fake breast had been attractive to someone. I never reported the incident to my parents—and I doubt any of my friends did to their parents.

The second incident taught me what I was supposed to do about perverts. I was 15 years old and still wearing my falsies. I was at a roller rink with my grade school friend, Judy. We were standing next to each other behind the railing, watching the roller skaters, when a man came up to us from behind. He put an arm around each of us—placing his hand along the side of my "breast". Apparently, he was also touching Judy's breast.

"Hey, you pervert," she said. She hollered loudly. "You creep. Get your hands off of me!"

"Yeah," I said. "You creepy pervert. Keep your hands to yourself!"

As people turned to look, the man dropped his hands and quickly scurried away. So that's what you're supposed to do, I thought to myself. I knew he didn't have a right to touch me. I just didn't know what to do about it. Now I felt empowered. I realized for the first time that I alone was in control of my body—and destiny. Perhaps I began to give off this new awareness because no pervert has every approached me since that day—and nobody has ever touched me without my permission.

One would think that with all the focus on my breasts that I would have noticed when suddenly I blossomed at the age of 16. But I didn't. One day my nipples felt slightly sensitive and I noticed a red stain in my underpants. My periods had finally started—and I realized that I had breasts. I called Karen into our bedroom to tell her the good news and to reassure her. She was two years younger—if it happened to me, it would happen to her.

Karen quietly confided that it had already happened to her. She had her period and her breasts. I was thunderstruck. I was her older sister and she hadn't told me. I thought we told each other everything. She had kept a secret from me—the first I knew about. Gradually I realized that it was to protect me. If I had known she had developed before me, I would really have been worried.

I was 15 years old when I went on my first formal date. A friend of Lorraine's had a brother I barely knew. I had only met him once or twice. Paul was a sophomore at an all-boys Catholic school and needed a partner for a school prom. The two sisters made all of the arrangements. Paul's parents drove us. Mama bought me a maroon dress with a round white collar and I received my first corsage from a boy. Paul was nice, but he couldn't dance. So we sat quietly and watched everyone else. It felt like I was out with one of my brothers.

As teens Karen and I and our friends went to sock hops and football games at all-boys high schools—De LaSalle, Austin, and Notre Dame. Our group of girls met groups of boys with whom we socialized. For special dances at our high school—the Anniversary Ball and Junior/Senior proms—we each invited a boy we liked and double-dated. The formal dances were held in our high school gymnasium. We had to bring our dresses to school in the days before the dance to be inspected by the nuns and approved to ensure they were modest enough.

Occasionally, we would plan other outings with the boys we met—a day at the beach, a basement party closely chaperoned by parents. But they were always group events. Even when we were invited as dates to a boy's school for a formal dance, we always double-dated. I can never remember single dating until I was a senior in high school. Wherever we went, Mama was a subtle vigilante when Karen and I were teenagers.

If we were at a friend's house and the phone rang, Karen and I would smile at each other. We knew it would be Mama needing to talk to one of us. "Colette, I've laid out the fabric and pattern for my dress on the dining room table," she said. "Do you know what happened to my pinking shears? I can't find them anywhere." Calling was Mama's way of checking up on us. She wanted to be sure we were where we said we would be. But she did it in a way that wouldn't embarrass us. And she did it frequently enough that we couldn't have lied about where we were going if ever we wanted to.

Another trick Mama had was flashing the porch light. When our dates pulled up in front of the house to bring us home, we knew Mama would be watching and waiting for us. We had five minutes at the most to say "good night". Otherwise, the light on the porch would begin its warning—on/off, on/off—until we climbed out of the car and came up the porch steps. Karen and I often chuckled about that porch light. If we had mischief on our minds, the front of the house would be the last place we'd look for it. But we were good girls and were not looking for that kind of trouble. Instead, we felt watched over and loved. Mama couldn't talk to us, but we knew she had our best interests at heart.

***

Growing up, I've had plenty of women who were role models for me—my mother, two grandmothers, seven aunts, and many great aunts from both sides of the family. All were full-time housewives except Grandma Taube who had a job outside the home when Daddy was young. Of course, I didn't know her then and Mama always talked negatively about Grandma working in a factory and not staying at home with her children. My sister Mary Ann quit her outside job and became a full-time homemaker when she married. From the time I was a child, I'd assumed my only career would be as a wife and mother.

Before Mama married, she'd taken pride in being a secretary.

Although I'd followed in her footsteps, it was just a job for me. I never considered a long term career as a secretary, and I knew that my chances of going to college to earn a degree were slim. None of my aunts had attended college, explored their potential outside the traditional roles of women, or pursued careers in professional fields. If I continued down the path I was going, I'd be the first woman in my immediate family to have a career. I wondered. Did I have the courage to be different? To pursue my dreams?

Chapter 31

When I saw my articles in print, my question was answered. I loved writing. It was something I was good at. I'd sold all of my assignments and saw them appear in inspirational magazines. There was no stopping me now. I had a second career. While I made copies of the articles and shared them with Mama and my sisters and brothers, I soon realized I didn't need their praise or approval. My sense of accomplishment and self satisfaction was enough. I was a published author!

For the final lessons of my writing course, the assignments included researching, outlining and writing the first chapter of a nonfiction book. I explored many subjects before coming up with the perfect solution. I'd write a "how-to" book on adoption. The process had changed dramatically. There were no up-to-date books available describing adoptions today. It was something I had personally experienced. I knew I could do it. I was excited.

I spent months researching adoption at the library. I talked with other adoptive parents. I contacted experts around the country. Eventually, I had an outline I was happy with. I completed the first chapter and sent it to my Famous Writers School instructor—and nervously waited for a response. Finally it came. He loved my book idea and my writing style! There were a few suggestions for changes—along with instructions for submitting the manuscript to prospective book publishers.

By late summer I had made the changes and generated a list of book publishers I would contact. I decided to start with the most prestigious. It was worth a try. I had nothing to lose. I mailed the outline for the book and the first chapter to the publisher on the top of my list and eagerly awaited a response. It was rejected and returned by the first two publishers. But I intended to keep trying. I had been warned that it's difficult for a new author to find a publishing house. I planned on making it a practice to send my work to a new source the same day it was returned. The manuscript was now with the third publishing house.

It was two years since I first started the writing course. I had received my Certificate of Recognition and congratulations for completing the course. Publishing all of my articles had greatly boosted my self confidence. Our older children were in school full-time now. Janette was 2-1/2. I was exploring new subjects to write about when I received a letter from Harper & Row. The envelope was thick—but not thick enough to hold my manuscript. I speculated on what could be inside. I decided to set it on the kitchen table. I'd wait until I laid Janette down for a nap before opening the envelope.

Finally, I tore open the envelope. "Oh, my God," I whispered. "It's a book contract!" I sat there stunned as my eyes raced over the details of the letter and the fine print of the contract. I had six months to write the book. I'd receive $750 when I signed and returned the agreement to the publisher and $750 when I delivered a complete and satisfactory manuscript. Thereafter, I'd receive a 10 percent royalty on books sold. Tears of joy flooded my eyes as I reached for the phone to call Jerry.

"I knew you could do it," he said. "I'm so proud of you. Don't make dinner. We'll go to the Chinese restaurant to celebrate."

I thought about calling Mama or one of my siblings to tell them. I decided to wait. I didn't want anyone to dampen my enthusiasm—to spoil my excitement before the contract was even signed. There was plenty of time to share the good news with everyone else. We'd tell the children at dinner. They were old enough to understand what was happening—and old enough to support the changes in routine that would be necessary for me to complete the book on time.

Figuring out a schedule turned out to be challenging. But we worked it out. On week days, I would go to bed early in the evening—an hour or so after the children were in bed. I would get up at 3:00 a.m. to write for a few hours before the rest of the family awoke to start their day. I'd try to arrange with a neighbor to babysit Janette mornings in her home. Hopefully, Nancy across the street—who had a daughter Janette's age—would be willing and able to babysit. Our girls liked each other and played well together.

I'd work from the time our older children left for school until they returned home at lunch time. These arrangements would give me seven hours a day, five days a week to write and do phone interviews. I'd estimated the book would include twelve chapters. The first chapter was completed. The in-depth research was done. Finishing the book well before our older children got out of school in June for summer vacation seemed possible.

Any additional library research or in-person interviews would have to be done in the evening or on the weekends when Jerry was home to be with our children—and I'd have access to a car. Occasionally, if necessary, Jerry could arrange for a ride to work. But he needed the car for his job and we couldn't afford a second vehicle. Perhaps when my book was published, we could get another car. That would be my goal—an additional incentive.

The next morning, Jerry mailed the signed contract. I called Nancy to see about babysitting. She was thrilled to learn about my book contract and more than willing to help out. "A book contract with Harper & Row—I'm impressed," she said. "What an accomplishment! I'd be delighted to have Janette over. Elise will be happy to have a playmate every morning. Since the kids started school, she's been kind of lonely—and bored. It'll be good for both of our girls. And, if it's all right with you, I'll plan some outings for them—to the zoo, the library, the park. It'll be fun."

We worked out the details—start date, information about Janette's usual schedule, what she liked for snacks, her nap time, etc. I assured Nancy that Janette had been potty trained for more than a year so that wasn't a concern. She objected to me paying her, but I insisted. "I don't want to impose," I said. "And I'll be using my store of cash from selling makeup and publishing my writings to pay for the babysitting. It's only right. Besides, it makes me feel good to know I'm compensating you for your time and trouble. You'll be earning the money and I'm sure there are things you can use it for."

Later that day, I called Mama to tell her about my book contract. Predictably, she wasn't excited. She didn't seem to understand what I had accomplished. She was more concerned about me taking time away from my family to write the book. And what I might put in it. I explained the arrangements I had made to find writing time—and to minimize the disruption to my family.

"It's just not right," she said. "Why do you need to do this? Why is it so important? Do you want everyone to know everything about you and your family? That's what will happen when you put things in a book. It's so public. How can you expose your family to that?"

"You don't understand," I said. "It's not an expose. It'll be a factual book—a 'how-to' for people who are considering adoption. Everyone in my family is excited about it—Jerry, the kids. And Janette is looking forward to having a playmate every morning. She'll just be across the street."

"Everything you wrote about before was personal. Don't get me wrong. It's good you can write about things. I'm sure that's some kind of a special talent. But it makes me uncomfortable."

"There is nothing about this book that should make you feel uncomfortable. And it's something I need to do. It's an incredible opportunity. You needn't worry about what I'm going to say in the book. You'll see what I mean when it's done. And by the way—thanks for saying I have talent. I appreciate that."

**

The schedule we had created seemed to be working perfectly. It was difficult at first to go to bed so early and get up while it was still dark. But I adjusted rapidly. It was nice to have the quiet time to work on my writing while everyone else was still sleeping. And it was a welcome break when the family got up. We had breakfast together every morning and talked about the upcoming day before going our individual ways. I found that writing was hard work—but so satisfying. I was careful to stay on target to complete the book on time.

I wrote and edited each chapter in longhand. Then I typed it on my manual Smith Corona using carbon paper to make a duplicate copy. I wanted the manuscript to be perfect—free of typos and erasures. Fortunately, my secretarial skills came in handy. But I waited to type the pages until I was certain it was the final draft. It would be tedious and time consuming to make changes later. I'd have to re-type any single page to make corrections, plus re-type subsequent pages if the word count on the corrected page changed.

I soon learned that I had to ignore the ringing of the telephone during my writing time. If I answered any calls, it would involve taking precious minutes away from my writing. I discovered that the hard way—by answering the phone too many times. So I warned my friends and relatives not to call me until the afternoon. Some people didn't seem to understand, but they respected my request and complied. Except Mama.

"I can't believe you won't answer the phone," she said. "How can you just let it ring? It could be something important."

"If it's a real emergency, I can be reached," I said. "I gave the school Nancy's telephone number. They'd call her and she'd come across the street and knock on my door to let me know. It wouldn't be a problem.

And Jerry can do the same if he needs to contact me. He knows her number."

"Well it's inconvenient for the rest of us. And pretty selfish I'd say."

"I'm sorry, Mama, but I need to meet this deadline. I have to preserve what little time I have to write." In reality, I had arranged a code with Nancy and Jerry. If they wanted to reach me for any reason, they were to let the phone ring twice, hang up, then call back. I would know it was one of them and answer. This would not be too disruptive as neither of them was likely to expect lengthy conversations.

"Well I tried to call you this morning and the line was busy."

"I was on the phone with my editor. Believe me; I spend as little time on the phone in the mornings as possible."

"Aren't you going to ask me why I was trying to call you?"

"Was it about something special?"

"Davey bought some property in Yale. He wants to move there. And he's got a new girlfriend. I think it's serious."

"Wow. Good for him. He's always wanted to live in the country. But he's sure been quiet about his new girlfriend. What's her name?"

"Her name is Debbie. But you don't understand. I think he's going to marry her."

"What's the problem? Don't you like her?"

"I'm afraid he's going to get married, move out, and leave me and Lorraine here alone."

I didn't know what to say. Mama talking about her fears was unprecedented. But surely she expected Davey would eventually marry. He was almost 24 years old. "Well," I said carefully. "You're happy living in Utica aren't you? The rest of us aren't too far away. You wouldn't exactly be alone."

"It's not the same. And I'm not particularly fond of where I'm living or this house. I only moved here because it was near Pa."

"Where would you want to live? In Yale? It's really out in the sticks."

"I hadn't really thought about living anywhere else."

"Well you always have options. If you wanted to be close to Davey nothing is stopping you from moving to Yale. But I think you're worrying a little prematurely."

"You're right. Lorraine and I could move there, too. Thanks, Colette. You've given me something to think about."

***

The holidays came. I was busy working on my book but still found time to do all of the things I did every year to make these times special. Davey got engaged as Mama predicted; the wedding was set for September. By March I had finished my book and sent it to Harold Grove, my editor at Harper & Row. I was proud of myself for meeting the deadline.

"I'm pleased with the book," he said. "It's great. And I want you to know that you're the first writer I ever worked with that actually sent a manuscript in on time. We always allow a few months extra as a cushion." He chuckled. "Good job!" Then he went on to outline what the next steps in the publication process would entail.

Initially, the legal department would review the manuscript to make sure there weren't any concerns. Next, an editorial assistant would read the manuscript, raise questions about anything unanswered in the text, check language usage and punctuation, and recommend changes. If any re-writing was necessary, the manuscript would be returned to me. Only after the revisions were made would the manuscript be set into type. Then the galleys would be sent to me for proofing and last minute corrections.

Once the editing was complete, I would be expected to provide a table of contents, dedication, epigraph or inscription, foreword or preface, and any acknowledgements I might want to include in the book. Thereafter, I would be sent the final galleys and asked to write the index. My editor estimated that these steps would take approximately three months. The schedule worked out perfectly for me, as I expected to be able to complete everything by the time our children got out of school for the summer.

As it turned out, there were only minor changes that were required. My editor and his staff were pleased with the final draft. The book was to be entitled, "Adoption—Is It for You?" At the last minute, I decided to include my maiden name on the book; it would be authored by Colette Taube Dywasuk. Daddy would have been proud to see his name in print. I turned the final galleys for my book over to the editor in late May.

In early June, Jerry completed his classes at the community college and earned his Associate of Arts Degree. We did not attend the formal graduation ceremony or have a party. He had decided he was going to go on to Oakland University and earn a Bachelor of Science Degree in Management. So we'd wait until he graduated from there to celebrate with family and friends. At about the same time, our children finished school for the summer—Jerry, Jr. completed fifth grade, Jeffrey, fourth, and Cheryl, third. We all went to the Chinese restaurant to celebrate our accomplishments. We were excited and proud of each other.

Chapter 32

During the summer we all took a break—Jerry from work and classes, the kids from school, and me from my writing. For our two-week family vacation we rented a pop-up trailer and traveled to Cumberland Falls and the Great Smoky Mountains. It was wonderful camping out, hiking, and swimming in the mountain streams. Jerry and I tried to plan family vacations—even when we had to manage on a tight budget. In the earliest years of our marriage, we had gone tent camping. The trailer with its built-in beds, cooler, and cooking stove was a huge step up for us.

When we returned in August, there was a letter waiting for me from my editor at Harper & Row. The galleys of my book had been turned over for production; the publication date would be January, 1973. I would receive my complimentary copies of Adoption—Is It for You? sometime in December. He wanted to know how many additional books I would like. The retail price of the book would be $6.95. According to the contract, I would receive 10 copies free; the rest would be provided at a trade discount of 43 percent. Jerry and I would have to sit down and figure out how many copies we'd need for family and close friends.

But there was even more exciting news. Harper & Row wanted to know if I'd be willing to update a book on adoption that had been in print for more than 17 years. The original author was ill and unable to revise it herself. Adoption and After had been a highly successful book. I had used it as a reference for my own book. I was honored to be considered for this project and quickly contacted my editor.

"I'll send you a contract," he said. "The original author is willing to allow your name—along with hers—on the updated version. And she's willing to share the royalties. Would you be able to start work right away?"

We discussed the details. I would begin work on the revisions in September, and complete them by next April. I would receive $1,000 upon signing the contract and $1,000 upon acceptance of a complete and final manuscript. In addition, I would be awarded one-third of all the royalties.

"The timing is perfect," I said. "It should be no problem at all to complete the revisions on schedule. Just send me a copy of the book and the contract."

"I want to allow you plenty of time. Don't forget. Once Adoption— Is It for You? is published, you'll need to do some publicity tours."

I hadn't realized this. "What does that entail?"

"You'll be going around the country meeting prospective adopters, appearing on radio and television programs, and in book stores to promote your book. I don't know if you remember, but it's in your contract. Harper & Row pays for all the expenses. Our publicist is lining up appearances right now. That's not a problem is it?"

"Of course not," I said. But I was flabbergasted. How exciting! How scary! I couldn't imagine me doing public appearances—maybe having to make speeches. I had absolutely no experience. For heaven's sake— I'd never even flown in an airplane. "Would my husband be able to come with me?"

"Your husband or whomever you want to bring as a traveling companion. Expenses are covered for two people."

"Great. I'll look forward to it. When will I know the schedule?"

I couldn't imagine what it would be like but I knew I would do what needed to be done to sell my books. I'd have to figure out who I could get to stay with the kids. And I'd have to start sewing some new outfits to wear. At least I'd have time to get ready.

"We'll get you the schedule sometime in December. Don't worry. We'll discuss everything with you before anything is finalized. But you can anticipate the publicity tours will begin just after New Year's."

***

Throughout the spring and summer Davey had been building his new house in Yale. He had the rough structure done by experts, but he was doing the finishing work himself. It would be ready for him and Debbie to move there after the wedding. Meanwhile, Mama had decided to put her house in Utica up for sale.

"Davey invited me to build a house next door to him," she said. "He has more than 12 acres—so there's plenty of room."

"What does Debbie say?" I wondered how I'd feel as a new bride with my mother-in-law living so close.

"She's all for it. She said it'll be good for their future kids to have their grandma nearby."

"That's great. It's good you like each other. Otherwise it could be difficult—you know, living so close."

"It'll work out. We'll be able to help each other. It'll be good for all of us. Just think. I'll be able to have the brand new house I've always dreamed of. And Lorraine and I will live out in the country, yet be close to town. It's perfect."

"I'm happy for you. Do you think you'll have any problem selling the house in Utica?"

"Not at all. The real estate agent said the market's good. I should be able to get all the money I put into it. We're already looking at house plans. We'll start building just as soon as we get an offer."

It was good to hear Mama so excited about something. But I had to chuckle to myself. It wasn't long ago that she had complained about us moving "way out in the country". Now she was talking about moving 60 miles from where we grew up in Detroit. Interesting.

***

In September, the kids started school. Jerry started classes at Oakland University. Davey got married and moved to Yale. I started on the revision of Adoption and After. And Mama sold her house, finalized building plans, and hired a contractor to begin construction of her house in Yale. It was busy. In December, the printed copies of Adoption—Is It for You? arrived. I was ecstatic! Holding a copy in my hands, sniffing the fresh ink, leafing through the pages gave me a feeling comparable to holding each of my newborns in my arms. This was something that I had created.

I dedicated my book "To my darling daughter, Janette...Forever special in my heart". The inscription read: "Not flesh of my flesh, nor bone of my bone, but still miraculously my own. Never forget for a single minute: You didn't grow under my heart, but in it." The quote was taken from "The Answer" (To an adopted child) by Fleur Conkling Heyliger, and had appeared in the April 5, 1952 edition of Saturday Evening Post.

For everyone else, I wanted to include a special message on the inside cover of their copy of my book. I took days figuring out what I would write to each of my children, my husband, my mother, my sisters and brothers, and the friends and neighbors who had helped out with encouragement, babysitting duties, or special favors. I had learned over the last year that although I wrote the book, it would have been impossible without the support of family and friends. Just before Christmas, Jerry and I took the children along as we delivered copies to everyone.

The comments and compliments were gratifying. "How impressive—I can't believe you really did this. Thanks so much. I'm honored to receive a copy from you. Now I can tell everyone that I know a real published author. I'm happy for you. I can't wait to read it.

How does it feel to see your book in print?" Mama's comments weren't the most effusive—but they meant the most to me. "Daddy would have been so proud," she said.

In early January, the first reviews of my book had begun to appear. My editor sent me copies from Virginia Kirkus Service, The Booklist, Publisher's Weekly, Book Review Digest, Child Welfare League of America, The New York Times. All the reviews were favorable and recommended Adoption—Is It for You? to readers. The New York Times noted: "this book should be of considerable interest to couples considering adoption." Articles about the book appeared in magazines and newspapers. Harper & Row informed me that the publisher had decided to print a second run, and then a third.

In February, the public appearances began. My first engagement was scheduled on a local television show entitled, "A.M. Detroit". I was both excited and nervous. Everyone I knew would be watching. Once I arrived at the studio and sat down to talk to the host, I realized that the only thing required of me was to make conversation about my book. I was able to tune out the bright lights and just pretend I was sitting in his living room making small talk. This worked perfectly for me. My television debut was a success. Everyone was amazed at how calm and self confident I looked and acted. I was amazed at how comfortable I felt.

After my first appearance, more local radio and television engagements had been booked. Now out-of-town promotional tours were being scheduled. First to Baltimore, then to New York, Chicago, and Los Angeles. There would be more radio and television appearances, but also bookstore signings and adoption group meetings. Jerry would accompany me. The schedule allowed time at home between tours. We found a young married couple who was willing to move into our house and supervise our children while we were away. The wife, Mary, had worked with Jerry. She was from a large family. We had socialized with her and her husband frequently. I felt confident the children would be in good hands.

"I can't get used to you gadding about," Mama said. "But I do like Mary and her husband. They'll do a good job with the kids."

"It'd make me feel better if I knew you'd be watching over them."

"Don't worry. I will be. But how much longer is all of this going to be going on?"

"Not long," I said. "My editor said the tours generally last only as long as the reviews are still new and fresh."

"Will you have to do publicity when your next book comes out?"

"I don't know. I have to finish the book first."

I was surprised to find how much I enjoyed flying across the country on the promotional tours. Over several weeks, I talked with hundreds of potential adopters in book stores and at adoption association meetings. It was exciting to meet so many people who were interested in my book. I gave spontaneous speeches, answered questions, and autographed countless copies. In New York I visited the Harper & Row offices—and met my editor. He showed me the room where unsolicited manuscripts were stored. It was a 20-foot square room piled high with 9-by-12 inch manila envelopes. I felt fortunate that my book had been selected to be published from among the hundreds that arrived each day.

Finally, things quieted down and I was able to get back to my writing. I followed the schedule I had assumed in completing my first book. With so much traveling, I was unable to meet the April deadline for Adoption and After. But I finished the revisions before the children got out of school for the summer. My editor was pleased with the manuscript; the book was scheduled for publication in early 1974.

As Adoption and After was a previously published book, he advised that the market for it wasn't expected to be as favorable as it had been for Adoption—Is It for You? Reviewers wouldn't write about it, so it was unlikely I would need to do many publicity tours, if any. At the same time, the number of children expected to be available for adoption had been dwindling. Roe vs. Wade had been decided in January, 1973, and abortion was now legal across the country. Women had other choices than to have their babies and place them for adoption.

***

During the winter, Mama's house in Yale had been constructed. It was a modest three-bedroom ranch with white aluminum siding and black shutters. A huge picture window in the living room faced the road which was connected to the house by a 50-foot gravel driveway. All of my sisters and brothers—and their husbands and wives—had gotten together to paint and wallpaper the rooms. Mary Ann's husband had built all the cabinets in the kitchen and bathroom. Mama and Lorraine moved into the house in early spring.

Although I had been traveling and couldn't participate with my brothers and sisters in the finishing of the inside rooms, I had promised to sew all the curtains and drapes. Mama was anxious to have the windows covered. Now I had time to complete the job. As I measured each window, Mama described what she wanted. I spent hours shopping for the various fabrics—and cutting and sewing. As each set of curtains and drapes was completed, Jerry purchased the hardware and hung the window furnishings.

Meanwhile, Mama set about planning where various shrubs would be placed along the front of the house, and where her forsythia, peony and rose bushes would be planted. She set flower pots and hanging baskets on the tiny front porch, and made lists of the annuals she would plant. She and Davey also planned to plant a vegetable garden behind the house—tomatoes, cucumbers, corn, squash and pumpkins. They wanted to have enough to can pickles and make corn relish in the fall. Now she was thinking of getting a dog.

"It's a collie," she said. "Already house broken. She'd be a great watchdog. And you know how much Lorraine loves dogs!"

***

When I was growing up, we didn't have many pets. With so many people living in such a small house, there wasn't room for four-legged animals. I did, however, have some goldfish. For my birthday one year my godfather gave me a small glass tank, goldfish food, a bag with blue stones, a small net, and 25 cents. Daddy took me to the 5-and-10-cent store to choose six goldfish out of the hundreds in the huge tank. I watched fascinated as the clerk dipped a small white cardboard container into the tank, filled it with water, and added a sprig of seaweed. Then she used a net to capture each of the fish I pointed to, and dropped the wriggling shape into the take-home box.

"Be sure to change the water and feed those fish every day," she said. "But don't give them too much food or they'll die." She showed me how to sprinkle just a few flakes onto the top of the water then closed the container and handed it to me by the thin metal handle.

When we arrived home, Daddy poured the stones into the bottom of the goldfish bowl, filled it with tap water, added the seaweed, and slid the fish inside. At first I sat for hours watching the fish swim around in the bowl. I gave each of them a name. It was winter so I covered the bowl with a towel at night so the fish could stay warm. I changed the water every day and fed the fish carefully.

But after a time, my attention wavered and I would forget about the fish—sometimes for days. Then I would overfeed them to make up for the missed meals. Soon I was flushing dead fish down the toilet; the fish bowl was empty. My fascination with fish was over. I never got more fish but my younger sisters and brothers took turns using the fish bowl over the years. They were much better pet owners than I.

One year for her birthday Karen got a green parakeet. She loved that bird and was determined to teach it how to talk. She kept the cage hanging from a holder in the corner of the dining room. Every day Karen would carefully clean out the cage, refill the water and seed holders, and lay fresh newspaper on the bottom. She taught the bird to sit on her shoulder. Sadly, someone startled the bird one afternoon when Mama had a pot of soup boiling on the stove. The bird flew off of Karen's shoulder, into the kitchen, and right into the pot of soup. She never wanted a replacement.

One summer a small gray cat started hanging around our house. We weren't allowed to bring the cat in the house, but Karen and I would put small dishes of milk by the back door and try to get the cat to let us pet it. "Be careful of that cat," Mama warned. "It's an alley cat. You don't know how many germs it may be carrying."

One afternoon, when we opened the screen door, the cat ran up the back steps into the kitchen. Karen and I started yelling. Donny tried to pick the cat up to take it back outside, but the cat hissed and clawed and actually jumped at his face. It was so frightening to see the cat with its back arched going after my brother, that Karen and I lost interest in befriending the potential pet. When we stopped putting the bowls of milk out, the cat soon disappeared.

I was a teenager when we finally got a dog. A black rat terrier followed Karen and I home from the bus stop, up the back alley, through the yard, to the kitchen door. Davey had been begging for a dog. "Davey," I called. I opened the back door and climbed the steps to the kitchen. "Look by the door. See what followed us home."

"It's a dog," he said. "It's so cute!" He ran out the kitchen door, picked up the dog and brought it into the kitchen for Lorraine to see. She got down on the kitchen floor and wrapped her arms around the dog. It began licking her face.

"You can keep it until somebody claims him," Mama said. "But that's it. We don't need a dog in this house. We have enough mouths to feed."

But nobody ever claimed the dog. He stayed. "Cookie" was the first of the many dogs that lived in Mama's house. She always professed to hate dogs. "They're a pain," she said. "But Lorraine needs a dog for companionship. It's for her that we have a dog." But the dogs sure loved Mama. She defended them as if they were her children.

Chapter 33

Early in summer, the first royalty statement arrived from Harper & Row. I gasped when I opened the envelope. My book had sold well during its first six months in print; I had earned over $5,000 in royalties. I called Jerry. "Guess what?" I said. "I got my royalty check today. Are you ready to go car shopping?" We bought a 1973 Tampico yellow three-door Ford Pinto hatchback. Although the salesman recommended I purchase the car on credit, I wrote out a check for the $2,600. It felt especially good to be able to pay the total amount up front.

"A brand new car," Jerry said, "your very first. And you earned the money on your own. That must make you feel good."

I looked at him. He understood. "It feels wonderful. Like all the hours I put into my writing course and into my book was worthwhile."

"I'm really proud of you." He pulled me against his chest in a hug. "My liberated wife."

I smiled. "You're right. I'm no longer homebound. Does that concern you?"

He laughed. "Not at all. It's funny. When you published your book one of the guys at work asked me if I wasn't worried about you leaving me now that you're becoming so independent. I think he was kidding but I'm not sure. That's how some guys think."

"I'm glad you're not like that. You've always understood about me having to write. In fact, you deserve part of the credit. I wouldn't have been able to do it without you."

"Hey—I'm happy to have a wife with so much talent. And let's face it. The money's nice, too."

"Yeah. We not only have a brand new second car—there's money left over."

"Maybe we should set your royalties aside in a separate savings account. We can use the money for special purchases."

"Sounds good to me."

***

Throughout the summer months, my children and I drove out to Yale frequently. I was putting the final touches on the window trimmings—and we helped Mama with her gardening. I loved the freedom of being able to come and go as I pleased, and the kids were enjoying exploring the countryside. There was a river that ran behind Davey's property; they fished and swam there. Late in August, Mama and I canned her vegetables. Debbie was pregnant and not feeling her best. Between us, we put up quarts and quarts of bread-and-butter pickles, stewed tomatoes, and corn relish. I valued the time I spent with my mother; she was happy and seemed so content.

***

From as early as I can remember, Mama always loved being outdoors. She had little time to enjoy the luxury of gardening during my growing up years and all the days, months and years she was nursing Daddy. But she made the most of the moments she had. She pruned her flowers and pulled weeds in between hanging the laundry. The smell of line-dried clothes and her favorite flowers—violets, lily of the valley, lilacs, bleeding hearts, peonies and roses—transport me right back to our yard on Mt. Olivet.

On summer evenings after we were all in bed, Mama would go out front to water the shrubs and grass. She would connect the hose to the outside faucet, attach the nozzle, and spray all the plantings. Then she would connect the hose to the sprinkler and move it from spot to spot on the lawn while she sat on the front porch steps drinking a cup of coffee. I would fall asleep to the soothing clack, clack, of the sprinkler and know Mama was nearby. I can still remember the sweet smells that flowed through the screens of my open bedroom windows above the porch—of fresh cool water hitting the hot grass and strong black coffee.

In July Mama had turned 65. "How does it feel to be so old," I said.

She laughed and gave me a shove. "It's funny," she said. "On the inside I feel the same way I did when I was 18. Then I look in the mirror and see this little old lady looking back at me."

I smiled. "Well you certainly don't act like a little old lady. Sometimes I think you have more energy than I do."

"Oh I have my aches and pains. But I try not to think about them. When you get older, it's important to just keep moving. You know, I still have a lot of living to do."

And Mama did like to keep busy. In addition to the gardening, she did her own cooking and house cleaning. She drove herself and Lorraine to town for shopping, church, and doctor appointments. She took up crewel embroidery and needlepoint. She stitched gorgeous complicated designs that everyone begged to own. She designed and sewed rag dolls and hooked rugs for each of her grandchildren. She relaxed by doing paint-by-number oil paintings and reading years worth of stories in old Reader's Digest Condensed Books.

Mama's one vice was smoking. She had started secretly when Daddy first took ill. Ironically, it was the doctor who suggested that she smoke "to relax tension". For years Mama was embarrassed about her smoking. She didn't think it was ladylike. So she tried to hide her habit from her children. She would smoke when she and Daddy were alone—which was rare—or when she was down in the basement washing and ringing out clothes.

All of us knew Mama smoked. You could smell the odor on her

clothes. But by unspoken agreement, we pretended we didn't. "Mama," we would call as we started down the basement steps. "Are you down there?" We knew she would be smoking and wanted to give her the opportunity to put out her cigarette and hide the pack. By the time we walked across the basement to the laundry tub, no cigarette would be in sight—but the air would still be pungent with the smoky smell.

Eventually, as we grew older, Mama began smoking in front of us—one by one. When Mama smoked in front of me for the first time, I felt special because it was like she was taking me into her confidence. Now Mama smoked openly. Sitting at the kitchen table, she always seemed to have a cigarette burning in the ash tray. I don't think any of us ever questioned her small pleasure—even as adults when we learned how unhealthy cigarettes are. Not that it would have done any good.

"I don't believe cigarettes are bad for you," Mama said. "It's hogwash. I know people who have been smoking for years and they're still kicking. Besides, it was a doctor who suggested I start smoking. If it kills me, it kills me."

***

In the fall, Janette started attending nursery school. It was a co-op program held twice weekly at the local Lutheran church. She loved it. I missed having her at home. I worked on the finishing touches to Adoption and After while she was at school or napping. When the galleys arrived, I proofed them—then provided the table of contents, forward and index. The work was not time consuming. I began to wonder what would capture my interest once this job was completed.

I spent a lot of hours doing research at the library. I wrote and published a few more inspirational articles and I explored some new book ideas. But there was nothing I was especially excited about. Household projects no longer satisfied me completely. Doing the washing and ironing, shopping and house cleaning just wasn't a full time job. I was restless. I promised myself I would come up with some new projects to fill my time after the holidays.

In January, the printed copies of Adoption and After arrived. It was satisfying to see my work in print—to distribute it to family and friends and to find copies of both books in the stores. But the revision did not generate the same public excitement my first book had created. The original had been in print since 1955. As the book itself was not brand new, reviewers tended to bypass it. Those that did make mention of it in their columns always recommended it. But there were no publicity tours.

During the winter months, I came up with another exciting new idea. I started exploring the possibility of going back to school to get a college degree. Of course, I had a lot of questions. Would it be worth spending the time and money to achieve this? Was it something I really wanted to do? I had established a career in writing without a degree. Why should this be important to me? Could I compete in a classroom? I recognized that a degree wasn't required for a writer, but the idea fascinated me. The more I thought about it, the more enthusiastic I became. I could learn so many new things!

Finally I decided to pursue the possibility. I would like to try it even if it was just to prove to myself that I could handle college work. And for Daddy who had always dreamed of his children going to college. I could do it for him, too. I talked with Jerry about the idea. As always, he was supportive. He suggested I talk with a counselor at Macomb County Community College (MCCC) to see what opportunities were available. When I did, the counselor recommended I take the College Level Examination Program (CLEP) testing.

"The exams include a battery of five tests covering the liberal arts," he said. "They're distributed nationally by the College Entrance Examination Board and were designed to gauge the learning an individual may have gained from work experience, personal reading, or noncredit study programs. It's possible to gain legitimate college credits through the program without attending classes. With your background, I think you'd be a perfect candidate."

This program sounded like the ideal way for me to get into the college mode. Study materials and test guides for those planning to take the exams were available as part of the College Without Walls program at the Warren Public Library. I could prepare over the next few months and take the testing in the fall. Whatever credits I earned through the program would be applied towards a degree. "Sign me up," I said.

In the meantime, the counselor suggested I plan on enrolling in one fall class and see how it works out. "A speech class might be worthwhile for you. SPH-100 is a Fundamentals of Speaking class designed to help students gain confidence in effective oral communication through varied speech experiences. It's not one you'd be able to receive credits for through the exams, and it'd be a good way for you to get started as a student. When you receive the results of the CLEP testing, you can figure out what you want to do next."

I thought it was a great idea. I'd definitely take the speech class in addition to doing the testing. Now that I had made a decision, I could hardly wait to begin college.

***

In June, my Dominican High graduating class held its 15th year reunion. As the school was all-girls, the organizing committee had decided only the women would be invited to attend—no husbands or significant others. My longtime friend and fellow graduate, Mary Nanni and I, drove to the reunion together.

"I can't believe it's been 15 years," she said.

"I can't believe we're in our 30s," I said.

"But I'm glad we've kept in touch."

"Me, too. I'd hate to have to go to the reunion by myself."

"I heard that some of the nuns that taught us are going to be there."

I immediately thought about Sister Eileen Therese—my high school English teacher who had failed me because she believed I copied my senior term paper. I explained to Mary what had happened. "I hope she's there so I can tell her about my books."

"I remember when that happened. I'd like to see her face when you tell her."

Sister Eileen Therese wasn't at the reunion, but several nuns who had taught us were there. I asked about my former teacher. They said she was living at the Dominican Motherhouse in Adrian. I told them my story and asked if they would tell her about my books.

"We'll be happy to tell her," one of the sisters said. She handed me a small notebook. "Write down the names of your books. I think Sister would like to know that one of her students has become a published author."

"And I think that she should apologize for not trusting and believing in you," another added.

We all looked at each other and laughed. I was unlikely to get an apology from Sister Eileen Therese, but it felt good to know she would be advised of her error in judgment. Teachers are supposed to draw the best out of their student and offer encouragement—not discouragement. For me it was now finished business. I only hoped Sister would learn a valuable lesson from the experience. Going to the reunion and seeing all my old classmates again was great, but being able to get my message to Sister Eileen Therese was especially satisfying.

**

The summer passed quickly. I enrolled at MCCC and started classes in the fall. Janette was now in kindergarten, so I was able to take the speech class while she was in school. I loved attending college. And I loved the class. It was challenging. Although most of the students were young, there was a sprinkling of men and women my age. I fit right in—and I did well. In November, I took the CLEP tests and learned that I was eligible for 18 credit hours—six each in Communications, Humanities and Social Sciences.

By the end of December, I had already accumulated 21 credits toward a degree. For an Associate of Arts Degree, I'd need 62 credit hours. I was determined to complete the requirements. I decided to carry a full load of classes in the winter semester. I could work my schedule around the hours my children were in school. If all went as planned, I could earn my degree in less than two years.

Meanwhile, Mama was pre-occupied with changes in her own life. Davey had built a greenhouse on his property which was located on a main road a couple miles from town. He and Mama planned on opening a business—Taube's Greenhouse. Mama planted flowering annuals and tomatoes. She nurtured the seedlings throughout the winter. When spring came, she would sell the plants to her neighbors. Now she was busy and always in a rush when I spoke to her on the phone.

"I've got to get out to the greenhouse," she said.

"I'm going to be going to school full-time now," I said.

"I know. You told me. While the kids are in school. I understand why that's important to you."

"You do?" I was amazed.

"Yes. It's like this business. I've always loved gardening and I'm good at it. Now I have a chance to turn it into a career."

"You mean like my writing?"

"Exactly."

"You'll be a huge success, Mama. I'm sure of it."

All through the years I had followed in Mama's footsteps, worried about her opinion, tried to please her. Despite her protests and disapproval, I managed to create a somewhat different life for myself. Yes, I was a wife and mother. But I also had a career. Now things were turned around. Mama was following my example. And she was showing me that you're never too old to follow your dreams.

EPILOGUE

After completing my Associate of Arts Degree, I was hired by Campbell-Ewald Company, an international advertising agency, to work full-time as a writer in the publications division. It was a dream job. CECO Publishing developed corporate newsletters, magazines and brochures for prestigious clients—like Bendix Corporation, Rockwell International, AT&T, Eastern Air Lines, as well as General Motors and its various corporate divisions.

My assignments included writing a variety of publications and magazine articles for widely diverse audiences. I'd interviewed famous people, traveled around the country, and wrote features about everything from growing tomatoes to careers in sales to following Janet Guthrie, who was the first woman to compete in a NASCAR Winston Cup stock car race, the Indianapolis 500, and Daytona 500.

While working at the agency, I attended evening classes at Oakland University to earn credits toward a Bachelor's Degree. Tuition reimbursement was provided by the company. It took me six years to earn a double degree in Marketing and Business Management. By then, I had taken a position as Marketing Coordinator with Sperry-Vickers, an international hydraulics company.

Again I attended evening classes—this time at the University of

Michigan-Flint campus—to earn a graduate degree. The company generously paid my tuition as I moved up within the department to become the Corporate Communications Manager responsible for a staff of ten writers, designers, photographers and video cameramen. It took three more years to earn an MBA.

I spent ten years in advertising management before accepting an appointment as Deputy to the Macomb County Clerk/Register of Deeds in Mt. Clemens. There I directed day-to-day operations and oversaw 60 government employees who handled everything from vital records—including marriage, birth and death, military discharge, business registrations and passport information—to circuit court filings, weapons licensing, land recordings, jury service and county elections.

***

In 1976 we had moved from Warren to a house on a small lake in Orion Township. At the time, Jerry, Jr. was just entering tenth grade, Jeffrey, ninth, Cheryl, eighth, and Janette, second. Through the years our children did well in primary and secondary schools, and moved on to graduate with degrees from high ranking colleges. Except Jeffrey. He was a junior at the University of Michigan in Ann Arbor when he suddenly suffered a cerebral hemorrhage. He died before we could reach the hospital that snowy winter night. Once again, tragedy had struck our family.

As any parent knows, there is nothing worse than losing a child. Jeffrey was a remarkable human being who contributed a great deal in the short time he lived on earth. Much of what he'd accomplished we learned about from the multitude of friends, co-workers, acquaintances and relatives who came to support us in our grief. Their hugs and stories gave us strength. Without doubt he was a son to be proud of— and we will always miss him. But we feel fortunate to have had him for 20 years, unlike Mark, who we never had an opportunity to know.

At the funeral home Mama took me aside to whisper: "It should have been me, not Jeffrey. He was such a sweet boy, so happy, so young.

I've lived my life. It should have been me."

Mama loved Jeffrey. Our children had spent a lot of time with her after she moved out to Yale. During the summers, they would stay for days at a time helping her plant her flower and vegetable gardens, playing cards and board games in her kitchen in the evenings, teasing and laughing with her. They shared some of the best years of Mama's life. She was healthy and had the time and freedom to do as she pleased. She enjoyed her grandchildren; they were self-sufficient and good company.

"Please don't say that, Mama," I said. I hugged her to my aching heart. "I love you so much. I wish it wasn't Jeffrey who had died, but I wouldn't want to lose you either. I just have to believe that God has some kind of plan. For whatever reason, it was Jeff's time—not yours."

Of course I've missed my son. Even though I believe he is still around me—watching over our family—the pain of loss never evaporates. There is an empty space that nothing fills. "You're so strong," somebody close to me said one day. I can't help but resent that remark. I don't feel strong. I feel like I have little choice. I can go forward and accomplish whatever God has planned for me, or I can stay stuck and wallow in sorrow and misery.

Another friend said: "God never sends you more than you can handle." I don't like that expression either. To me it infers that if you're weak you won't have troubles and if you're strong you'll get more than your fair share. Nobody wants these kinds of challenges in life. They're difficult for anyone to deal with.

My philosophy is this. Everyone has problems. Life is not perfect. There are some really bad things that happen that you just can't do anything about. You are not in control. During those times, you have to learn to accept. Crying or screaming about unfairness just doesn't help. No matter what you do, the outcome is still the same.

A death of a loved one is one of those times. Your choice is to stay stuck in the tragedy or allow yourself to move forward. That doesn't mean you are over it. The sorrow will always be a part of you. It simply means you've accepted the irreversibility. Death is inevitable. So is aging. Both are a part of life. Strong or weak, each of us will eventually experience the loss of youth and the loss of those we love. Where, when and how are the only variables.

"I love you" were three words rarely spoken in our house when I was growing up. By their actions, we assumed our parents cared for and loved us. Jeff's death initiated a kind of miracle in my extended family. From the time Mama whispered "I love you" to me at Jeff's wake, all of my sisters and brothers began to end every good-bye with these same words—and hugs. Mama did, too. And the practice soon spread to husbands, wives, children, nieces, nephews, cousins and close friends. Somehow, Jeff's death made everyone realize how important it is to let each other know we care. Separation, temporary or permanent, happens. Nobody knows which good-bye will be the last.

***

Mama operated Taube's Greenhouse for many years. Her neighbors in Yale counted on purchasing their annuals from her every spring. Davey and she kept the business open until Mama grew bored with it. At 88 years old, she was still healthy, but slowing down. She was recuperating from gall bladder surgery when she called me one day at work.

"I need you to take me to the doctor," she said.

"What's wrong?" I asked. "Are you okay?"

"I'm perfectly fine. This is just a post surgery exam."

"Debbie can't take you?"

"I want you to take me. You're the one that's responsible for making decisions about my health care."

"Are you sure there's not a problem?"

"No problem. I just want you to be the one to go with me."

"Okay, Mama. I'll do it."

A few days later, I picked her up and we drove to see her doctor in

Port Huron. It was a warm, sunny spring afternoon in May—Mama's favorite time of year. I realized that it had been a very long time since she and I had spent any one-on-one time together. I was happy she had asked me to come. When we arrived at the doctor's office, she insisted I go into the examination room with her. It wasn't a problem. I had assumed she would want me there.

I sat in a chair while the nurse prepped Mama for her examination. As soon as the doctor entered the room, Mama took charge. "Doctor, this is my daughter," she said.

The doctor walked over to me and shook my hand. "It's very nice to meet you," he said. "Your mother is always bragging about you." He turned to Mama. "Now let's see how you're doing, Mrs. Taube."

Mama had been bragging about me?

As the doctor examined her, Mama continued. "My daughter is the mayor of Lake Orion. She just got elected. It's a really important job."

"You're right. It is." He turned his head to look at me. He smiled. "Congratulations."

"There are more than 30,000 people who live in that town. And everyone knows her."

"You must be very proud of your daughter."

"You bet I am."

Twenty years after we moved to Orion, I had been approached by community activists who encouraged me to run for Township Supervisor. At the time, I was serving on the Orion Township Public Library Board—an unpaid elected position I had chosen as a way to give back to the community. I had no further political aspirations, but I agreed to run. To my surprise, I was elected in a landslide. I hadn't realized how many people our family had come to know over the years. I was serving the first year of a four-year term.

All through the election and inauguration, Mama had never given any indication that she was proud of me. Or, for that matter, at any time in my life. I was amazed. I got up out of the chair and went to stand next to the doctor. I looked down into Mama's face and smiled. "Did I just hear you say that you're proud of me? I said.

She frowned. "You know I am," she said. "I've always been proud of you."

"No, Mama. I really didn't know that. You've never said it before. I've always wondered how you felt about me having a career."

Instead of responding, Mama looked up at the doctor who was quietly removing her stitches. "Hey. That one hurt. Be a little gentle here. I'm an old lady!"

The doctor smiled. "Don't pull that little old lady stuff with me. I know how tough you are. You went through emergency surgery with flying colors. And you're doing great."

"Even though I'm a smoker?"

"Yes. Thanks for reminding me. I wanted to talk to you about that."

"Forget it!"

Everyone laughed. Obviously, the doctor and Mama had had this conversation before.

After we left the doctor's office, we drove along Lake Huron to Lexington for lunch. Mama wanted to look for the restaurant she said Daddy had taken her to when they were dating. Along the way Mama directed me to stop at a viewing spot high above the lake to look at the shimmering water. She pointed out other landmarks as we drove. Finally, we found the place. Although a restaurant with a different name was now operating out of the building, it didn't matter to Mama.

"I came to this restaurant with my husband 52 years ago—before we were married," she told the waitress. "My daughter brought me here to find it." Her brown eyes were sparkling.

The waitress smiled and touched Mama's shoulder. "It must have good memories for you," she said.

"All good memories. The very best."

***

Like Mama and Daddy, Jerry and I have a strong marriage. We love and respect each other—and enjoy each other's company. I'm amazed I could have chosen so well when I was so young. Our children have grown up to be fine citizens—responsible, self-supporting, loving, kind, and successful in their chosen careers. And I believe I've been a good role model for my daughters—as my mother has been for me.

Although Daddy strongly impacted my life, Mama was the person I measured myself by. She has profoundly affected who I've been, who I am, and what I aspire to be. Was Mama a good mother? Although I've often silently questioned her parenting techniques and her ability to mother, I've never questioned her dedication, her selflessness, her goodness, her strength, or her love.

Mama bore twelve children and raised ten to adulthood. She was a good woman—the best. A dedicated mother who worked harder than any woman I have ever known in my life. Her strength and endurance was absolutely remarkable. She did what had to be done for the survival of everyone in her family. She gave her all. She did her duty. She dedicated her life to her children.

I once read somewhere that mothering has little to do with biological reproduction—there are women who bear and raise children without ever mothering them, and there are those who mother all their lives without ever giving birth. My mother was never warm and fuzzy—or a person you could turn to for advice. Instead, she nurtured in each of her children the skills we needed to survive—and expected us to learn by her example. After that, she assumed we were perfectly capable of making it on our own. Like she did.

Each of us brings to parenthood experiences from our own childhoods. These experiences shape our lives and influence how we behave—the opinions we dish out, the actions we take, even the thoughts we think are all guided by our belief system which was forged in childhood. We use what we consider positive and improve on what we consider negative. But it isn't until our own children are grown and raising our grandchildren that we have a glimpse of whether or not we did well.

Although there are some things I'd like to change if I had to do it over, I believe I have done very well as a mother. I have taken the incredible strengths and values of my parents and added more one-on-one mothering. And I have raised strong loving wonderful children who are testament to my parent's legacy—a legacy of love, of wisdom, of faith, of courage, of happiness, and of security.

Throughout my life, I have served in many roles, held many positions, and faced many challenges. I've overcome personal obstacles, built success out of the circumstances of my life, shattered the glass ceiling—even walked on hot coals. But when I look back over my life, I am most proud of what I have achieved in my first career—as a wife and mother. My children and grandchildren are my delight. I look at them and know I did well. I consider the family I raised with my husband to be my greatest accomplishment.

Our grandsons are fine young men. Over the years, when I've asked them, "What do you want to be?" they've always answered: "I don't know, Grandma. I haven't decided yet what I'll study in college." For them, attending college and earning a degree has been assumed. They've grown up knowing they have choices. And the importance of learning has been passed down to them through the generations. Whatever they decide to become, whatever path each takes, I know it will be wonderful and that I will truly be proud of each of them. They are my legacy.

Acknowledgments

First, I'd like to thank my husband, Jerry Dywasuk, who's been so supportive and patient even when I reached several frustration points in writing, editing and producing this book. He's always been there for me in every area of my life.

Next there's my family—my children Jerry Dywasuk, Jr., Cheryl (Dywasuk) Haffey, and Janette Dywasuk who never questioned whether this book would eventually see the light of day. And, of course, my sisters and brothers who periodically teased and nagged me about finishing it—while letting me know they were getting more and more impatient while waiting to read it.

The ones who read the early drafts made this a better book for their input—my dear friend and fellow writer, Lynn Arbor; my brother David Taube and his wife, Debbie; and the grammar couple, Ken and Phyllis Cory, who made particularly sure my use of "I and me" and "lie and lay" were accurate.

I especially want to thank my niece, Nikki Botwinik, who spent years researching our family history and made my job so much easier by providing the facts I needed to make my book as accurate as possible. And my daughter, Janette Dywasuk, who spent countless hours patiently—and with great talent—designing and producing this book.

Finally, I want to thank all of my readers who love Detroit as I do. I am grateful to have the opportunity to share what it was like growing up and living in such a great city more than 60 years ago.

About the Author

Colette & Jerry's Wedding Day
1960

Colette Dywasuk was born in Detroit and has resided in the metro area her entire life. She earned a Master of Business Administration from The University of Michigan, as well as a Bachelor of Science in Marketing and Business Management from Oakland University.

Colette worked in advertising/marketing communications and government offices for over 20 years, served in elected office as Treasurer, Orion Township Library Board for four years, and then as Supervisor of the Charter Township of Orion in Michigan from 1996-2000.

Colette has published a variety of articles in nationwide religious and inspirational magazines, and also published two nonfiction books with Harper & Row: Adoption—Is It For You? (1973), and the revised edition of Adoption And After (1974). She is the mother of five children, two deceased, and currently lives with her husband of 55 years in Shelby Township, Michigan.

About the Author